APPROACHES TO A PHILOSOPHICAL BIOLOGY

Approaches
to a
Philosophical
Biology

MARJORIE GRENE

BASIC BOOKS, INC., PUBLISHERS

New York / London

© 1965, 1968, 1969, 1968 by Marjorie Grene
Library of Congress Catalog Card Number 68-54140
Manufactured in the United States of America

7/1969
Pohl.

FOR

Monica

AND

FOR

Merle

Preface

The aim of this book is simple: to bring to the attention of English-speaking readers a number of European scientists—or scientist-philosophers—whose reflections on the conceptual foundations of biology deserve more attention than they have so far received.

What we think, basically, about the nature and functions of living things in general makes an important difference to what we think about ourselves. That what we think about ourselves makes a difference to the lives we lead should need, since we are conscious and self-conscious beings, no argument. But thinking about the subject matter of biology, and hence about ourselves as living things, is dominated, in the English-speaking world, by two dogmatisms, one of which confuses, while the other prevents, any attempt to achieve a new perspective. The first is the Darwinian tradition, with its accordionlike ambivalence; the other, especially in the last few years, is the outspoken physicalism of many biochemists, biophysicists, cyberneticists—of all those who proclaim with gusto the imminent reduction of the biological sciences to physics and chemistry. True, there are exceptions, but the twin orthodoxy is still imposing and vociferous.

The European tradition, however, is broader, and I think we have something to learn from it, whether as students of philosophy, as practicing biologists (though only a few of these will listen), physicians, psychologists, social scientists, or simply as people concerned with the general beliefs on which our work or our everyday thinking rests. What it has to say to any or all of these I hope will become clear in what follows.

Admittedly, some of the work of all of my subjects, and much of the work of some of them, has been translated, and, indeed, two of them, Straus and Goldstein, both of whom came to America as exiles in the thirties, have published in English as well as German. Their major philosophical *opera* had been published, however, in 1934 and 1935, respectively, in their native language, and they remain, like my other subjects, Portmann, Plessner, and Buytendijk, essentially European thinkers imported in translation. But translation is difficult, and it seemed to me worthwhile to add to such transposition of their own words into English an introduction by a native speaker of the general tenor of their views.

These views, though exhibiting individual differences sufficient to demand the five separate essays that follow, are also sufficiently convergent to justify an exposition within the covers of a single book. Indeed, it was through the writings of Portmann, which I happened on first, that I came to the others as writers who had influenced his biological philosophy. There are others whom I might have included. Merleau-Ponty I excluded because his work is by now well known, if not positively fashionable, and also because he is purely a philosopher, while all the others, with the possible exception of Plessner, have come to philosophical reflection from the demands of one branch or another of empirical science. And it is the philosophical reform demanded—as Goldstein perhaps most directly argues—by biological practice that is at issue here. V. von Weizsäcker's *Gestaltkreis*, although it represents in essential respects an advance on Gestalt theory, seemed to me at the same time to issue finally in a kind of fixation on the "circle" that was best left alone. Some reference to his work will be found in Chapter 3. E. Minkowski's *Le Temps Vécu* has also contributed to the European movement I am concerned with; but I found, I confess, his concept of an *élan mental* too indigestibly Bergsonian to permit a convincing exegesis of his major work. I may be wrong about either or both of these omissions; but I hope that the writers I *have* presented may stand for a general trend in biological philosophy, and should this style of thinking come to receive the attention it merits, others may yet convince me of the equal importance of those whose work I have, with apologies, seen fit to neglect.

I am grateful to the Werner Reimers Stiftung für Anthropogenetische Forschung for a grant-in-aid of European travel in 1965 and to the University of California, Davis, for research grants in 1965–1966 and 1966–1967.

I am also grateful to Mrs. Geraldine Bradbury for typing the manuscript and to Mr. George Gale, Mrs. Tosca Arbini, and Mrs. Diana Hewitt for their invaluable help in seeing it through the press.

MARJORIE GRENE

University of California, Davis
July 1968

Contents

Contents

APPROACHES TO A PHILOSOPHICAL BIOLOGY

I

Adolf Portmann

1

The dramatic advance of biological research in the past few decades has been proceeding on two very different fronts. The triumphs of biochemistry, in its detailed study of the nature and regulation of metabolic processes; the startling advances of molecular genetics, in particular DNA "code-cracking"; the revelation, through the electron microscope, of a whole new world of complex organization at the minutest level: In short, those fields of research designated by the package title "molecular biology": these form one such ever-widening front of advancing knowledge. A little less conspicuously in the headlines, but as ingenious in its methods and certainly as significant in its philosophical implications, is the almost equally new and equally rapidly growing science of animal behavior, or ethology, which studies, not the minute component parts of animals, but their action patterns, whether as individuals or in groups.

The difference in the research procedures of these two groups of scientists is obvious. One set works chiefly analytically. What the visitor sees in their laboratories is blackboards full of calculations, expensive electrical and electronic equipment, carefully isolated preparations of the appropriate tissues or micro-organisms or metabolic substances; but anything that *looks* like a plant or an animal is conspicuous by its absence. True, molecular geneticists still perform breeding experiments, but usually with bacteriophage or other borderline organisms invisible to the naked eye. Even in electron microscopy, where techniques of looking, of "pure observation," are undoubtedly crucial, the structures "seen" are far indeed from our ordinary field of vision.

Ethologists, however, must *watch* devotedly hour by hour and week by week, animals, living animals, in laboratory conditions, in zoos, or, best of all, in the wild, managing or submitting to their environments in a very great variety of species-specific ways. They do, indeed, perform experiments of great ingenuity and sophistication, interfering with the environment of their subjects in such a way as to infer from altered or constant behavior the fundamental action patterns which certain situations call forth. They spend much time, for example, trying to discover whether a given action pattern is "innate" or "learned." In every case, it is not tissue cultures, proteins, or genes, but whole, individual animals or groups of animals they are observing. However abstract and elaborate their theoretical explanations of such behavior, they never escape this base: it is *what animals do* that they are talking about, and this is a very different subject matter from that of their molecule-oriented colleagues.

True, some very eminent ethologists have sometimes insisted that, so far as their program goes, they hope eventually to translate their statements about the behavior of animals, of great tits or sticklebacks or chimpanzees, into statements solely about muscle contractions or glandular secretions, and these would in turn be smoothly translatable into the terms first of biochemistry and ultimately of the science of sciences—as they consider it—mathematical physics. Whether this "ideal" is realizable we shall have to consider in terms of the positions taken by the scientists we shall be meeting in these chapters. For the moment, however, it is sufficient to notice that what, say, biochemists and ethologists *now* spend their time doing are two very different sorts of things. Their activities differ, in particular, in the directness of their relation to the ordinary *perceptible* world of living things that surrounds us and of which we form a part. True, it is a far cry from the amateur "bird watcher," for instance, to Lorenz's research as director of the Max Planck Institute; but the ethologist's skill is an extension and extrapolation of the primal fascination described by Lorenz himself as "that mysterious charm that the beauty of living creatures works on some of us." [1]

Take as typical of the ethologist's activity an example from the work of G. P. Baerends on digger wasps, quoted by Portmann in his book *Animals as Social Beings*. Of a particular female under observation, Baerends reports:

On 24th July, 1940, 000 completes the first stage of Nest 61; on 25th she opens Nest 68 (unknown to me till then) and brings food here later. When I am putting in a plaster nest here, I find the young larva with its first caterpillar. It seems to me not quite healthy, and I find that the wasp, after her next unladen visit, has stopped looking after the nest. On 26th she inspects Nest 61, but the larva has not yet emerged (A). On 28th she digs Nest 84; when she arrives there with her first caterpillar, I have a caterpillar in there for her. She throws out the strange caterpillar, puts her own in, and lays an egg on it (B). On 30th she again inspects Nest 61; I have previously replaced its contents with a cocoon. She closes the nest, and I do not see her there again (C). Now she begins to dig Nest 356, but does not supply it with food till 2nd August, because the weather in the two days between is very bad. On that day she also visits Nest 84, but the larva here has not yet emerged. So she brings no food here (D), but builds a new nest, which, however, is destroyed by me in trying to replace it with a plaster nest. On 3rd August she again visits Nest 84, into which I have previously brought six caterpillars. She then closes the nest (probably for good, but this I cannot say for certain) and stops bringing food here (E). On 4th she works first on the first stage of Nest 340, and finishes this stage; later she comes to inspect Nest 365 and then takes a caterpillar there as food. On 5th she digs Nest 423, brings the first caterpillar there and lays an egg on it. Then she inspects Nest 356 in its third stage. Before she brings a caterpillar there, I replace the larva with a caterpillar and egg; she brings in her caterpillar, without letting herself be disturbed by the larva's absence (F). After an hour, however, she makes an inspection here. There being no larva in the nest, she stops bringing food here (G). The contents of the nest afterwards rot from the rain. On 6th she opens Nests 340 and 423; the eggs have not yet been hatched, and she stops bringing food here (H and I), but digs a new nest 440. From 7th to 14th the weather is very bad, and it is not till 14th that she starts on the third stage of Nest 423. On 16th I take the larva out of the nest, and she makes an inspecting visit, after which she closes it for good, without there being a larva in the nest (J). Then she begins on the second stage of Nest 440—and I give up my observations of her.

Although, therefore, this wasp has been disturbed in many ways, she has always reacted "logically" both to the nest's natural content and to its content as altered by me [Fig. 1–1].[2]

What is the ethologist watching? He is observing the behavior of an individual living being. Plainly, that is not altogether the same thing as watching a sunrise or taking pointer readings. Nor indeed is it the same as observing in detail the pattern of a butterfly's wing or a peacock's tail. The latter example can in itself illustrate what I mean. To describe in detail the pattern of the peacock's tail is not the same activity, for exam-

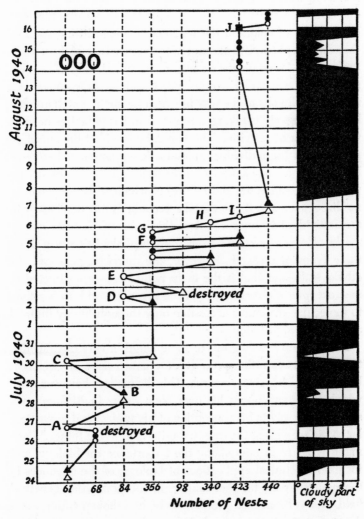

FIGURE 1–1. Diagram of activity of digger wasp ooo from July 24 to August 16, 1940. The black on the right shows the cloudy parts of the sky: the increased activity on cloudless days (July 26 and August 14 and 15) is striking. Such a diagram gives some idea how much the wasps' success in rearing depends on the weather.

ple, as to watch the use of his fan by the peacock in courtship display. Even apart from the study of the physical nature and distribution of colors in the feathers, one can distinguish further the morphologist's account of the appearance of the pattern itself from the ethologist's study of its functioning of the life story of its possessor. The ethologist is watching the animal in a manner analogous to the way in which he might watch another human being. He is taking account of an individual as in some way a center of activities. This is *not*, be it said at the outset, to predicate of the individual animal a "consciousness" like ours; but it *is* to acknowledge the existence of a center of drives, perceptions, successes, and failures of which, although we have no direct access to it, we do take account in our dealings with the individual in question. And this acknowledgment clearly marks off the ethologist's from the morphologist's study. Both these types of research, however, the morphological *and* the ethological—and that is the main point here—are directed to macroscopic, visible features of the organic world, rather than to molecular structures accessible only through highly indirect and analytical techniques.

I have been drawing out to some length a very obvious distinction between the procedures characteristic of different branches of biological research. This distinction, however, with which Portmann opens his own *New Paths in Biology*, may serve us as a key to his conception of his subject and in particular to his account of the essential criteria of living things.[3] Portmann is far from minimizing the importance for biology, and for man's technical applications of biology, of the advances in the molecular or, for that matter, in the population-genetical field. Nor is he in fact, professionally, an ethologist, but a student of comparative morphology and comparative development. But he does oppose, for good reasons, which I shall shortly examine, the tendency to *reduce* biology to its physico-chemical base. Instead, he suggests a starting point for a new and richer philosophy of living things—a philosophy which will permit respect for all facets of biologists' activity, including in particular those which bear directly on plants and animals as they strike our human senses. It is from this general contrast between the imperceptible and the perceptible, which he has emphasized in many of his writings, that we can best approach his thought.

2

Let us return for a moment to the second of the two types of research we have mentioned, that is, to the ethologist and the morphologist taken together. We may describe them as students of *perceptible organic form.* For if the ethologist studies behavior, it is still perceptible form in the spatiotemporal sense that he is investigating; for example, in the sequence of the digger wasp's nesting activities quoted above. This whole class of perceptible patterns in space and time Portmann calls *authentic phenomena,* as distinct from all the rest of the subject matter of all the sciences, including that of molecular biology, which he refers to collectively as *inauthentic phenomena.* This distinction is both more important and more revolutionary than it appears at first sight, and it will need, I think, a brief historical excursion to see what is entailed in it.

The term "phenomena" has a venerable history. Astronomical theory was traditionally concerned to "save the phenomena," that is, to find a formulation in terms of the mathematics of the circle which would be consistent with the movements of the heavenly bodies as seen. Positivist philosophers of science, such as Duhem, have interpreted the whole of scientific activity in these terms. Theories, from this point of view, are constructs, in themselves empty of meaning, intended to guide the observer from one set of "phenomena" to another. Yet in its transformation through the intellectual revolution of the seven-

teenth century, the reference of the term "phenomena" itself
has been strangely altered. The modern positivist's "phenomena" are not what appear to the ordinary stargazer, let alone to
the ordinary natural historian, bent curiously over leaf or
chrysalis. For a philosopher like Duhem, it is the "phenomena"
accessible to the ingenuity of the mathematical physicist that
count, and these are, in general, data obtainable only in highly
contrived experimental situations. This change, like so much in
the scientific revolution, can be documented in the writings of
Galileo, on the one hand in his dictum that "nature is written in
the mathematical language" and on the other in his exclusion of
color, sound, taste, and smell from natural realities, that is, his
insistence on what Locke was to call the distinction between
primary and secondary qualities. Both these innovations, which
are, indeed, closely linked to one another, are announced in
Galileo's polemical work *The Assayer,* and it is worth looking at
both passages in some detail to see how his program and that
of the then new mechanical philosophy are related to Portmann's distinction.

The first passage runs:

> Philosophy is written in this great book, the universe, which
> stands continually open to our gaze. But the book cannot be
> understood unless one first learns to comprehend the language
> and read the letters in which it is composed. It is written in the
> language of mathematics, and its characters are triangles, circles,
> and other geometric figures without which it is humanly impossi-
> ble to understand a single word of it; without these, one wanders
> about in a dark labyrinth.[4]

So authoritative is the place of mathematical physics in our
conception of scientific knowledge that we take this pronouncement as the enunciation, trail-blazing in its time, of
what is now a truism. Applied mathematics is the paradigm
case of science, science the paradigm case of knowledge; *of*

course someday all we know or can know will be statable in strict mathematical form. But let us think again and ask, first, what Galileo's statement really means, and second, whether it is true.

The language of nature, Galileo tells us, is one that we must learn. Certainly; all languages must be learned. But this is a language, he seems to be suggesting, which by no means everybody knows. It is not like one's mother tongue, assimilated in infancy by any normal human child; for certainly he is convinced that at least the wretched Sarsi, against whom his polemic is directed, has never learned it. The language of nature, then, is in some sense a foreign language. And indeed, for most of us, the language of mathematics, which *is* for Galileo nature's language, has to be learned in school, not at home; it is a secondary and artificial acquisition. It belongs, in other words, not to the life world, but to the secondary, painfully constructed world of learning. But how do we learn such a secondary, a foreign language? Either its alphabet is written like our own, and we have to learn the meanings of the words; or there is a foreign alphabet, a different kind of character, to be learned before we can get as far as trying to understand the words. The latter situation holds for nature as Galileo sees it: not even the letters of its language form part of our ordinary environment, for, he insists, we have to learn them too. And again, this is, of course, true of the language of mathematics: we have to familiarize ourselves with its formalisms before we can make use of them in order to understand what they have to teach. To the ordinary person, then, the language of nature bears to the perceptible surface of the things around him a relation rather like that which, for a native English speaker, a page of Chinese or Arabic bears to a page of ordinary English prose. Until he is trained to do so, he cannot make out so much as its constituent elements, let alone their meaning. In short, the universe that "lies open to our gaze" is, if Galileo is correct, a volume written in a secret code, which only the trained cryptographer can interpret. The rest of us can only "wander in a dark labyrinth."

Is this true? Are all of us blind to nature who have not learned to decipher the applied mathematician's code? Is there no mother tongue of nature that we have learned in early childhood and on the ground of which we acquire the second, formal speech of mathematics?

Two aspects of our conceptual situation obstruct an honest answer to these questions. One is the product of that very revolution in which Galileo was engaged. The "naturalistic" world view which it engendered has been often described; but what is seldom acknowledged in such expositions is the sediment of ordinary, prescientific human experience out of which this, like any world view, developed and which it cannot wholly replace. In other words, the "objective" world of science, and especially of applied mathematics, must be distinguished from the "life world," the world shared by all human beings, in and out of which it develops.[5] "Nature" within the main tradition of modern science, in other words, is an *objectified* nature, and this is Galilean nature. If, moreover, Galilean nature was a construct of the seventeenth-century revolution, so is it a construct, within the life world, in the life history of each of us. We have each of us a dwelling place on this earth, a biological environment, within which, and transcending which, we assimilate, in the process of education, the intellectual framework of our culture. The distinction between the *environment* (*Umwelt*) of animals and the *world* of man (*Welt*) can be transposed into a distinction between the primary and secondary worlds of man himself. As human beings we dwell primarily, and immediately, in the life world; as participants in modern Western culture we acquire, as we mature, the intellectual framework of modern objective thought, within that primary frame. But— and this is the point in our present context—as we acquire our cultural heritage, we come to dwell in it also. We assimilate it to our persons and identify it on the one hand with our primary world and on the other with reality itself. So nature comes to *mean* to us Galilean nature, and the existence of the primary life world is ignored.

Second, most of us live and have always lived in an urban, industrial environment. Man is an earth-dwelling animal among other animals; urban man lives densely jammed among other human beings, indeed, but his nonhuman environment is chiefly one of artifacts. He is cut off by roads and pavements from earth itself, by smog and steam from the sky, by electricity from hewing wood and drawing water, by processed and packaged foods from man's age-old wrestling with the elements in heaven and earth to gain his sustenance. He may make parks and gardens for his own amusement, climb rocks for sport, or relax at the seaside in the sun. But the abstract language of mathematics may well be, for him, the only language of nature he has ever learned. Yet he sleeps and wakes; he has been born and will die. And he is in the first instance part of a biological unit, the family—and we have all been told how difficult it is for him to mature successfully into full humanity if he has been deprived of this normal biological beginning. Even in his technocratic world, moreover, he needs to re-create for himself analogues of nature, not only islands of living nature itself in parks and zoos but colored surfaces and artificial rhythms to fill in the unnatural emptiness of life seemingly founded in artifact and abstraction: the demands of the life world persist. But in an industrial environment these needs are disguised and neglected, and the sophisticated city-dweller can easily identify the objective world of science and technology with "nature" itself. He is a Galilean to the point of denying the existence of nature in the primary sense.

If, however, we can, by acknowledging them, hold in abeyance these disabilities, we must admit that, taken at its face value, Galileo's pronouncement is false. Of course nature includes the geometrical shapes which are his favored mathematical "characters" but much more too: colors and sounds and tastes and smells. This is, indeed, just what Galileo denies in the other crucial passage I want to examine here. Swayed by the authority of physics and its mythology, we have too sheepishly followed him in his denial and again have overlooked the full implications of his statement. In the passage in which he initiates the distinction between primary and secondary qualities (or, strictly speaking, revives the ancient Democritean distinction), he puts his thesis as follows:

> Now I say that whenever I conceive any material or corporeal substance, I immediately feel the need to think of it as bounded, and as having this or that shape; as being large or small in relation to other things, and in some specific place at any given time; as being in motion or at rest; as touching or not touching some other body; and as being one in number, or few, or many. From these conditions I cannot separate such a substance by any stretch of my imagination. But that it must be white or red, bitter or sweet, noisy or silent, and of sweet or foul odor, my mind does not feel compelled to bring in as necessary accompaniments. Without the senses as our guides, reason or imagination unaided would probably never arrive at qualities like these. Hence I think that tastes, odors, colors, and so on are no more than mere names so far as the object in which we place them is concerned, and that they reside only in the consciousness. Hence *if the living creatures were removed,* all these qualities would be wiped away and annihilated. But since we have imposed upon them special names, distinct from those of the other and real qualities mentioned previously, we wish to believe that they really exist as actually different from those.[6]

How true, we say. This is the story of Eddington's two tables: the hard, brown, smooth, coffee-stained or ink-stained object in my study which is my table and the buzzing congeries of billions of subatomic particles which is the physicist's table, the

real table. But think of the condition on which the whole construction depends: "if the living creature were removed." This
great book of nature, in other words, would be a nature deprived of life. And a fortiori it would be a nature without ourselves. But surely it is our world, the nature we live in, and the
nature that we are, that we are trying to read. Yet the letters of
Galilean nature exclude the language of life, including the life
of man. And this is quite literally so: for modern naturalism
has, and can have, no adequate concepts for the interpretation
of organic phenomena nor for the disciplines that deal with
that most strange though most familiar animal, man.

Yet we do have a world of color and taste and smell and
sound which is not just part of our individual subjectivity but
part of our biological environment, genetically determined as
much as our more "mechanical" powers are determined. To
this, of course, the Galilean answers: but all these perceptions
are "determined" by physics and chemistry: sound waves, light
waves, and the chemistry of taste and smell. And it is true, of
course, that *conditions* for all our perceptive powers, and those
of all animals, are given by physicochemical laws. But in its
qualitative nature, perception has laws of its own, which do not
indeed contradict the laws of inorganic nature, but are nevertheless not identical with them.

Portmann presents as an example of this fact the human
"world of color." Color perception has its own laws which are
laws of "the living creature," and this is both our nature and the
nature of the world as the human living creature's world. It was
this aspect of color vision that was the primary theme of
Goethe's *Farbenlehre*, not in contradiction, but in supplemen-
tation, of Newton's more artificial experiments. Goethe's "color
circle" presented a sequence of *seen* hues with their own intrinsic order—an order that was simply not discoverable in terms
of the physical theory of "pure" colors. Physicists have recently
begun to pay attention to Goethe's results; moreover, the work

of E. P. Land on color vision, though controversial, has raised dramatically the question of laws of visual perception distinct from the physicist's classical trichromatic theory. To put it briefly: Land has shown that the superposed projections of two black and white pictures, one through a red filter, can produce, for the spectator, a picture filled, not, as one would expect, with a uniform pink, but with a variety of colors, including greens and blues, strikingly similar to the colors of the original subject. Whether or not this result "disproves" the classical theory, it certainly suggests—and very powerfully—that the laws of vision are more subtle and complex than the theories of Young, Maxwell, and Helmholtz would have led one to suspect.[7]

Such laws, of course, by no means invalidate the physicist's investigations of isolated colors nor the classical laws of color mixing where the physicist's special conditions prevail. No one is suggesting that they do. But the point is that there are natural laws characterizing many levels and dimensions of reality. The laws of more complex entities, such as organisms, do not indeed conflict with the laws of physics and chemistry, but neither are they "determined" by them. And to investigate adequately the regularities of such more complex existences, the scientist needs to apply his analytical techniques to the *natural* context: he has to take account of the living world of his subject. It is on the reality and significance of this richer context that Portmann is insisting.

It is, then, the whole range of perceived and perceptible phenomena, the nature which would not be at all were the living creature, with his sense organs, not existent or not at least possible, that Portmann calls *authentic phenomena*. What for Galileo is authentic because independent of living things, and existent out of all relation to them, is for Portmann *inauthentic*, just because of its want of such relation. It is not genuinely appearance because it does not and cannot appear *to* anyone. And conversely, what for Galileo is a "mere name," given real-

ity only by the living creature's presence, and therefore inauthentic, is for Portmann authentic, just because it does, or can,
properly be said to *appear*. His nature is nature with living
creatures in it, not, by a contrary-to-fact condition, reasoned
away, and its qualities, rather than being "mere names," call on
us to name them.

True, this is not a simple reversal: movements are also "authentic" for Portmann insofar as they appear to our perceptions, and they are, of course, truly part of nature for Galileo.
Yet even the motions apparent in full natural reality are not
what the physicist studies: from Galileo's inclined-plane experiment on, he has studied progressively more abstract relations
of ideal motion, contrived through ingenious experiment, remote from the movements of everyday life. Rivers flowing,
plants growing, fishes swimming, birds flying, our own changes
of attitude, our speech: all these, not the physicists' pointer
readings, are authentic phenomena. Nature for Portmann is in
the first instance nature seen and heard, not nature reasoned
out in the physicist's dream of a mathematically ordered world.

Authentic phenomena, then, are the perceptible surface of
the things around us: rocks, clouds, stars, and above all the
pullulating variety of plant and animal life as seen and heard.
Now, most modern biologists, it must be admitted, would
make short work of this conception. They would agree in fact
with Galileo: such surfaces will appear mere names once science has "explained" them, and such explanation, they insist, is
partly imminent, partly already achieved. Granted, such biologists argue, that colors, sounds, smells, tastes, do indeed enter,
in important *functional* ways, into the life histories of plants
and animals. They are confident, however, on the one hand,
that such matters can be explained as effects of underlying
macromolecular causes. And on the other hand they insist that
all such macroscopic functions with all the perceiver-per-
ceived relations they entail are also to be explained by mechan-

ical causes, in particular by the so-called "mechanism" of natural selection. Bees are attracted by colored petals; the colors of flowers are therefore "explained" by pollination through the flight of bees. Thrushes take more pink and brown snails on the green leaves in summer, more yellow snails on the brown earth in winter; color polymorphism in the common land snail is thus "explained" by the resulting alterations in "selection pressure." And, of course, both the colors of the snail shells and the vision of their predators, the thrushes, are themselves explained in physicochemical terms. It all boils down in the long run to matter in motion in the classical Galilean form.

To this purely functional interpretation of authentic phenomena Portmann makes two objections. First, he does not agree that all the great multiplicity of situations in which animals *appear* to other animals can be interpreted *exhaustively* in terms of natural selection. Selection can indeed explain the change of such phenomena, but not their origin. Thus color polymorphism can, of course, be maintained by change of selective pressure; but the snails and their colors must pre-exist for selection to work on them. Nor is mutation, the major complementary principle of neo-Darwinian explanation, adequate to account for the origin of complex patterns. Not only are nearly all mutations deleterious but they too are, again, minute deviations from complex genetic formulae already in existence. To extrapolate these two well-established principles of micro-evolution to the whole range of living phenomena in their whole development is, Portmann believes, a procedure unjustified by the present state of our knowledge.

Second, the range and complexity of authentic phenomena, Portmann argues, far exceed those functional needs which alone natural selection can explain. To explain the elaborate pattern of the peacock's tail, for example, by natural selection in the orthodox fashion meant attributing to the female a kind of artistic connoisseurship in her preference for the more clearly elaborated and "harmonious" effect. Recent experiments with these and allied species, however, have suggested two more plausible but restricted explanations for the functional aspect of the peacock's fan. First, the female displays from an early age a marked response to small kernel-shaped objects; this is plainly a drive connected with feeding behavior and would account for the selective advantage of clearly developed eyes in the fan. Second, the fan and the whole courtship dance seem to furnish an over-all index of the liveliness and individual superiority of a given male. Now, both these explanations again are selective; in neither context, however, need we invoke the anthropomorphic conception of a developed artistic taste on the part of the female. But what then of the whole intricacy of the pattern, which is, relative to both these ends, superfluous? We cannot explain them, Portmann insists, by reference to any automatic external control, but must acknowledge that they have a value of their own:

> We know of many patterns that exist without any possibility of direct natural selection and the special formal properties of which can in no way be attributed to selection. The morphologist is led to the assumption that the genetic endowment of an organism includes special systems of factors whose role is directed to the development of complex patterns. Such genetic factors are directed to these achievements just as other genetic processes are aimed at the construction of a brain, a kidney or a heart.[8]

This is not, be it noted, to deny the importance of selection in general and of the selective control of patterns in particular. Indeed, Portmann himself has published a textbook on protective coloration.[9] What he is denying is simply that the whole intricate detail of living pattern is to be explained *solely* in selective terms. Sometimes and in some respects it is so and can be shown experimentally to be so. But not therefore always and in all respects. Selection explains the maintenance of some patterns—as in stick insects, for example—but not the maintenance in all their detail of all patterns, nor, indeed, the origin of any. To claim that it *must* do so is to make an unwarranted extrapolation supported in its comprehensive import, not by experiment, but by the demands of an oversimple methodology and an overdogmatic metaphysic.

Further emphasizing and expanding this point, and more directly contradicting the neo-Darwinian reduction of all organic phenomena to their functions, Portmann divides authentic phenomena further into two classes: *addressed* and *unaddressed*. By *unaddressed phenomena* he means such appearances of living things as do not have their *raison d'être* in being directed to the sense organs of other animals of the same or other kinds. The superfluity of detail in the peacock's fan, over and above its selective utility, would be such a phenomenon. So is the black pattern on the wing of the mother-of-pearl butterfly, where size and background color have been shown to be the necessary conditions for mating behavior, but where the lively black pattern can vary or even be absent without effect. "The pattern as such," Portmann comments, "however 'optically' it may affect us, is in the details of its form, even in its existence or non-existence, functionally insignificant. . . . Yet it is there."[10] Such phenomena are unaddressed in the sense that they do not have their meaning in an act of vision. Even more plainly "unaddressed," moreover, are the patterns of animals without vision, where a "technical," selective explanation of shapes and colors is on principle impossible. Portmann describes the dramatic variations and arrangements of color in sea snails, which the marine biologist observes, and which to him, again, are optically effective, but which can have no optical significance for their eyeless owners, nor, presumably, in such elaborate detail as they display, for the inhabitants of their normal environment. Even if they serve to warn off predators, *any* bright color would suffice to meet this need; the whole detailed pattern, and the variety of patterns, far transcend the selective demand.[11] Yet there they are: the oranges and blues and purples and golds in glowing regular array. From a Galilean point of view, this riot of color and immense diversity of constant form must be in some so far wholly unintelligible way purely coincidental to the mechanisms of living, while these in their turn must be but epiphenomena of the working of inorganic laws. Yet that "the living creature" does display to our perception colors, sounds, smells, and, at higher levels of life, responds to these displays in others is a massive fact of the living world around us, a puzzling, even a mysterious, fact, but still a fact. We have no right, in the name of science, to deny the fact just because our favored kind of explanation, a Galilean explanation, could not allow it to exist.

On the contrary, the appearance of living things, the way they show themselves in surface pattern, in rhythms of movement or voice, constitutes for Portmann one of the two basic characters of living things as such. This fundamental character of life he calls *Selbstdarstellung*, life's showing of itself on the surface. The concept is difficult to render in a single English word; with some hesitation, I shall translate it as "display," emphasizing, however, that its meaning is wider than the usual biological concept. Ordinarily display means an active posturing of an animal, as in courtship display and the like. As a rendering of *Selbstdarstellung*, however, I am using "display" in a sense similar perhaps to its use in merchandising. It includes active display, but also all the passive show of animal shapes and patterns. These, Portmann has demonstrated, have their own laws, clearly genetically determined with as much complexity and regularity as any more "functional" characters. All animals but the very simplest have an outer layer, a skin, marked in characteristic, often symmetrical and highly complex patterns, in contrast to the less regular arrangement of their internal organs. Even in very simple transparent animals, Port-

mann points out, the internal organs are often knotted up in
the corner as if not to interfere with the symmetry of the over-
all body design. For such species, moreover, as for the sea
snails, visible patterns cannot (except partially and indirectly)
serve a "useful" purpose, because they have no eyes; yet pattern is nevertheless constant, intricate, and universal in these
cases as it is also in all higher forms of life. Why? No one can
say; but it is a basic character of living things that it is so.

By hardheaded evolutionists, Portmann will doubtless be accused of "teleology," "vitalism," and "mysticism." What of these
charges? Note, first, that it is the neo-Darwinians whose
thought, in this context, is overteleological. They must have a
"function" for everything, because otherwise selection could
not control it. Descriptive laws, simply accepting a massive
body of phenomena, though not "explaining" them, they cannot stomach, if these phenomena plainly resist their favored
form of teleology, that is, "improvement" through the external
control of natural selection. Portmann, on the contrary, is not
invoking any mysterious "purpose" for display; he is simply
acknowledging its existence, admitting openly a massive reality
to which Galilean thinkers must close their minds, as well as
their eyes. The patterns of animals, feathers, scales, and so on,
are indeed, he insists, in principle "explicable" in terms of their
foundation in a genetic basis, as all persistent characters are.
And they may someday be explicable not only causally but in
the sense that we may find some new—other than functional—
perspective out of which to understand them. For the present,
however, we should honestly admit the existence of organic
display as a given, an ultimate, fact of the organic world. We
have no adequate theory to explain the fact; only an adumbra-
tion of causal laws, in genetics, which could account for its persistence and modification, though not for its ultimate origin.

Is this "mysticism"? In a sense: openness to unexplained phenomena is openness to mystery, and Portmann likes to stress
the mysterious complexity of life in a way which intensely irri-

tates mechanistically minded biologists. But why is it "unscientific" to admit the unexplained, to turn afresh to the phenomena? To face and acknowledge mysteries may be, not the rejection of science, but the first step to discovery. Besides, are not scientists supposed to pride themselves on "open-mindedness"? Yet it is scarcely "open-minded" to deny the very existence of the whole range of non-Galilean phenomena which constitute most of the living world and therefore of our own lives as living beings.

Nor, finally, is the acknowledgment of display as a basic character of living things a renewal of "vitalism." It does, indeed, involve resistance to reductivism: to the view that life is "nothing but" statistical variations in the gene pools of populations. But it has nothing to do with any addition of a mysterious "life force" over and above the obvious appearance of the things themselves.

3

It is from Galileo's rejection of secondary qualities that I have tried to approach Portmann's concept of authentic phenomena and of display as a basic character of living things. "Display," however, is not simply color, sound, smell, as such, but the exhibition to the senses of animals of perceptible forms and patterns characteristic of other animals, whether of their own or other species. It is display *of*—what? Living things are not mere surfaces, nor are they, as used to be said, simply "sacks full of functions." Just as their superficies, their appearances to one another, form a significant, indeed essential, aspect of their nature, so does what very broadly speaking one can call their "inner life." A second essential character of living things, in other words, inseparably allied to but contrasted with display, consists in the fact that organisms are *centers* of perceptions, drives, and actions. This is most plainly true of ourselves and of mammals close to ourselves, as we feel, in the scale of living things. We *know* that we are conscious and that our awareness of our own identity somehow matters through all the variations and vicissitudes of our actions upon and passivities to our natural and cultural environments. We know, moreover, that our conscious thought is only a narrow center of a much broader field of unconscious processes. The totality of our "sentient" life far outruns its self-conscious, wide-awake core: it ranges from the narrow circle of focal awareness through a continuum of gradations all the way to the wholly unconscious. Indeed, many of the transactions through which we both master and submit to our environment, and through which we make it a human world, are on principle entirely out of range of consciousness; yet they are nevertheless *our* achievements. Such, for example, is the achievement of color vision.

We do indeed *see* the colors and know that we see them, but we cannot "see" or in any direct way apprehend what our nervous system has done to achieve this end. Taking consciousness, then, as a narrow center of a much wider range of inner dealings with the outer world, we may extend this extension to include another phenomenon which, again, in our experience of the world, we immediately and indubitably confront, namely, the fact that other animals, especially higher mammals, appear and behave, in a way analogous to our own, as "centers of doing and letting be." Stimulus-response theory, for all its vaunted "objectivism," cannot explain away the massive confrontation with animals as living centers: the experience, for example, of Rilke watching a panther pacing his cage:

> Der weiche Gang geschmeidig starker Schritte,
>   der sich im allerkleinsten Kreise dreht,
> ist wie ein Tanz von Kraft um eine Mitte,
>   in der betaubt ein grosser Wille steht.

> Circling, revolving, lithe prowling strength soft-footed,
>   The narrow ring he treads is like a dance,

> A dance of power with at the center rooted
> A great will stupefied, a will in trance.[12]

Rilke's poem begins with the "look" of the panther (*sein Blick*), all but destroyed by the bars of his captivity. And it is, indeed, on those occasions when we meet the eyes of an animal with our own—just as we encounter our own kind "face to face"— that we acknowledge most directly the centered depth of animal life. A dog, unnaturally bound to human life, directs to his master a mute appeal that seems at first sight to make him, like a Hegelian slave, a personality only in relation to another, fuller personality. Yet, turned back into itself by the impassible barrier that language erects between ourselves and other creatures, his look displays at the same time a structured resonance of mood, of character, sometimes almost of something analogous to wisdom.

But the most eloquent animal countenances belong to our closer kin, the apes. The quality of this life, so familiar to us, yet so foreign, Portmann illustrates with the picture of a male gorilla from the Basel zoo, or of a gorilla mother and child. How rich a center of experience meets us here: the muteness of the gaze serves but to deepen the reverberation of the mood that confronts us. Whatever our *theories* of animal behavior or animal evolution, we must acknowledge quite simply and factually the presence here of a center in which the living being's dealings with its environment are drawn together and from which they radiate.

As we move further from our own obvious near kin, the life we confront seems more alien to us, but at a few removes the centered structure is still clearly there; even a kind of awareness is still undeniable. A case from H. Bruhin's study of deer strikingly illustrates this:

> The position of a male with high social standing is abruptly shattered as soon as he loses his antlers. In the spring of 1951, in

the Basel Zoo, I was able to watch the moment when a fallow-buck sank to a lower level (a, β, γ, here describe the levels in social rank). On April 18th, at 3:45 P.M. the herd of five males and eight females were begging for food from the zoo visitors. Suddenly they were slightly startled by a playing child, so that some of them trotted off, including the a male. He happened to graze with the right side of his antlers the branch of a fir-tree lying in the enclosure. Immediately this half of the antlers fell clattering to the ground. Obviously upset, with tail raised, he sniffed at the piece he had just lost. Almost at the same moment the β buck realized what had happened, and attacked and pursued him vigorously. The other three yearling antler-less γ bucks took scarcely any notice of the occurrence nor did the does. After about half an hour both the a and β bucks had more or less calmed down and were again begging for food. But the former a buck was not tolerated at the fence by his rival, and therefore kept right at the back of the enclosure. There was only an indication of a social clash between a and γ bucks. Up to the evening the one-palmed animal carried out peculiar head movements, as were observed by Heck (1935) after the loss of antlers. On 23rd April the β buck also shed his first antlers. From this time on there was the same social ranking as had prevailed before the a animal shed his. In this case it can therefore be clearly established that the antlers, "representing a particular social position," also lose their significance as representative organ when one half is lost, and this loss results in its owner going down the social scale.[13]

That the stag "knows" about his antlers is confirmed by many other studies, notably, for example, those of Hediger on the psychology of animals both in captivity and in the wild.[14]

Now, admittedly as we move still further from styles of living like our own, it seems strange to speak at all of an animal's "knowing" what it is doing, to speak of "consciousness" or even in some more tenuous sense "awareness." Yet in some way even a hydra moving its tentacles or an amoeba its pseudopodia is showing in the broadest sense a kind of "sentience" and through this, again, is controlling the patterns of its relation to the surrounding world. Looking downward across the continuum of life, we find universally some such principle, which is unlike anything in the inorganic world. Mechanists like Loeb, early in this century, hoped to reduce all living processes to "tropisms"; Fraenkel and Gunn twenty-five years ago made a similar attempt to explain animal orientation in purely mechanical terms. But animals do not simply *move;* they *behave.* They do not simply display *reactions,* as acids and bases do, they perform—to borrow a psychologist's term—*transactions.* But transactions demand an agent, an individual center of giving and taking, of doing and ceasing to do. However strange to us the "inner life" of animals, especially of invertebrates, remote as they are from our own patterns of living, we must in some extended sense admit the presence of such centers of experience where there is animal life at all. Even plants, although we should scarcely ascribe to them awareness in any sense at all, are still organized centers of growth and form.

This second pervasive and essential character of organisms Portmann describes by the phrase *Weltbeziehung durch Innerlichkeit,* again, a difficult phrase to make viable in English. "Relation to the environment through inwardness": a hopelessly awkward expression! "Inwardness" alone, on the other hand, is too exclusively subjective and fails to convey the *relatedness* that Portmann's concept entails. I shall use, therefore, a neologism, "centricity," to convey what, as I understand it, Portmann means, and say that centricity, along with display, is a fundamental character of living things. Again, this statement is not meant to explain anything, but to acknowledge the existence of a range of phenomena too often neglected or even denied. But if we cannot, obviously, get inside the skins, so to speak, of other organic beings and feel how their way of living feels, we need not deny that such lives exist and have, in a way forever inaccessible to us, their own style of significance. In a passage reminiscent of our earlier reflections on the Galilean language of nature, Portmann writes:

> The inwardness of these forms, widely different from our own organisation, speaks to us through its appearance. That we cannot translate this language into human words is no reason not to see the appearance itself. If, in a distant country, I attend a dramatic performance, of which I understand not a single word, I shall not on that account assert that nothing at all is being presented, that nothing is happening but a random noise.[15]

Not that centricity cannot be studied. It is indeed not only a quality of life acknowledged at the boundary of science but a domain of life accessible indirectly to analytical methods, as the experimental ingenuity of modern research into animal behavior has amply proved. Portmann has described some of these studies in his book *Animals as Social Beings,* from which I have already quoted, and there are numerous other places where one can read about them, like Tinbergen's *Social Behavior in Animals* or Lack's *Life of the Robin* or Lorenz's *King Solomon's Ring.*[16] What Portmann is emphasizing, however, is an implication of all this work which ethologists themselves, reared in the faith of "pure objectivism," often fear to face. Thus he says, for example, in discussing the phenomenon of *territory* (in a chapter on "The World of the Dragonflies"): "The realization that territory is a biological fact has helped to obtain full attention for the subjective spheres of owning and defending it, and has made the most subjective thing of all, the individual's experience and social impulses, a field for new objective research."[17] This frank avowal of the existence of the *subject,* not simply as a fringe phenomenon, but as the object of scientific research, may have, like the concept of display, far-reaching consequences for our thinking about nature, about science, and about ourselves.

Revolutionary concepts, however, are hard to take seriously.

Perhaps we may strengthen our grasp of this concept by considering some objections that might be made to it by more orthodox biologists.

Our most immediate and massive experience of centricity comes from our own experience of our own inner life; the inner core that holds together the threads of organism-environment relation in other species we can never directly know. What Portmann is doing in counting centricity a basic character of all life, therefore, is to extrapolate something we know in ourselves and apply it, if in diminished form, to all organisms. Yet Portmann hesitates, as we have seen, to follow the extrapolation of the neo-Darwinian's basic concepts, mutation and natural selection, from experiments on present-day selective change, where they undoubtedly do serve as adequate explanatory principles, to the whole panorama of phylogeny, where, taken by themselves, they do not seem adequate. How, then, it might be objected, is he justified in extrapolating what may well be a unique character of our own, the possession of consciousness, to the whole living world? To this objection there would be several answers.

First, Portmann is by no means alleging that "consciousness" or "mind" is to be predicated of all animals, let alone plants as well. Consciousness as we experience it is one expression, one style, of centricity. Even in the human individual it forms in fact only a narrow band in the much wider spectrum of mental life. And so, since even our own awareness is by no means wholly focal, we need no great imaginative effort to extend a generalized concept of sentience of some sort at least to other animals. Second, consciousness in us, or sentience in a broader sense in animals generally, is again but the inner expression of centricity as such: of the fact that organisms are centers of metabolism and development, of ordered reaching out toward an environment and taking in from it, of birth and death. It is this centered dynamic, dependent as it is on the existence of *individuals,* that *is* characteristic of all life and is *not* characteristic of inorganic phenomena.

Third, one reason for approaching the general concept of centricity *from* our own consciousness as its characteristic human expression is that it is this expression, this dimension of centricity, which we know most intimately and indubitably. We also know, immediately and massively, that some similar structure characterizes other higher animals; and, finally, even as we try in imagination to lessen the intensity of centricity in its aspect of inwardness, we are still *describing,* and describing what is common to the living forms we see before us and around us here and now. We are not suggesting abstract explanatory theories nor extrapolating these to a vast and remote past, but only trying to pin down with a fitting phrase a description of a common quality of our present experienced world. Portmann's extrapolation, therefore, is less adventuresome than the Darwinian, since it is descriptive and contemporary, rather than explanatory of an inaccessible past.

To such an answer, however, it might be objected that, however plainly "descriptive" the concepts Portmann is introducing, they exceed the scientist's brief in a way in which the Darwinian extrapolation from present to past does not do. For even if centricity is not equivalent to consciousness or sentience, it does involve a reference to inwardness—not just to a geometrical center or a midpoint of centripetal forces or the like, but to a literally *subjective* center. And such a reference, it would be alleged by the orthodox biologist, is obviously nonobjective and therefore nonscientific. The Darwinian account of evolution as the product of chance mutation and external selective control, on the other hand, invokes, its adherents believe, no concepts not compatible with strict scientific mechanism: it is "life" in Galilean terms. And it is true, indeed, as we have seen in our discussion of display, that Portmann's reflections about living things cannot be contained within the frame of Galilean science. Rather they arise from an effort like that of the phenomenologists to overcome the abstractions of the Galilean tradition and return "to the things themselves."

Moreover, such a return, and in particular the acknowledgment of centricity as a pervasive character of living things, permits not only a truer account of nature in general but a reassimilation in reasonable terms of human nature to the living world. In the main tradition of modern naturalism, man must appear either as wholly alien to nature, like Galileo's "living creature," or as reduced to meaninglessness, simply one more expression of the laws of matter in motion. The achievements of man, art, religion, legal and political institutions, science itself, *can* have no significance in a naturalistic one-level world, where there *is*, on principle, nothing but particles in a four-dimensional space-time continuum. Admittedly, if mechanism were true—if the book of the universe spread before us *were* Galilean—we should have to resign ourselves to this dismal fact: the only appropriate philosophy would be one of absurdism or of despair. Yet why should we so resign ourselves? In loyalty to the "facts"? But the naturalist interpretation of man is itself in palpable contradiction of the "facts" of our experience, even of living nature other than man, let alone of the massive human fact of consciousness, of the inner lives we do in fact lead. It seems intellectually justifiable, therefore, to try to revise our thinking about nature in such a way as to assimilate harmoniously to our basic view of things those aspects of our experience, so close to our deepest hopes and needs, which Galilean science must either deny or exile to some limbo of paradox and anomaly. And it is this more harmonious philosophy, this reintegration of man *into* nature, I believe, that Portmann's account of the characters of living things can help us to achieve.

One more warning, however. Portmann is not in the least denying, but only supplementing, the great storehouse of biological knowledge accumulated by a more mechanistically oriented science. In particular, he is not denying the importance of *self-maintenance* as a characteristic of organic nature. In fact, we may add self-maintenance here, parenthetically, as a third basic character of living things. For all the intricate mechanisms of reproduction, growth, metabolism, regeneration, learning behavior, and so on are, of course, rightly interpreted by biologists as devices for the preservation of the individual and the species. Many biologists, however, would make self-maintenance, or "survival," the sole explanatory principle for all organic phenomena. And where they are in fact studying in detail particular physiological or genetic mechanisms, there is, again, nothing wrong with this. But it is in the philosophical implications of their work, when they think about them, that they go astray.

Animals must indeed be adapted to their environments if they are to survive, and such techniques for survival do form a very substantial, perhaps even the major, segment of the totality of living structure and process. But biologists, under the guiding influence of Darwinian theory, often treat living things as *nothing but* aggregates of such techniques. Life, they seem to believe, *is* adaptation. And adaptation is the fitting of the organism into its internal and external environment in such a way as to enable it to survive; in other words, it is the sum total of *means to survival*. Now, the governing concept in this kind of thinking seems to be *utility*. Organisms are understood as aggregates of devices useful for survival. Thus a woodpecker's beak is useful for getting insects out of trees; the brooding habits of fishes and birds are useful for keeping the young alive; the colors of snails are useful in hiding them from hungry thrushes; and so on through the whole vast variety of living functions and forms. Utility, however, is a doubly relative concept. A use is a use not only *for* something—in this case, survival—but also to *someone*. Birds, fishes, snails: in every case there is an individual or a group of individuals, that is, a species, to whom the activity or pattern or process in the case is useful. How is the biologist to interpret this term of the adaptive relation, the individual woodpecker who gets his meals or the individual snail who does not get eaten by the thrush? There are two alternatives. Either the individual is itself simply useful for some further end, or it is intrinsically valuable and presupposed as such in the original predication of utility. In the former case, we have to say, as Dobzhansky has done on occasion, that the whole life of multicellular organisms is *nothing but* a device for the self-duplication and recombination of the only part of living things that can survive indefinitely, namely, the genes. In other words, a hen is an egg's way of making another egg[18]—an amusing, but also surely an absurd fashion of looking at all the achievements of all living things, including the whole of human culture as well as all the immense variety of plant and animal life. The other alternative is to acknowledge frankly that mechanisms for self-maintenance, however complex and fascinating in themselves as objects of study, are all of them instrumental in relation to the intrinsic value of the entities so maintained. And that is just what Portmann's criteria of display and centricity are meant to convey. Living things as they display themselves to the world and as they carry on, out of their own centered existence, ordered transactions with their environments, are significant in themselves. The criterion of self-maintenance, important though it is, must be counted only as a third character in subordination to the other two.

In this connection it is revealing, as Portmann points out, that the first great experimental embryologist, Wilhelm Roux, insisted on the need to refer to *Innerlichkeit*, "inwardness," as a pervasive character of life. Roux's *Mechanics of Development* is one of the great landmarks in the advance of modern biology toward the ideal of exact experimental science. Yet this great founding father of objectivism asserted that for every characteristic living process, development, reproduction, metabolism, heredity and the like, one should really put the prefix "self-" ahead of each such term.[19] So in self-maintenance generally, in all the processes through which the living individual achieves and preserves its being, the self that is so maintaining itself is necessarily presupposed as the significant entity, the center of action, experience, success, and failure, whose being all its manifold techniques for survival subserve.

The social life of animals, as Portmann interprets it, plainly exhibits the balance between self-maintenance and centricity as dominant features of organic life. He writes:

> The observer of social life must time and again be shifting his attention between two different aspects. In one of these, society is an organization where the individual has value merely by being a member of it: it is considerably limited in possibilities of self-expression, but contributes towards achievements only realisable in society and is integrated with other individuals for purposes which can be seen only in judging the whole. In the other aspect, equally essential and indeed complementary, the individual finds complete fulfillment only in and through social life, which allows the greatest possible "individuality" and vitality for individuals.[20]

In the first of these aspects, social life is geared to the maintenance, not, it is true, primarily of the individual, but of the species. In the selective process it is those characters which increase the probability of an organism's leaving descendants that are favored. Portmann mentions as one example of such a process the breeding habits of the Emperor penguin as compared with its near relations:

> During the reproductive season, when these penguins live on land, the conditions of existence are more than forbidding. In Terre Adélie, where they were thoroughly investigated by the French Antarctic expedition, they lived in temperatures of from −13° to −31° (Fahrenheit) and endure snowstorms which rage at eighty miles an hour. According to the expedition's doctor and biologist, J. Sapin-Jaloustre (1952), "a human being is blinded

by the ice mask which forms on his face in a minute, whatever his protective clothing; his breathing is laboured, and he finds himself incapable of the slightest effort. A small area of naked human skin freezes in about 40 seconds. If he moves as much as 50 yards from his shelter, he will have lost all his physical faculties including seeing and hearing and any kind of bearing, and will never find his way back!"

In such conditions, in the dark winter of the Antarctic, the Emperor penguins breed. Besides many favourable physical dispositions, they are helped to survive by special modifications in behavior: e.g., their strikingly motionless waiting in one place, which avoids loss of energy; and perhaps also the production of sounds as means of communication instead of the very "detailed" gesture-language used by other penguins. The conspicuous absence of many typically penguin ceremonials is bound to work in those border regions of life as a species-preserving economy in the metabolism.

These giant penguins are remarkably peaceable, without any aggressive urges, any need for a breeding couple's territory, or any hierarchical order. This is particularly useful at the beginning of a snowstorm, when the colony throng together in a narrow space, forming the so-called "tortoise-shell," whereby they face the raging blizzard as a compact mass, exposing to it only the smallest possible area of their bodies and completely protecting within the shell the chicks which are specially endangered.

They only become combative where an egg or a chick is concerned, for in Sapin-Jaloustre's description, "the drive to possess and nurse a chick is common to all the adults, and is so powerful and striking that Wilson called it 'pathetic.' Immediately a chick emerges from the skin-flap of the parent-bird's stomach, or is left by the parent bird, those penguins which have no chicks vie with each other to take charge of it. Pressing and pushing, the old birds peck dangerously, trying to thrust the chick on to their feet (on which the chicks are isolated from the ice surface of the ground). In the process the chicks are roughly handled, and their skin is often injured. Many are thus destroyed by love! Wilson tells us that they often try to escape and hide in cracks in the ice, to avoid this terrible devotion—that they prefer to starve or freeze to death!"

It thus happens that an egg has many hatchers, a chick many protectors, not only the actual parent birds. By and large, all eggs and chicks are cared for by the whole colony. "This communal brooding and rearing of young by a succession of old birds means a considerable economy, compared with the family structure of the Adélie penguins (the smaller Antarctic species) at the same stage of reproduction. The old birds can thus afford to spend four or five times as long in the fishing which is so necessary in this climate—all the more necessary just now because they must assuage the chicks' hunger as well as their own." [21]

We can see how such a species would have developed from a species like the King penguin, living in slightly less severe conditions. Any small mutations "which weaken penguins' normal drive for a brooding territory and limit aggressiveness to the drive to possess an egg or a chick" [22] would clearly have selective value, and the accumulation of many such mutations would finally issue in a pattern of behavior adapted, as the Emperor penguin is, to the most severe Antarctic conditions. The advantage, finally, of the birds' adapting themselves to this rigorous habitat is the access it gives them to an abundance of food and at the same time the absence of predators in that forbidding environment.

In general, variants in territory-possession, associated as this phenomenon is with reproduction, are clearly functions of the need to preserve the species: or strictly speaking, in selective terms, they are phenomena in the absence of which the species in question would have become extinct. Yet at the same time, territory-possession is not only a device for species preservation but marks the enhancement of individual life as well. Portmann cites, for example, R. A. Hinde's study of the social life of the great tit:

In winter the tits live in small flocks which roost and fly out foraging together. Among these flocks are the pairs which reared a brood together in the summer, sometimes keeping a little more "on their own," though without cutting themselves off from flock life. In early spring the males especially often have moments of aggressiveness against each other. The flock slowly disbands, because its members become increasingly affected by new inner states. The males are the first to break loose, and soon they are seen pairing up in a chosen area: the flocking season is once again over. The male now looks for favourite spots in his territory where he can sing. There are a great many of them when the pair first separate from the flock, but soon he shows greater selection, and there are only a few such points, to which he is tied by habit. Finally he develops a clear preference for a particular place, which he defends fiercely. He also defends the area round it, though with less intensity the further he gets from the favourite haunt.[23]

The tits come to "own" a brooding territory: . . .

So there develops what biologists call "ownership behavior," for it shows a striking resemblance to the human drive toward ownership: M. Meyer-Holzapfel (1952) has made a thorough comparative study of this drive in human beings and in animals. Such a comparison is far more than a piece of "biologist's license" to bring nearer home a bird's life. For in the case of these tits, for instance, their inner state, as revealed by external forms and behavior, can best be described by reference to familiar human experience, however uncertain the relation may be between that experience and the birds'. At any rate the tit pair "owns"—in a real sense—a brooding territory, which can be expanded in the brooding time or shrink somewhat (as careful investigations have shown).

This territory belongs to the pair: the favourite places make it into a specially attractive environment, in which very soon the nest will occupy a new favourite place. The individual tit is now a creature with its own private space, containing centres of particular importance. This space has its structure, like a magnetic field with lines of force which the physicist makes visible; indeed considering the progressive intensity with which it is defended, we might speak of the tension of the field and the intensity of the various points in it—as long as we manage to keep in mind the special, non-homogeneous character of a living "magnetic field." [24]

This kind of limited spatiality, Portmann continues, serves to enhance the individuality of the single animal:

> The male tit singing in his look-out is recognized from a distance by other tits in the vicinity as a particular bird. The territory thus adds distinguishing marks to those of body and behavior, it becomes a part of the whole individual, also an expression of his capacity for self-assertion. It has its inner side in the bird's experience: he knows his territory exactly, recognises it again when he returns there. Even the cuckoo, laying her eggs in other birds' nests, is governed by familiarity with her territory: although in choosing the nests she shows a preference for those belonging to particular species of song-birds, she will still, if need be, lay eggs in any unfamiliar nest (as many observers have reported) rather than go outside the bounds of her territory. [25]

Associated with such individual ownership behavior, moreover, is the mutual value to each other of a mating pair:

> In the roaming phases one bird will recognize and seek out his or her mate in their territory. Here as often, preservation of the species and enhancement of individuality go hand in hand. [26]

In a real sense, moreover, Portmann argues, a territory becomes *home:*

> An inner attachment to this place develops, it becomes a "home" associated with special values and feelings of familiarity and safety. Home is a place where through peace and security essential moods of every higher animal find most satisfaction. M. Holzapfel has shown the importance of such a home for a craterspider: if it has caught a fly in its web, its "appetite for home" is greater than its appetite for the prey, and it does not start sucking the fly's blood till it reaches the "soothing" atmosphere of its favourite haunt. We have seen earlier how "home-like" are sand-wasps' sleeping places. All these examples point to the de-

liberate satisfaction of a drive, which fosters a positive mood within the animal.[27]

This is only one instance among many. The existence of social ranking, for example, as in the case of the stag quoted earlier, is a conspicuous example of individuality in social life. Or again, the greater ferocity of combative behavior in mammals as against birds, Portmann believes, also reflects their increased individuality.

Ownership behavior, the sense of home, focuses organisms at a center in space. But centricity is expressed in time as well as space, in rhythms of living as well as in the cherishing of a dwelling place. Portmann reminds us that, as zoo keepers know, animals can be bored, needing to "fill time" as we do. Quite generally, he suggests, those aspects of social life which heighten individuality give meaning to life as it passes. So termites, for example, are more active, more "lively," in the presence of their royal pair, or bees of their queen.

Nor is time simply a stretch, waiting to be filled. Ordered process, rhythm, is indeed the fundamental expression of centricity. In a paper on "Time in the Life of the Organism," Portmann writes: "Every form of life appears to us as a *Gestalt* with a specific development in time as well as space. Living things, like melodies, might be said to be configured time; life manifests itself as configured time." [28] I can cite here only two examples from this remarkable paper. First, consider the duration of a minimal impression, or *moment*, in the life of a given species of organism. Experiments devised to measure such minimal durations indicate that the human moment lasts only about $\frac{1}{18}$ second; a dog's moment is roughly equivalent to ours, while the snail needs $\frac{1}{4}$ second, but the fighting fish only $\frac{1}{30}$ second to register an impression. Portmann comments:

It is hard to say what consequences such differences in the duration of the moment have for the animal's subjective experience and the structure of its world, and the scientist will do well not to say too much about the inner world of the snail or fighting fish—that is, the nature of their experience. Still, these animal experiments are of great value in that they show us once again how dependent our experience of the world is on our structure, and how significant a question it is whether this structure is adequate to the apperception of hidden reality. The infinite variety we may expect to find in this realm of "relations with time" is suggested by motion pictures of hummingbirds in flight. In the space of ⅛ second these tiny creatures, while remaining in one place, effect a complete revolution on their longitudinal axis and another on their transverse axis; at the same time they complete four wing beats. From this we may infer an amazing reaction velocity, which must in turn be reflected in the nature of the hummingbird's experience.[29]

Second, and obviously, the most dramatic integration of rhythms of living with larger temporal rhythms is the phenomenon of bird migration. Portmann, having warned of the extreme complexity of the processes involved, presents as one example of the correlation of bird life with the annual cycle the life of the arctic tern:

This delicately built white sea bird, related to the gulls, breeds in the entire Arctic Zone; its most southerly breeding grounds are situated on the German islands of the North Sea. The eggs are set down in the sand, without a nest, and after a hatching period of from 20 to 23 days the chicks slip out. Let us pause to consider for a moment that in this hidden period all the organs required for the bird's migratory habit are built up in the egg by inherited processes: the slender wings, the special character of the nerve centers, the special hormone apparatus—all are achieved by an unconscious process of development. It is not without reason that in this connection some biologists speak of developmental instincts. Just as the adult animal acts "instinctively," so the plasm of the species "instinctively" regulates the temporal sequence of formative processes. The species in its first state as pure plasm builds up all its organs.

For roughly one month the chick remains in the "nest." Here

the young, intensively fed by their parents, grow quickly. At the end of this period the migratory drive awakens in consequence of hereditary processes of development. "A hereditary drive awakens." This is easy to say, but what riddles such a statement creates! It implies an almost inconceivably complex assembly in the organism. We conceive of this assembly primarily as occurring in the embryo of each individual bird, but we must also think of it as an assembly that came into being down through geologic ages in the process of the evolution of the species. This historical process has transformed a sedentary bird into a migratory bird. Concomitantly there must have been corresponding changes in the germ plasm, which in each new generation produce the time-responses of a migratory bird with its annual rhythm. This evolutionary process impresses us with the significance of temporal structures for the organism. And what a powerful drive it is that "awakens" in our tern! Long before the older birds and uninfluenced by them, the fledglings start on their first journey, which is literally a world tour. The Northern European terns cross the Continent and follow the coasts of Africa. In the distant south of Africa they sometimes meet American birds of their species, which may have flown from Labrador, crossed North and Central America, and then traversed the Atlantic. Sometimes the journey continues on into the Antarctic for these terns have been definitely observed as far south as the sixty-sixth parallel. When they fly away from our latitudes, it is summer; and when they arrive in their "winter quarters," it is again summer with its long days. For a few weeks the terns remain in the southern summer. In the southern autumn, just as our spring is coming on, the unknown urge drives them northward again, where the days have once more begun to grow longer. In the first part of May they are back in the North Sea territory, in their hereditary breeding grounds. Twice a year the little white bird effects this immense flight that carries him almost from pole to pole, from one summer to another, from a life in the long light days of the northern hemisphere to another with equally long and bright days in the southern half of our earth. Experiments with banded birds have shown for certain that this species has a longevity of at least twelve years, but for all we know they may live longer. An aging tern, then, has carried out at least twenty-four flights, each measuring almost the entire length of a meridian. We have little knowledge of the physical performance required by these journeys, and even the biologist surely reflects too little on the extraordinary inward processes of a bird engaged in migration. This transformation of many structures in the course of the interval from breeding time to migration period also belongs to the picture of the bird as a being in whom the dimension of time is extraordinarily filled with varying content, with transformations of structure and action—an extreme example of configured time.[30]

Nor is the wonder we feel in the face of such phenomena a mere "subjective" addendum to what is "really" a story merely of mechanisms of survival more complicated than most:

There is no doubt that bird migrations represent a solution to certain ecological problems, that they enable the bird to exchange unfavorable seasons for more propitious ones. But if we consider all the aspects of these migratory phenomena in their immense variety, it becomes increasingly plain that they surpass elementary practical needs, such as the preservation of the species. All necessity is transcended in these great formative processes, into which tellurian events are integrated as wonderful alarm-signals for the awakening and enrichment of organic life in time. The passage of clock time, meaningless in itself, is employed for the enrichment of life. It need hardly be added that human life is a magnificent configuration of time in this same sense, offering in its successive ages ever new possibilities of development in time and hence of living riches.[31]

4

As the passage just quoted indicates, Portmann's account of the characters of living things has important consequences also for our view of man's place in nature. Although he started from research on invertebrates, moreover, Portmann's comparative study of morphology and development led him, as long ago as 1937, to a comparative investigation of the ontogenesis of mammals and in particular of primates—an investigation which has produced important results for the theory of human nature and development.[32] Portmann's theory is closely allied to the arguments we shall be studying in later chapters; but, like them, it has, as against more widely current conceptions, revolutionary implications both for the philosophy of the biological sciences and for our philosophical self-knowledge. Again, we may see this more plainly if we approach Portmann's work in this field too by a brief historical detour.

Generalizations in the history of ideas are almost always oversimple, and doubtless the present one is no exception. Portmann's own account, for example, of men's changing views, in the past two hundred years, of our relation to the apes presents fascinating variations of which I can here take no account. But I think that speaking very roughly and generally we can distinguish four different views of man's place in the natural world. There was, first, the popular medieval conception of man as the microcosm set firmly within the macrocosm which he mirrored. Here we had our place, a little lower than the angels, in a neat, many-leveled, statically ordered cosmos. The seventeenth-century intellectual revolution, bursting open this tight little order, left us, in the terms Descartes handed down for our forebears, the only spiritual beings in an otherwise machinelike universe. There were mathematicians' minds, and the matter spread out in space for their contemplation, and, except for the God who made them both, no more. Man himself, of course, was a strange hybrid of the two finite substances, minds and bodies, a delicate and, as it turned out, unstable synthesis. For its time, however, Descartes's vision was definitive, and Western thinkers since then have had to start from the heritage he left them. But starting from the Cartesian concept of man and nature, there seem to be but two alternatives left. As men's confidence in God and in their own immortal souls dwindled, they could either deny the existence of anything mindlike in the universe—the issue accepted by the recurrent materialisms of the last three centuries—or take the works of human reason—as Hobbes did three hundred years ago—as *artifacts*. In other words, they could see nature, including all animal life, from the point of view of a pure materialism, but contrast with it the *cultural* life of man, which is not born but *made*. In the nineteenth century, the triumph of Darwinism seemed to many the triumph of materialism pure and simple. In its twentieth-century version, however, Darwinian theory has not only become, through its mating with genetics, much more subtle and statistical in its interpretation of natural change. In the writings of Huxley and Dobzhansky especially, it has also placed over against the mutation-selection model of all evolution up to Homo sapiens a new brand of evolution, *cultural* evolution, characteristic of human history (and prehistory) alone. This is change through tradition, through teaching and learning, through religion, arts, and science, through all the articulate devices of human imagination and inventiveness.

Now, of these four views, Portmann's position is in harmony with the last, but with two significant differences. First, as I have already pointed out, he is not convinced that the technique of evolution over the whole stretch of life's existence is explained by the concepts of micromutation and selection. While, of course, accepting evolution as a fact, and a fact of very great significance for biology and for the study of man, he prefers to leave the great question of ultimate origins as for the present unanswered and perhaps even in some ways unanswerable. Second—and this is the main point in the present context —his comparative study of ontogenesis and postembryonic development has led him to modify the dichotomy of nature and culture and to emphasize the rootedness of man's social life in his *biological* nature. It is this integration of man as a uniquely cultural animal into a solid biological foundation that enables us, through Portmann's eyes, to see ourselves once more *both* as human beings and as at home in the natural world: because we are *biologically* formed to be *cultural* animals.

The context within which Portmann develops this thesis is an investigation of the comparative development of mammals. Animals can be divided as to their postnatal development into two classes: nidicolous species, that is, those whose young are born relatively immature and remain for a period "in the nest" before venturing independently into the world; and nidifugous species, that is, those whose young are relatively free-moving and even free-feeding at birth or shortly thereafter. Among birds the more primitive species are nidifugous; it is the more highly developed types that produce helpless and sightless young needing a protracted course of parental care to prepare them for the adventure of living. Among mammals, evolution has taken the opposite course: the young of relatively primitive species are nest-dependent, while the newly born offspring of higher mammals are ready with their first breath to disport themselves on their own four feet. One has only to compare newborn kittens with a newborn foal to see the difference. Associated with this striking difference in mobility are two other important contrasts: the young of nidicolous species are usually born in large litters and have their sense organs relatively undeveloped at birth, while nidifugous young are fewer in number per parent but as wide-awake to their surroundings at birth as they will be in maturity. A comparison of the ontogeny of the two types shows the evolutionary process involved in the last of these contrasts. In the embryos of nidicolous species, the eyelids are formed early, then close, and birth occurs before they reopen. In nidifugous species, the stage of lid-closing, now meaningless in the life of the organism, is retained, but birth is postponed till later when the eyes have once more opened.

Now, where does man fit into this classification? Nowhere, it seems. We are born helpless, but with our eyes and ears wide open. Even though a baby does not focus on objects for the first few weeks, he does respond to colors very soon indeed and to sounds as well. He takes from the first moment a powerful sight of notice. In other words, we have retained the sensory characteristics of the higher mammals (as well as the small number in our litters!), but have reverted in other respects to an earlier pattern in our infantile way of life. We have become *secondarily nidicolous*. Thus the evolution of mammals as a whole shows a change of course: from nidicolous to nidifugous, and then back again to a new kind of nidicolous state. That this is so is strikingly confirmed in comparative studies of postembryonic development by Portmann's associates at Basel. In nidicolous animals, as one might expect from the condition of their sense organs at birth, the brain has to develop during life to from 8 to 10 times its size at birth; while for nidifugous species this figure is on the average 1.5 to 2.5—somewhere around 2. This holds even for our nearest kin, the anthropoid apes; they are still nidifugous. For even though the baby clings more closely to its mother than do other nidifugous animals, it does so, so to speak, by its own volition: it is free-moving. Moreover, the rate of growth of the brain from birth to maturity is still the "normal" one of about 2. With man, however, this figure has sharply altered: his brain has to develop from birth to maturity to *four* times the natal size: a clear reversal of the evolutionary trend. Moreover, the proportions of a human infant are much further from those of the adult than are the proportions of a newborn ape from the mature individual. But at the same time the human infant is much heavier at birth than any newborn anthropoid, almost twice as heavy, even among peoples who are comparatively slight in build when full-grown. On all these counts, our pattern of development is unique among mammals.

What is the significance of all this? Let us look at the comparison a little differently. Instead of comparing the newborn young of each species, let us ask: when does man reach, in behavior and in physical proportions, a stage of development comparable to that of the newborn young of other highly evolved mammals? It is usually at about a year that the child takes his first steps and so assumes the upright posture characteristic of his kind, and at this age also his build has come much closer in its proportions to its eventual adult shape. At about twelve months, also, he begins to act like a person: that is, he begins to speak, and he begins to perform what we recognize as voluntary, responsible actions. Taking the pattern of nidifugous development as our model, therefore, we see that man is born prematurely and achieves the status of an ordinary nidifuge at about twelve months of age. This hypothesis is further confirmed by a comparison of the rate of growth of the human baby and the young of closely related species. Thus the apes show a steady development from birth to maturity, while the human baby changes with an amazing speed, in fact, a rate of growth comparable to that of the embryo, up to a year, then slows down to a rate similar to that of "normal" postembryonic development. If we look at ourselves as mammals among other mammals, therefore, we see that we should be born twelve months later than we are: it is at that period that we emerge like other advanced mammals into the world of our peculiar kind, that we take on full human nature.

But what is this "full human nature"? Portmann has mentioned its three chief characters: upright posture, speech, and rational action. Now, all these have to be *learned* by the infant in its first months through contact with human adults or in particular with one adult, his mother or foster mother. Of course parental care, and social life in general, are essential, in a host of intricate and marvelous ways, to a host of other species as well. But nowhere else in living nature on this planet does this pattern of premature sociality occur. Looking at it from the perspective of evolution and of comparative development, Portmann calls this unique period of postembryonic, yet still embryonic, growth the period of *social gestation*. To take its place alongside a newborn orang or chimp, at an analogous level of development toward the adult form, in other words, the human being demands not only nine months in the physical uterus of the mother but a further twelve months in the social uterus of maternal care. We must be careful also, Portmann warns us, not to take this lately developed pattern in evolution as a mere addendum to an otherwise "ordinary" mammalism ontogenesis: our unique pattern of development is not an "afterthought" tacked onto a standard embryogenesis. The human attitudes and endowments which we must acquire in infancy are prepared for very early indeed in embryonic growth: thus the first preparation for the upright posture, in the development of the pelvis, occurs in the second month of the foetus's growth. The preparation for the acquisition of speech, moreover, involves glottal structures very strikingly and thoroughly different from those of any other species. And the huge size of our infants relatively to the young of apes—born more "mature" but very much smaller—is probably related, Portmann conjectures, to the immense development of the brain necessary for the achievement of human rationality—a development which begins, again, very early indeed in ontogenesis. In short, the whole biological development of a typical mammal has been rewritten in our case in a new key: the whole structure of the embryo, the whole rhythm of growth, is directed, from first to last, to the emergence of a culture-dwelling animal—an animal not bound within a predetermined ecological niche like the tern or the stag or the dragonfly or even the chimpanzee, but, in its very tissues and organs and aptitudes, born to be *open to its world,* to be able to accept responsibility, to make its own the traditions of a historical past and to remake them into an unforeseeable future.

Not only the first year of life, moreover, but the further pattern of human development testifies to the fact that, even in their physiological foundations, our lives are so ordered as to facilitate social learning, the perpetuation and modification from one generation to another of traditional lore. The postponement of sexual maturity to a date relatively later than is

characteristic of other species permits a long period of appren-
ticeship and the gradual assumption of responsible adulthood.
And at the other end of the time span, the prolonged and gen-
tle slope of human senescence provides opportunities for rising
generations to profit from the richer experience of the old and
wise. Thus at every level and at every stage of our existence we
live out the uniquely flexible, uniquely creative pattern of configured time that is man.

From this vantage point, then, we can see at one and the
same time how wonderfully various are the modes of life of
many, many kinds of living beings and also how wonderful is
our own scheme of life, unique in its intricate order, as every
specific life history is, yet unique among all these uniquenesses
in its "natural artificiality," in the dimension of cultural evolution which is not only added to, but enmeshed in and expressed
through, every level of the many levels of order that converge
to produce a human life.

This is a zoologist's contribution to our understanding of ourselves, founded, not on a mere wish to overcome our alienation
from nature, but on careful morphological and developmental
research over many years and with the help of many hands.
But its implications for what is sometimes called "philosophical
anthropology" should be clear. Without suggesting a sentimen-
tal reversion to a once stable but now vanished "scale of nature," Portmann's findings nevertheless allow us to accept a
secure place *within* the natural world. Yet a place with a
difference, too. We need no longer try, absurdly, to see all the
achievements of men's minds—art, science, and religion—as
epiphenomena to molecules in motion, or, alternatively, to set
them, as mere conventions, over against the single level of
change that is thought to constitute the balance of the organic
world. Admitting from the start the intrinsic significance of life
itself in a thousand thousand forms, we can acknowledge too
the deep-reaching and far-flowing consequences of our own

natural-and-cultural, biologically determinate, *and* traditional form of life.

There is one more point about Portmann's view of man which I ought finally to mention—a point which I have touched on already at least indirectly in introducing the concept of display.[33] Each of us lives, I pointed out there, in a primary life world, out of which and within which the world of science, or of any other highly articulate discipline, develops. Portmann has repeatedly emphasized the importance of giving due heed to *both* these aspects of our lives. By the world of primary experience he means, however, something more inclusive than the concept of a "life world," as I introduced it earlier, may at first suggest. The world in which, from infancy, we come to live, and the human world shared by members of all cultures, does, of course, include the surface of experience, the colors, the sounds, the rhythms of movement that confront us on all sides. But it includes also our feelings, our desires, our dreams, the creative aspirations of artists, the vision of saints and prophets, even the delusions of the insane. No single term can adequately characterize this whole range of primary experience; perhaps we can still speak here of the "life world" if we remember that it is more than the plain, open order of "common sense" to which we are referring. Such a life world, then, with all its opacities and ambiguities, stands in contrast with the limited but lucid sphere governed by the operations of the intellect—and that means, in our culture, by the operations of science and technology. Human nature comprises both and can dispense with neither.[34]

I can perhaps point to the nub of Portmann's dichotomy by returning once more to Galileo's polemic in *The Assayer*. Galileo reviles the unhappy Sarsi for quoting poetry at him; and this was, indeed, on Sarsi's part, an irrelevant answer to a scientific argument. But it is the grounds of Galileo's objection that are revealing. It has been truly said, he remarks, "that nature takes no delight in poetry." With this truth, he goes on, Sarsi seems to be unacquainted: "He seems not to know that fables and fictions are in a way essential to poetry, which could not exist without them, while any sort of falsehood is so abhorrent to nature that it is as absent there as darkness is in light." [35] This is indeed the perspective of modern objectivism. As the "mathematical language," the instrument of an impersonal reason, is seen as the sole medium of truth and light, so poetry has come to be mere taletelling, at best invention and entertainment, at worst obscurity and untruth. And it is not only poetry in the narrow sense, the craft of making verses, that is here exiled from reality but the whole work of the imagination: myth and metaphor, dream and prophecy. In the bare mathematical bones of nature there is truth; all else is illusion. Yet that "all else" includes the very roots of our being, and we forget them at our peril. Indeed, even the scientist himself, no timeless, placeless spirit, derives from his aspirations and imaginings, his dreams and disappointments, the sustenance, the very existence, of his enterprise. Galileo himself, passionately evicting poetry from nature, has evoked the ancient metaphor of darkness and light. Portmann uses the same image to adjure us: "In a world in which the apparatus of gleaming glass, the bright research laboratories and men and women in white have acquired an almost symbolic value, we must look again and see how great is the darkness out of which the light that fills the bright spaces of the intellect wells up." [36] We must try, in other words, to achieve anew a whole vision of our nature—a revision which by its very character research alone is unable to provide. And Portmann is not speaking here, remember, as a writer or artist envious or ignorant of the achievements of science and technology. He is speaking as a scientist—a scientist looking beyond science to the wider, if obscurer, problems of our lives. So he says:

> I myself work every day, through research and teaching, at the advancement of knowledge, and it is out of my own inner impulse

that I have chosen this work. Hence perhaps my readers too will see the demand of the present hours more clearly if, out of the very passion for research, I emphasize the inevitable narrowness of every image of man that is formed through natural science alone, that does not draw its powers from all the sources of man's being.[37]

NOTES

1. K. Z. Lorenz, in *Physiological Mechanisms in Animal Behavior, Symposia of the Society for Experimental Biology,* IV (Cambridge: Cambridge University Press, 1950), 235.
2. A. Portmann, *Animals as Social Beings,* trans. by O. Coburn (London: Hutchinson, 1961), pp. 108–109.
3. A. Portmann, *New Paths in Biology,* trans. by A. Pomerans (New York: Harper and Row, 1964); *Neue Wege der Biologie* (Munich: R. Piper, 1960). The translation is inadequate at some crucial philosophical points, especially in the rendering of *eigentlich* and *uneigentlich* and also in the omission of some important passages.
4. S. Drake, ed. and trans., *Discoveries and Opinions of Galileo* (Garden City, New York: Doubleday, 1957), pp. 237–238. Galileo Galilei, *Il Saggiatore* (Florence: Edizione Nazionale, 1965), VI, 232.
5. This thesis has been most clearly articulated and defended in Husserl's late work. Husserl's thesis is paralleled in Portmann's own work in the distinction he makes between *Welterleben* and *Weltwissen,* between our primary experience of the world and the intellectual understanding of it we acquire through education, and in particular through science.
6. *Discoveries,* p. 272; *Il Saggiatore,* pp. 347–348.
7. See A. Portmann, "Der biologische Beitrag zu einem neuen Bild des Menschen," *Eranos Jahrbuch,* XXVIII (1959), 459–492, especially pp. 466–472.
   T. Holtsmark, "Goethe and the Phenomenon of Color," in M. Grene, ed., *The Anatomy of Knowledge* (Amherst: University of Massachusetts Press, 1968), pp. 47–71.
   E. P. Land, "Color Vision and the Natural Image," *Proceedings of the National Academy of Science USA,* XLV (1959), 115–129, 636–644; "The Retinex," *American Scientist,* LII, No. 2 (1964), 247–264; "Color in the Natural Image," *Proceedings of the Royal Institution of Great Britain,* XXXIX, No. 176 (1962), 1–15.
8. A. Portmann, "Gestaltung als Lebensvorgang," *Eranos Jahrbuch,*

XXIX (1960), 359. I shall return to this point again in connection with Portmann's account of the social life of animals.

9. A. Portmann, *Animal Camouflage*, trans. by A. Pomerans (Ann Arbor: University of Michigan Press, 1959).
10. *Neue Wege*, p. 148.
11. See *Animal Camouflage*.
12. Trans. by H. Lucas (unpublished).
13. Quoted in *Animals as Social Beings*, pp. 182–183.
14. See H. Hediger, *Wild Animals in Captivity* (New York: Dover, 1964).
15. *Neue Wege*, p. 225.
16. N. Tinbergen, *Social Behavior in Animals* (New York: Wiley, 1953). D. Lack, *The Life of the Robin* (London: H. F. and G. Witherby, 1946). K. Z. Lorenz, *King Solomon's Ring*, trans. by M. K. Wilson (New York: Crowell, 1952).
17. *Animals as Social Beings*, p. 26.
18. T. Dobzhansky, *The Biological Basis of Human Freedom* (New York: Columbia University Press, 1956), p. 17. For further development of my argument here, see Chapter 2, Section 1a.
19. See *Neue Wege*, p. 59.
20. *Animals as Social Beings*, p. 160.
21. *Ibid.*, pp. 170–171.
22. *Ibid.*
23. *Ibid.*, pp. 175–176.
24. *Ibid.*, p. 176.
25. *Ibid.*, p. 177.
26. *Ibid.*
27. *Ibid.*
28. "Time in the Life of the Organism," in *Man and Time* (Princeton: Princeton University Press, 1957), III, 312.
29. *Ibid.*, p. 311.
30. *Ibid.*, pp. 317–319.
31. *Ibid.*, p. 320.
32. See especially A. Portmann, *Zoologie und das neue Bild des Menschen* (Hamburg: Rowohlt, 1956); "Die Stellung des Menschen in der Natur," in *Handbuch der Biologie* (Constance: Hachfeld, 1961), IX, No. 19, 437–460; *Vom Ursprung des Menschen* (Basel: Reinhardt, 1958). Cf. also A. Portmann, "Beyond Darwinism," *Commentary*, XL (1965), 31–41.
33. See, for example, "Der biologische Beitrag," pp. 459–492; "Welterleben und Weltwissen," in *Erziehung und Wirklichkeit* (Munich: R. Oldenbourg, 1959).
34. Portmann has put this contrast sometimes as that of experiencing the world (*Welterleben*) and knowing the world (*Weltwissen*),

sometimes as that of the Ptolemean and the Copernican in each of us. I have not been able to find two English phrases to carry smoothly the connotations of *Welterleben* and *Weltwissen,* and I am not quite happy about the other pair. As earth-bound creatures, tied to the history of our species and the traditions of our community, we may be said to be Ptolemeans; as free-ranging analytical intellects, to be Copernicans. And perhaps, since Kant, "Copernican revolution" has indeed come to mean any basic change of perspective which reverses a more naïve or natural point of view. Yet Copernicus himself was still so deeply imbued with neo-Pythagorean mysticism, and Ptolemy himself so sophisticated a mathematician, that I prefer to approach the contrast without using these particular names.

35. *Discoveries,* p. 238.
36. *Nationalzeitung* (Basel), February 16, 1964.
37. *Ibid.*

2

Helmuth Plessner

The abolition of final causes from nature was a common theme of scientific revolutionaries in the seventeenth century, and philosophers of science still occasionally argue that teleological concepts should be excluded from all science, including the science of life. Yet biologists still talk in terms of functions, that is, of means and ends, and their attempts to dispense with such language and reduce their subject to terms of pure mechanical cause and effect are halfhearted and silly. Other philosophers, therefore, and reflectively inclined biologists continue to oppose "reductivism" and argue for the essential inclusion of teleological concepts in biology as a complement to simple mechanical causes and effects. What generally escapes the notice of both sides in this long-standing controversy, however, is the

t what is needed for the adequate philosophical founda-
biological thought is neither to get rid of teleology nor
on it as the self-sufficient partner of causality, but to
supplement both cause-and-effect thinking and means-end
thinking by reference to the still more basic concept of standards or norms.

To put it in Aristotelian terms—which are not strictly adequate in this context, but will perhaps indicate roughly what is
involved—biology needs to rely not only on material and efficient but on final causes, and not only on final causes but on
formal cause as well, and on formal cause most fundamentally.
Formal cause for Aristotle is not, of course, or not primarily,
shape or contour: it is the defining principle, the operating
principle that makes a given kind of thing the kind of thing it
is. In the *Metaphysics* Aristotle draws together the concept of
form, which is the equivalent of formal cause, and his peculiar
concept of each kind of thing's *being what it is:* that is, the
type or norm or standard that makes it *this* kind of thing and
not another. It is form in this sense, meaningful or significant
form, form as generic standard, that is fundamental to the
study of living things. It is true, of course, that Aristotelian
eternal species have vanished from our world; living things for
us are products of evolution, concretions out of flux. But, short
of the problem of the origin of life, we do have to deal with a
multiplicity of present kinds of plants and animals, and could
we not, did we not, in ordinary life and in biological research,
rely on our recognition of such kinds, of the differing styles of
living that separate them from one another, and that unite the
phases of individual development, and separate the individual
from its environment, we could neither begin nor continue to
practice biology at all. Of course, we want to find out with all
possible precision what organisms are made of—Aristotelian
material cause—and the sequence of processes—efficient
causes—which subtend the ends of life, its final causes: as, for

Final +
formal causes
(Impt.)

example, the processes of metabolism subtend the end of nutri-
tion, or nervous processes the ends of perception, action, and
thought. Yet all these have their ultimate importance within a
context that lies beyond the concept of "ends": the intrinsic
significance of each variety of life itself, the standard by which
we judge each kind of organism to be or to fail to be the kind it
is. Without reference to such norms there is and could be no
biology at all.

In introducing the concept of biological norms via Aristotle's
four causes I have come a long way around from my present
subject, the biological philosophy of Helmuth Plessner. Aristotle has often influenced biological thinking (even Darwin
professed to admire him), but Plessner's thought springs primarily from different and more modern philosophical roots:
from two diverse traditions which he both opposes and in a
way reconciles, that is, neo-Kantianism and phenomenology. I
am concerned here, however, not with the full scope of Plessner's philosophical thought, but with his contribution to philosophical biology, and I hope that Aristotle's distinction between
final and formal causes may help us to focus on Plessner's
thesis that we should take norms or significances rather than
means-end relations or functions as basic to biological thought.
Again, it must be confessed, this thesis—that norms rather
than ends must be taken as fundamental to our thinking
about living things—forms a relatively minor strand even in
Plessner's argument about biology, let alone in his philosophy
as a whole. I have introduced it here, however, because it
shows clearly the contrast of his position with the major stream
of biological thought, at least in the English-speaking world.
After dealing in a little more detail with this point, I propose to
move on to two other background problems from which, somewhat more centrally, Plessner's philosophy has emerged: that
is, the problem of the methodology of the social sciences, and,
as the final step in my introductory section, a more general bio-

logical controversy which forms an important strand in Plessner's development, the conflict between the Gestalt theory of Köhler and the vitalism of Driesch. These background topics are admittedly also partial; I could not here reconstruct the whole milieu of German thought in the early twentieth century which is the soil of Plessner's philosophizing.

To return then to the problem of means and ends. Let me look briefly at the structure of modern biological, and in particular, evolutionary thought.

"Evolution is progressive adaptation, and consists in nothing else." [1] This pronouncement in the early 1930's by one of the chief founders of neo-Darwinism expresses succinctly the model which had dominated much of nineteenth-century thought, still presides over the thinking of most biologists, and, at one remove, holds social science too under its spell. Science is in the first instance the study by mathematical means of inorganic nature: this has not only in fact been the case historically; it is also held, conceptually, to be the ideal of what science *ought* to be. Thus Kant, whose great synthesis still dominates modern methodology, insisted that only what can be mathematically formulated can be scientifically explained. What does one add to this situation when one adds the study of life? Again, the Kantian answer, by and large, is still accepted: one adds means-end relations. Kant's definition of the organism as an entity where all is reciprocally means and ends sounds quaint and pompous, but what is basic to it, and still retained in modern biological thought, is the principle that organisms differ from other objects of scientific study in that they exhibit in some way or other the adjustment of means to ends. "Organs" are by definition instruments, that is, means, by which plants and animals utilize the opportunities made available by their environments, both internal and external, the end of such utilization being, presumably, self-maintenance or survival, both of the individual and of the species. And organisms are conceived, in these terms, as aggregates or complexes of such instrumentalities: taken as wholes they are adaptation machines, mechanisms for their own or their descendants' survival. Thus both the parts and partial functionings of organisms and their character as wholes are interpreted in terms of the relations of means to ends.

Admittedly, it was the *abolition* of teleological thinking that was thought by both its adherents and its enemies to be the triumph—or the disaster—of Darwinian biology. Natural-selection theory, which, as Shaw said, threw Paley's famous watch into the ocean, was supposed to have overcome the reference to divine purposes behind nature through reducing the myriad and marvelous structures of life to mechanically necessitated changes effected in a medium of minute random variations in the genetic material. The vast increase in the knowledge of this material and its ways of persistence and change has not altered by a jot the fundamental antipurposive model which still, and more consistently than ever, lies at the base of Darwinian thought. Yet purposiveness is not identical with teleology. Darwinism did indeed banish from nature conscious purpose in the sense of the Deist tradition, but not means-end relations, or teleology in a more general sense. What was abolished by Darwinism and its modern heirs was in fact not Paley's watch, but only the watch*maker*. The artifact model of nature, and with it the emphasis on function, on the relation of means to ends, persists. Indeed, from the beginning it was plain to some at least, both adherents and critics, that what Darwinism had done was not so much to abolish teleology as to house it securely within nature—an unconscious teleology, to be sure, but nevertheless a teleology. Contemporary biologists in this tradition, moreover, have recently become more clearly aware that directedness, or as Huxley calls it, the telic aspect of organic phenomena, is essentially involved in their own view of the living world. Darwin himself had already made it plain that only adaptive phenomena could be controlled by natural selection: only what is useful, that is, a means to an end, can be selected, either weeded out as unfit, or, by elimination, left to survive as fit. And modern Darwinism is even more thorough in its teleology than was Darwin: for whatever is not on the surface adaptive is held to be necessarily tied to some adaptive character. Since mutation and selection are held to be *the* major mechanisms of evolution, and evolution the mechanism by which life has come to exist and survives, whatever exists in the organic world has been and is a *means* to survival as its *end*. The continuous refinement of adaptation—progressive adaptation—is evolution and is life. To exist is to be adapted; to persist is to be better adapted. This axiom of adaptivity, as we may call it, continues to dominate not only evolutionary biology itself but many related disciplines: physiology, functional anthropology, sociology, and so on.

Yet adaptation on its own, or progressive adaptation on its own, as neo-Darwinism takes it, is by no means self-explanatory or indeed explicable. For one thing, the concept of evolution as identified with progressive adaptation is basically ambiguous. On the one hand such adaptations are supposed to be mechanically self-generating, through mutation and natural selection, and so to entail no teleological reference. Yet on the other hand adaptation is itself a teleological concept: it is adjustment of something to something for some end. To interpret organisms as adaptation machines, therefore, is to interpret them as complexes of means for ends, and therefore teleologically. Second, if the means-end reference is admitted, one must ask further: means to what end? But the "end," for Darwinism, dare not be some "higher" form of life, the next "level" to which evolution aspires: that would be to reintroduce a forbidden version of "unscientific" teleology. It must, then, and is usually said to, be *survival* that adaptation is "for." But in that case the whole "theory" becomes a tautology, a complicated way of saying simply that what survives survives. Finally, and fundamentally, the trouble is, really, that the concept of adaptation is essentially a relative one—relative to the existence of two things: the *subject* to be adapted and the *environment* to which it is to be adapted. Plessner makes a similar point, in his early book, *Die Einheit der Sinne*,[2] in the context of an analysis of sense perception. Referring to physiological investigations of perception, he points out that perception cannot be explained wholly in terms of adaptation, since there must be *something there already to become adapted. Adaptability*, which is a potential relation between organ, medium, and object of perception, must precede adaptation. Thus the adaptable entity, the organism which *can* achieve adaptation, must be assessed in its own right, by its appropriate norm, before the detailed conditions of its adaptation can be specified. The same is true in the context of evolutionary theory, or indeed wherever the attempt is made to rely on adaptation as a principle of ultimate explanation. Adaptation is a cryptoteleological concept, but teleology, even when explicit, is itself dependent on the prior evaluation of the ends evoked. And in the case of evolutionary biology the end is not simply survival but the survival of—a type, a mode of living adjudged as significant in itself. That is the only judgment that can fill in the tautology of survival-for-survival-for-survival.

1b

Plessner's emphasis on the priority of norms to goals, which he stated in 1922 and again in 1928 in the book I shall be chiefly examining, *Die Stufen des Organischen und der Mensch*, seems to me to lay the groundwork for a fundamental revolution in biological thought.[3] Indirectly, through his collaboration with Buytendijk and through Buytendijk's influence on Merleau-Ponty, it may also be said, through the influence in turn of

Merleau-Ponty on contemporary philosophy, to be bearing fruit. As I have presented it, however, in the context of evolutionary theory, this theme by no means forms a leitmotiv of Plessner's own thought. On the contrary, his major contribution to the philosophy of biology seems to have been motivated in the first instance by response to the predicament not so much of biology—certainly not of evolutionary biology—as of the social sciences.

Historical method and historical judgment were among the great achievements of the nineteenth century. Yet history felt itself, so far as its method went, uneasy vis-à-vis the natural sciences, and this uneasiness increased as the study of man extended from the properly historical disciplines to the social sciences in general. Indeed, the crisis of the *Geisteswissenschaften* dominated much of German philosophy in the early decades of this century, and Plessner discusses two of the principal responses to it. One was that of the neo-Kantians, and the other the *Lebensphilosophie* of Dilthey.

The neo-Kantian response to the problem looks at first sight very reasonable. In Kant's time there was no body of historical knowledge comparable to that of the early twentieth century, let alone established disciplines of sociology or economics such as there were beginning to be fifty years ago. But Kant had proceeded in his critical inquiry from the fact of the existence of established sciences to the question of the grounds of the possibility of their existence. Why not then do this for the newly matured historical and human sciences? There are several reasons, according to Plessner, why this venture could not succeed. For one thing, as I have already mentioned, Kant equates science with knowledge mediated by the tools of mathematics: the range of theoretical knowledge for him is coterminous with mathematical physics; indeed, with the dubious exception of empirical psychology, it *is* mathematical physics. But the disciplines that deal with human history and institutions, however much they may use statistical or other mathematical techniques, can never, so long as they do deal with human agents and actions, be mathematical disciplines. Nor can they operate with the abstractive experimental techniques characteristic of the exact sciences. However strict the impersonality and objectivity with which historical evidence is weighed, no matter how elaborate the scientific techniques employed, moreover, Plessner points out, these are only the beginning, only the preliminary for historical understanding, not, as for the exact sciences, the heart of the matter. Kant believed that, given the right, purified principles of physics, given the right way of asking questions of nature, the smooth progress of scientific knowledge would follow in a sense automatically from this correct beginning. Whether or no this is true for science— and many philosophers of science would now question this conception of the automatism of scientific progress—history and the social sciences certainly do not proceed in this automatic way. They depend at every stage on human judgments of human affairs. Even if, Plessner points out, we could envisage a uniform panorama of historical movements proceeding by strict Kantian causality (which one would not expect Kant himself to have envisaged for human, and therefore morally oriented, actions), such a vision would be brought up short by the task of biography, where person-to-person encounter is inevitable.

Further, the very situation that called forth philosophical inquiry into the grounds of the possibility of historical and human disciplines shows up their inaccessibility to the Kantian type of question. Natural science for Kant was, and had been since Galileo, as he thought, a firmly established, smoothly proceeding discipline. There was absolutely no doubt of its existence, only a question about the a priori grounds on which this obvious certainty was founded. But what led philosophers— and historians—to concern themselves with history was precisely the *un*certainty surrounding its methods and results. Historians can be as scrupulous as scientists in their attempt to use evidence fairly, and yet they can never, unless they are very naïve indeed, be wholly convinced or convincing about the irrefutable and irreversible nature of their results. The situation of history and the social sciences, therefore, resembled, not so much that of natural science as Kant saw it, as that of metaphysics: a discipline which does not progress smoothly and of which we want to ask not, given its undoubted existence as a science, *how* it is possible, but *whether* it is possible as a science at all. The answer for metaphysics, in Kant's view, was negative; and he might well have given a similar answer for the social sciences had he been in a position to inquire about them. A positive answer, given the disquietude of historians and social scientists themselves, could not be generated by the Kantian method.

The alternative, obviously, seemed to be to let the exact sciences and their subject matter, nature, strictly alone and describe the procedures of the historical and human disciplines as something unique in themselves, with their own characteristic methods, quite distinct from those of science. Dilthey is the most eminent of the philosophers who adopted this alternative. Nature, he said, was merely the backdrop for historical action; let the scientists explain it as they liked. What the historian needs to do, by contrast, is not to *explain* phenomena, but to *understand* the actions, aspirations, decisions, of human beings. Science explains, but history understands. Dilthey's effort was a grandiose one, but again there are at least two reasons why it was not adequate to solve the basic problem which the growth of the historical and social disciplines had raised.

First: in general, Plessner argues, a conflict between two spheres like that of nature and history cannot be resolved by setting the two over against each other. It can be resolved only on a level which transcends them both. In effect, the concept of understanding must be, not set over against explanation, but expanded to include scientific explanation, historical interpretation, and, indeed, the insights of the arts as well, as so many of its forms. Again, the character of the Kantian critique shows how this comes about. Kant started from the given of a steadily progressing, securely established science. But this given was itself a cultural given. It was, as we see now, after the revolutions of physics in our century, itself a historical phenomenon, which has to be assessed historically as well as cognitively, which has to be *understood*. Only a philosophy, therefore, which comes to terms with the human condition as such, and understands the range and variety of modes of understanding, can rightly interpret the methods and principles of *either* science *or* history or the contrast between them. Such a philosophy, however, it must be said, would not be a once-for-all completed structure of human reason such as the Kantian critique was meant to be; it would be itself a part of history. Nor does this statement generate an infinite regress except in the sense that our understanding of ourselves is always in process, always incomplete, reaching beyond itself to shape the future in the light of our understanding of our past.

This seems to take us a long way from the philosophy of biology. But not really. This becomes clear when we consider the second reason why Dilthey failed. There can be no resolution of the problem of the *Geisteswissenschaften,* Plessner declares, without a general philosophy of man: "a philosophical anthropology." But a philosophical anthropology is in turn impossible, he says, unless it is itself founded on a philosophy of nature, not, indeed, in the Kantian sense of a set of principles for the inorganic world, leaving the life sciences to be guided by a vague set of "as if's" or "regulative principles," but in the sense of a philosophical examination of the question *what it means to be alive*. History is not a sequence of pure ideas any more than it is a sequence of physical causes and effects. It is an interpretive record of what people have done. And social science generally studies neither thoughts and feelings and desires as the expression of subjectivity nor the physical changes that sum up to movements of population, wars, inventions, or what not. It studies the ways in which people behave. Behavior, however, is neither a subjective nor a physical category; it is carried by persons, neither as minds nor as bodies nor as a kind of hybrid of the two, but as characteristically psychophysically neutral whole entities. These cannot be grasped as such from the side either of subjective understanding or of physical cause-and-effect relations, but only as a specific variety of the general category of *things alive*. Dilthey did indeed call his philosophy *Lebensphilosophie;* yet he treated the whole of nature, including organic nature, as mere backdrop. Given the predominance of the exact sciences and the philosophically backward state of biology, this was perhaps excusable. But it is just this impasse that we need to transcend if we are to understand ourselves and our history—and our scientific ventures too as part of what it is to be human. To overcome the conflict of *Naturwissenschaft* and *Geisteswissenschaft,* I have already emphasized, it is necessary to interpret both scientific explanation and historical interpretation as modes of understanding. But understanding can be understood, not as the work of a pure mind, but as the achievement of human beings, that is, of the peculiar kind of living beings that we are. Thus Plessner comes squarely to the problem of the nature of living things as the problem which must be faced if the human disciplines are to be given adequate philosophical and methodological foundation. It is this task which he faced in his major work.

1c

The more immediate biological background of Plessner's argument in *Stufen* is contained in the controversy between Köhler and Driesch about the relation of biology to physics: one of the recurrent controversies about the reducibility or otherwise of the biological sciences to physicochemical terms.

Looking back now at the history of experimental psychology since its inception, we may be inclined to think of Gestalt psychology as one of the movements that have helped to emancipate the study of behavior from the fetters of an abstract, mechanistic way of thinking. Experimental psychology before Gestalt was atomistic: it was the association of elements of sensation or of utterance (for example, nonsense syllables) that was the chief subject of study. By contrast, the discoveries about the importance of form in perception by the Gestalt school seem to have shown up the absurdities of mental atomism and to have opened the door to a richer conception of mental life. The mind, from an associationist point of view, was simply, as Hume called it, "a bundle of sensations," and all "higher" categories were banished to the limbo of metaphysical nonsense. But if perception is of wholes greater than their parts, the reduction too of mind to its parts, and a fortiori to a mechanical summation of such parts, seems also to have failed. There are after all no "minimum sensibles," but only the achievement of organized perception; and the perceiving agent, it would seem, needs henceforth to be taken seriously as himself a whole that is more than the sum of its parts. Yet this was not the interpretation that Gestalt psychologists themselves placed on their discoveries. Or at any rate it was certainly not Köhler's interpretation: his principle of isomorphism, to which he clung faithfully throughout his career, expressed his confidence that physical configurations could be found which exactly correspond to and produce the perceived configurations described by Gestalt psychologists. The laws of *Gestalt* would be explained in physical terms, and "mental" or "vital" categories therewith reduced to physical. It is true that the whole is greater than the sum of its parts, but this is also true, in the last analysis, of the physical world which is, on this view, the only "real" one. In the classical mechanism-vitalism controversy, therefore, Köhler stood firmly on the side of mechanism. *Gestalten*, though not aggregates, are nevertheless explicable in "mechanical," that is, in classical-physical, terms. Against this reductivism Driesch was, of course, the most eminent exponent of a vitalist position. On a classical-mechanistic basis there is no explaining how, as he had firmly established it can do, a half sea-urchin embryo can grow into a whole sea urchin. In terms of exact, analytical techniques and precise physical concepts there is simply no way to get a normal whole animal out of half the stuff it ought to be made of. There comes a point, therefore, Driesch insisted, where exact analysis breaks down, and here the biologist has to postulate an additional "vital" force, an entelechy, as he called it, which takes over the operation. Although Driesch borrowed this term from Aristotle, his "entelechy" is, as Plessner rightly points out, very different from the Aristotelian concept. The latter simply has nothing to do with exact methods and would be meaningless in a modern experimental situation, even as a limiting factor. Driesch simply borrowed the name, not the concept, in order to specify what he believed to be the nonmeasurable, nonenergic power of life which takes over at a point beyond the range of exact, measurable physical processes. The entelechy represents a type of order not only more than aggregative, as *Gestalten* are, but more than reducible to physical terms. *Gestalten* could be physically explained, so Köhler thought, in terms of field concepts or the like; entelechies, Driesch was confident, transcend physical explanation altogether.

Who was right? As is so often the case in fundamental conceptual controversies, both sides, and neither side. Köhler was right in refusing to stop at a given point and say, "Here and no farther." There is no limit to the applicability of exact methods to the analysis of organic phenomena. Even before the publication of Plessner's work, Spemann had already brought biology a great step forward beyond Driesch's simple conception of the embryo as a machine plus some outside nonmechanical something. Indeed, as Plessner says, it was Driesch's concept of a machine that was too simple: that was why he had to stop and add some wholly nonmechanical factor to explain the complex and flexible course of development. And since Spemann's time, of course, the immense progress in genetics, virus research, and other branches of microbiology, as well as in experimental embryology itself, has shown plainly how much farther than Driesch anticipated exact methods can go in the elucidation of organic process.

Does that mean that Köhler and mechanism were in the right? By no means. For if there is no entelechy superadded to the machinery of living, neither is life thereby reduced to matter or to self-generated, self-operating mechanisms. Every biologist, no matter how sophisticated and precise his techniques, starts by inquiring about some structure, some process, of the things we call "living." The quality of being alive confronts him as the problem he has to "explain." But it is not, for all his analysis or syntheses, explained "away." Living things are still living things after, as before, the analytical biologist's experiments. We put our questions to and get our answers from, says an experimental embryologist, "the embryo alive." [4] And "alive" here is not just a word; or better, it is a word that designates an irreducible quality. We know of such relations also, Plessner writes in the Preface to the second edition of *Stufen*, "in the sphere of the inorganic. A given quality of color is defined by a given wave length, but as a quality it only corresponds to it, even if it appears as just this color only for a seeing subject by means of a normally functioning retina and nervous system." [5] The basic criteria of life, or *modals* as he calls them (following Helmholtz), are, he says, qualities of this kind, "the genesis of which can be analytically comprehended, and thus made operable, insofar as this is possible for qualities." [6] But this is not to reduce them to quantities. And the problem Plessner faced in *Stufen* was not the elucidation of the *origin* of the quality of life, as the physicist studies the mechanism by which visible color is produced. It was the elucidation of the "logical position" of the essential qualities of life with which he was concerned, a problem which had eluded both the dogmatic mechanism of Köhler and the simple-minded vitalism of Driesch.

This is a philosophical, not a scientific, problem, which does not, and, during most of his working hours, need not worry the experimenting biologist. It can, and should, however, worry the philosopher reflecting on the nature both of knowledge and of things known. He wants to know what kind of quality this is, how the things said to be alive can be uniquely characterized and how they stand related both to one another, if there are essential differences between them, and to the rest of the furniture of the universe. Sometimes, indeed, such philosophical problems do also come to the notice of practicing scientists as well, when, as in current theorizing about the origin of life, they have to ask themselves what criteria to accept in determining whether or no a system of known chemical composition is to be described as "living." This only pinpoints a problem which is there in the background even when, as they do most of the time, experiments can proceed smoothly without reference to such underlying philosophical themes.

2a

Plessner's book *Die Stufen des Organischen und der Mensch* was first published in 1928 and reissued in 1965. In the preface to the second edition, Plessner speculates on the possible reasons for its having been so long ignored or nearly ignored (though, as I have already mentioned, its indirect influence has been deep if not wide). As far as the German philosophical audience goes, there were two important reasons. For one thing, the publication in 1927 of Heidegger's *Sein und Zeit* had as it were cornered the market for philosophical surprises. And for another, the influence of phenomenology in many quarters amounted at that period to a resuscitation of idealism; the down-to-earth realism of much of Plessner's argument was from this point of view also uncongenial to the *Zeitgeist*. It was an unlucky turn of fate that this was so: for Plessner does himself, it seems to me, profit from the phenomenological revolution, though without the heavy emphasis on the new "method" and its new certainty which makes much phenomenological philosophy so difficult for the outsider to penetrate. Moreover, he, like Heidegger, has something to say about such concepts as time, death, and destiny, and not, like Heidegger, only in terms of human existence cut off from living nature, but in terms of the significance of those concepts for organic being as a whole. But this is just the corrective that *Sein und Zeit* needs: the analysis of human existence is necessarily distorted unless it is grounded in an adequate philosophy of living nature.

There is no good, however, in reconstructing a history of ideas that failed to take place, in wondering, for example, what would have happened if Merleau-Ponty had read *Stufen*. Better late than never: let us look at the main outline of Plessner's argument and see what foundation it provides for a new approach to philosophical biology. Again, I shall not attempt to convey this argument in the fullness of its philosophical background. German idealism, in particular, forms for Plessner a tradition to be reckoned with, if chiefly in criticism, while for the mid-twentieth-century English-speaking reader his references to it provide chiefly stumbling blocks for the understanding of his own position. I shall therefore ignore much of this aspect of the book and try simply to reconstruct the core of the argument. Nor can I render literally much of Plessner's terminology; I can only follow the argument in outline and hope to remain faithful, on the whole, to its general theme.

Plessner's exposition begins, as any argument must which attempts to come to grips with the foundations problem in biology, with the sharp alternative set by Cartesian dualism. Is there, Plessner asks, in truth the strong disjunction envisaged by Cartesian thought between the inner and the outer aspect of living things? For Descartes himself, of course, such a dichotomy obtains in fact only in the case of human beings. Animals, let alone plants, are simply machines; in our case an "inner" nonmaterial soul has been mysteriously added. But the point is—and it is for the philosophy of biology, and, in the context of Plessner's investigation, for the social sciences, a point of fateful importance—that within the Cartesian heritage, which is the principal heritage of the modern intellect as such, within this tradition there is no alternative for any form of life except to be either a mere body spread out in space, completely "external," or a bit of subjectivity, completely and secretly "within." In terms of the central tradition of modern thought, in other words, it is inconceivable that there should be real entities which do not fall into one or the other of these categories. The seeming unity of mind and body must be only a seeming: either everything is really matter or really mind, or where both kinds of things do undeniably show themselves there are two substances somehow, if unintelligibly, combined. It is just this conceptual framework which, up to our time, has made a rational foundation for the biological and social sciences impossible.

The first step then is to look to see whether living things do in fact display a two-aspect character which does not fit the rigid Cartesian alternative. If we examine carefully the things we perceive and the way we perceive them, we notice that there is in this respect an experienced difference between inanimate and animate objects. We do, of course, always perceive only a given aspect of any single thing; we cannot see, for example, all around a tennis ball, nor can we feel its texture simply by seeing it. But the multiplicity of aspects in such a case does add up to the total object. There is nothing that resists a total grasp, through several senses, of the object as a totality. Perceiving a cat is different: the cat is present to me in a fashion which cannot be wholly specified in terms of particular views from particular positions or through different senses. The cat confronts me in a way in which the tennis ball does not. It is just this resistance to specification, of course, just this confrontation with life, which has long made people suspicious of the Cartesian theory of the bête-machine. But the statement of a disturbing fact is not enough; a philosophical theory cannot rest simply with pointing to facts; it must provide us with concepts through which to understand those facts. Not that we want to call down some pretty ideas from a Platonic heaven; that is no good either. What we must do as philosophers is, Kant-fashion, to discover through what categories we do in fact understand the phenomena which experience presents.

Plessner's procedure in this situation is as follows. He asks, in Chapter 3 of *Stufen*, what would be the distinguishing character of living things as perceived objects which would make them resist the Cartesian alternative of outer and inner? This distinguishing criterion, call it for the moment A, he then takes as a postulate for the development of his argument. He asks: given, hypothetically, A: do the acknowledged characters of living things, such as development, self-regulation, organization, and so on, follow logically from A? Such characters are usually listed, empirically, as ultimate qualities of life. They are, if any, those characters which cannot be reduced by analysis to other qualities. In other words, they are organic *modals*. And what Plessner will have done if he succeeds in deducing them from his initial postulate is to produce a *theory of organic modals*.

Another way to put the situation schematically is in terms of the conflict between Köhler and Driesch discussed above. Living things appear to be totalities which are not simply physical forms or *Gestalten*. A theory of organic modals should demonstrate the basic characters of living things as just those characters which make it possible for a *Gestalt* to be not only a *Gestalt* but a genuine totality. It does this, again, by taking as its starting point a *perceptible* difference between organic and inorganic bodies and deducing the other, indirectly apprehended characters from this difference.

What we need, then, is a property directly present to us in our immediate awareness of living things, not an abstract character or one which needs to be gleaned from a complicated chain of experiences—like the characters of metabolism or reproduction. We can find this, quite simply, by considering under what circumstances a shape "looks alive." Plessner refers in this connection to Buytendijk's systematic study of such judgments. Proceeding from the presentation of simpler to more complex shapes, he found that a certain irregular regularity both of shape and motion makes us react to forms as living or like living. Everyone will know this experience from watching animated cartoons. It is, to put it briefly, a certain plasticity of form, "freedom of form within form," that constitutes the immediate criterion of life. In the case of animated cartoons, of course, life is simulated; one's judgment here may be, humorously, or even seriously, in error. But the question is to establish the minimal criterion by which we judge a body to be alive—whether or no in a given case it "really" is so. It is a question here of the intuitive perception quite naïvely and ordinarily involved in such judgments. Consider again the example of the cat contrasted with the tennis ball. A cat playing with a ball, for example, confronts the ball in a fashion different, to our perceptive apprehension, from the way in which the ball confronts the cat. There is a difference here analogous to Merleau-Ponty's distinction between lived, bodily spatiality and objective spatiality. An inanimate object, a house or a mountain or a pebble, simply fills space. In Whitehead's terms, it is "simply

located." But a living thing *takes* its place. It not only has a
position in the co-ordinate system of space and time; it has *its*
place. The venerable concept of natural place, so hampering to
the perspectives of physics, is essential to biological thought.

The concept we need here, however, is not *only* spatial. It is
a question of the whole way in which an organism "takes its
place" in all environment: arises in it, is dependent on it, yet
opposes itself to it. Plessner tries to sum up what is intended
here in a single term: *positionality*. This is the fundamental
concept which he puts, hypothetically, at the head of his argument and from which he proceeds to elicit, first, the other characters of living things in general, and then the distinctions between different styles of living—notably between plants and
animals, animals and men.

Before I try to explain what Plessner means by this term,
however, I must ask the reader's patience. This is a difficult
concept to grasp at first meeting, but it does, I believe, gain in
intelligibility as the argument proceeds. It may help at this
point to anticipate some of the difficulties.

For one thing, positionality, if we take it, as I have been
doing, as identified with "natural place," seems to apply, as in
my feline example, more readily to animals than to plants.
Plants too have natural places—or, in modern language, ecological niches—but they do not seem, as animals do, to *take*
their place. They can exist only in certain environments, and
disintegrate outside them; but so can crystals, for instance,
keep their shape only out of solution. If positionality is to serve
as a basic concept for philosophical biology, it must mean,
therefore, more than *just* natural place.

Would Buytendijk's formula "freedom of form within form"
do better? It does apply to plants—to the shape of a leaf, for
example, as against a crystal. But positionality is not, or at any
rate is not *only*, a concept of shape, or even, more generally, of
physical form. Plessner has argued recently that his theory is

confirmed by modern evolutionists who hold that the origin of life can be located as the first establishment of an entity enclosed in a semipermeable membrane. And the concept of positionality does indeed have to do, as we shall see, with the way in which an organism establishes its boundary over against a surrounding medium. Yet positionality *is* not the boundary or the shape described by the boundary: it is the *way an organism bounds itself* that is essential. It is a question not only of a *Grenze* but of *Begrenzung*.

To put it this way, however, again seems to lead us back to a distinction involving an active aspect, which seems, at least at first sight, say, inappropriate to the description of the higher plants. Yet, as I hope to show in what follows, Plessner's basic concept and the theory he builds upon it are neither arbitrary nor meaningless. Perhaps the best crutch I can ask the reader to lean on at this stage is yet another example from modern biology: Sir McFarlane Burnet, in his work on immunology, argues that the ability of a living body to "know" its own cells from invading material is a deep-rooted property of life.[7] Now, of course, a cell, or indeed an organism, with few exceptions, cannot be said to "know" anything in a conscious or intentional sense. Yet it is some such power of distinguishing itself from the environment of which not only immunological phenomena but the very existence of semipermeable membranes are the biochemical expression. I think that is the sort of thing Plessner is after: natural place, plasticity of shape, semipermeable membrane, immunological activity, all express facets of the one very general, and essential, character of *positionality*, which he is taking as common to all living things.

With this warning, then, let me return to Plessner's argument and see, first, how he introduces his basic concept, and then what he proceeds to do with it.

The hypothesis which Plessner puts at the head of his argument is a statement about the nature of the *boundary* between

a living thing and its medium. A body, he argues, can have one
of two relations to its boundary. Either its boundary is merely
the point where it stops, and identical with its contour or outline, or its boundary is a part of itself, not merely a virtual in-
between between body and medium but an actual boundary
belonging to the body and setting it over against the medium
and indeed over against the body itself whose boundary it is.
Plessner puts these two possibilities diagrammatically:[8]

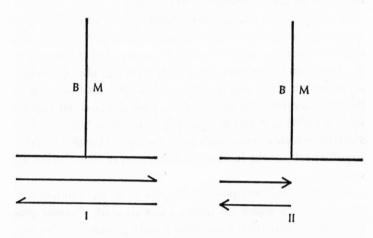

The first is characteristic of inanimate objects. A pebble or a
box simply is where it is and stops where it stops. Living things,
by contrast, have their boundaries as part of themselves, or,
strictly, as part of the bodies which they are. In the one case we
have the relation: B ←I→ M. (*The* Body ←In-Between→ Medium.) In the other, B ←B→ M, where the relation of the body
to its boundary is a relation of *itself* to *itself*.[9] In this situation
the body is placed over against the body and beyond it and at
the same time directed in *to* it. This relation of a body to its
boundary is, physically speaking, paradoxical, but nevertheless
it does not contradict the physical existence of the boundary
as such. It appears rather, Plessner says, as a *marginal phenom-*

enon of a physical system. Moreover, it is a phenomenon which cannot be specified even in an exhaustive listing of the explicit sensed characters of the body, but which is nevertheless presented directly to perceptual awareness, even though when we try to specify the character in question all we manage to state is the characters of the system as a *Gestalt*. Again, if this seems mysterious, I must ask the reader to be patient and to keep in mind the various expressions of positionality through which I have already tried to exemplify its meaning.

Of course, if we can accept this concept and work with it, as I hope we shall succeed in doing, we do have here exactly that double-aspect character we were in search of as a way out of the Cartesian dichotomy. For a body with this kind of boundary structure is not simply divisible into inner and outer; it is, through its relation to its boundary, *both* directed *out* beyond the body that it is *and* back *into* it again. It is this boundary structure which Plessner calls *positionality,* and which he takes hypothetically as the fundamental character of those bodies we call living.

Having established positionality, then, as the fundamental character from which his theory takes its start, Plessner proceeds to consider what follows for a body possessing this property. First, positionality entails process. The double-directedness of a living body beyond the body and back into the body can be realized only in change. But this is not change simply, as a rock wears away or the tide ebbs. A living body becomes something and *has* this process of becoming something as a property *of its own.* Ebb tide is ebb tide, not an entity which ebbs. A living body, in order to take on the two-directional relation to its boundary by which we have defined it, must change, but it is at the same time an entity undergoing change, itself exhibiting the process which it undergoes and being the end product toward which the process tends.

Organic process, in other words, is change governed by *type.*

Inorganic forms change, but they change simply. They are "typical" rock formations and "typical" cloud formations, but they are "typical" simply in an inductive sense: because that is how they often occur. If we "explain" them, moreover, it is by showing that, given certain conditions, they follow necessarily (by logical necessity) from the laws of physics or chemistry. Organic process, however, displays an essential tension between the series of physicochemical changes through which it is necessarily exhibited and the type toward the realization of which it moves. Inorganic forms are *Gestalten* simply. Organic form stands in an essential relation to a "*Gestalt*-idea," a type which is its norm.

From the very shape which organic bodies exhibit, therefore, or, better, from the way in which they exhibit it, from their positionality, it follows that they exist on more than one level. They exist essentially in relation to the types they realize. Given the concept of type, or *Gestalt*-idea, moreover, such types are themselves comparable in terms of near or far likeness, of "kinship"—quite apart from, and prior to, any theory of factual descent. I have tried elsewhere to show how theories of evolution which attempt to make phylogeny prior to morphology import surreptitiously a concept of type into their arguments. Plessner here shows why this is so: the very way in which living bodies enter into our experience, as bodies having the property of positionality, already entails their essential relation to morphological principles. The particular type or level attained by a particular living thing and its relation to others, both morphologically and phylogenetically, is, of course, a matter for the empirical scientist to determine. Plessner is not, one must say explicitly, suggesting a return to the *Naturphilosophie* of the early nineteenth century. But he *is* saying that the possibility of systematics is a logical consequence of the perceptible character of living bodies—not a fortunate accident which just happens to suit the convenience of biological research.

Let me amplify this point a little in relation both to the history of philosophy and to the problem of taxonomy. Plessner's insistence that the possibility of classifying organisms is no mere happy chance recalls Kant's statement to the contrary in the *Critique of Judgment*—his statement that it *is* a happy accident that nature conforms to our regulative idea of order.[10] Nature, for Kant, of course, was Newtonian nature. It was the reality knowable by classical mechanics, and only that reality, which, he had demonstrated in the first *Critique*, was constituted, as far as its form goes, by the principles of our understanding. The range within which we can basically make sense of the real world, in other words, is coterminous with *non*living nature. When we come to the living world, what we add, in Kant's view, is, as I have already pointed out, a mutual means-end relation characteristic of organized beings. Ends, however, over against the one-level cause-and-effect reality of Newtonian nature, are conscious purposes, yet not our purposes which we know from within. What then? Presumably God's purposes. These, however, we finite and fallen beings cannot know; we can only act *as if* living nature were planned according to such purposes and proceed thankfully in the light of the happy chance that things do work out this way. We have, then, on the one hand, sheer mechanical necessity, whose principles are formally entailed by our intellectual categories, and, on the other, inscrutable purposes to which, fortunately for the practice of biology, organic phenomena just happen to conform. The heart of natural science, which is physics, stands out of all positive relation to cosmology and theology, but in an essential, internal relation to the structure of our intellects. Biological "science," insofar as it is not reducible to physics, exceeds the constitutive principles of our intellects, but stands in an external, though expectant and respectful, relation to a theologically oriented cosmology. We cannot expect to understand this "happy accident," but we approach it with piety in the service of faith.

Most contemporary biologists are unacquainted with the Kantian *Critiques;* they seem to think of Kant, for some obscure reason, as the founder of idealistic *Naturphilosophie*— just the sort of aprioristic morphology which he thought to be radically *im*possible. But despite their happy innocence of philosophy, their thinking is still, as I said earlier, dominated by the Kantian synthesis. They have, of course, and rightly, no wish to serve the ends of theology, and so, wanting the "regulative" principles which, for Kant, linked the inspection of living things to faith, they fall back onto the need to reduce biology to physics. Indeed, within the Kantian perspective, biology could not mature into a proper science on any other terms. Only physics is science.

What happens, in this situation, to biological taxonomy and systematics, the whole business of classifying organisms? One of two things. Classification may be identified with genealogy, as it was in the heyday of classical Darwinism and is again by some neo-Darwinian systematists. Descent in this case is thought to determine type. But how is descent known? One would suppose, by similarity of type. But there is no such similarity, the neo-Darwinian argues: there are simply overlapping congeries of characters which sum up to something we call species, genus, and so on. What there is fundamentally, "in reality," however, is: gene pools of changing populations and the statistical relationships established in respect to these. I do not want here to go into the conceptual difficulties of such radical evolutionism in taxonomy; suffice it to mention that the model of population genetics when applied to paleontology is itself at high abstraction. If the field paleontologist were not himself an excellent judge of the specimens he in fact discovers, he could not make the elaborate extrapolations he in fact makes to a vanished flux of vanished molecules of hereditary material.

Many biologists, indeed, admit the difficulty of a purely genealogical taxonomy. What alternatives are left them? Some try to evade the problem by insisting on the purely conventional nature of classification. Taxonomy is just a game of ours, they insist, by which we sort out objects purely for our convenience. The aim of "real" classification so long pursued by naturalists was wholly illusory. This theory, however, is plainly contradicted by practice. For example: a botanist defending the mere-convenience theory of classification illustrated it by referring to the case of a plant useful for medicinal purposes. This plant had been imported from India, but was for the time being unavailable; scientists therefore sought a substitute in the same family and found, indeed, a "related" plant with similar curative properties. This shows, the botanist explained, that the classification was made merely for convenience, since it enabled the doctors to find what they were looking for. But surely what it did was to enable them to find a *really* similar plant: it *did* have the same property and did in fact cure people of the same illness. If the classification is a convenience, it is a convenience based on natural similarity. Using it is like remembering that I always put all the herbs on one shelf and the spices on another, not like remembering that I always put the ketchup beside the shoe polish. There is, of course, a conventional aspect to classification, but the convention is at least partly based on and directed to natural similarities and dissimilarities.

Yet in terms of the modern tradition it is difficult if not impossible to find an alternative to the interpretation of classification as always and necessarily genealogical on the one hand or always and necessarily purely conventional on the other. A group of taxonomists have, indeed, recently been attempting with sophisticated statistical methods, to develop an alternative which they call "numerical taxonomy," and as one might have guessed they have been loudly accused of being "typologists," Platonists, and what not. Plessner's argument shows, however, that, whether or no it succeeds, their endeavor is philosophically justified and indeed fundamental. For the very perceived, experienced character of living things is such that they must be capable of being ordered according to types. Again, this is not *Naturphilosophie* in the aprioristic sense: Plessner is not trying to tell taxonomists *how* to classify organic phenomena. That is a matter for empirical research and statistical analysis. The philosopher cannot tell the scientist *how* to classify his subject matter, but he can tell him that he must classify it *somehow* and that the nature of the subject matter, as both common sense and scientific experience display it, demands that he do so. He need neither dogmatize his efforts in the direction of Darwinian orthodoxy, pretending to himself that he never refers to types or norms and surreptitiously doing so, nor need he, on the other hand, disguise his efforts to comprehend natural systems as mere conventional shufflings of meaningless tags. If he is dealing with living things at all, he is thinking in terms of their trueness to type; and if he is thinking in terms of trueness to type, he is thinking, Plessner argues further, in terms of levels which can be hierarchically ordered. There is no need to be ashamed of such activities, which are part and parcel of our ordinary grasp of the things around us: as much so as recognizing the difference between a toy snake and a real one or between a doll and a baby.

I am, in the main, trying here to exhibit the outline of Plessner's argument and to take my reader with me in following its course. Whether or no my summary of it is convincing, however, there is, it seems to me, a gap at this point which must be mentioned for the reader's reflection before I go on to the balance of the argument. It concerns the very title, and therefore a major theme, of his book: *levels* of organic order. It is, I believe, a central, if not the central task of philosophy in our time to teach us to think in terms which will reasonably permit the acknowledgment of levels of reality. For the tragic fragmentation of our culture—in particular, in terms of the argument before us here, our inability to erect the disciplines concerned with living things in general and with ourselves in particular on

a rational philosophical foundation—all this is intimately related to the insistence of modern science-oriented thought that
there are no degrees of being, that things just *are* or *are not*. If
that were true, everything would be strictly meaningless—in
relation to the ideals men cherish, strictly absurd—as so many
artists and thinkers have indeed held it to be. Plessner is concerned to rectify this fateful error, and he does indeed, as I
hope I shall show, articulate most convincingly the distinctions
that do display themselves between the great levels of organic
being: between plant, animal, and human life. His aim, however, in the chapter I am now concerned with is, as we have
seen, to *deduce* the characteristic powers and functions of living things from positionality as a basic property of such things.
And he has indeed, it seems to me, shown conclusively how the
relation between individual and type follows logically from the
positional character of the sort of object we call "living." This
argument does therefore demonstrate, as I have argued, why
morphological judgments are necessarily involved at the very
root of biological research. Types, however, are not the same as
levels of order. Living things could fall each one under some
type, without those types, being necessarily themselves hierarchically ordered in relation to one another. There could be an
anarchy of Forms; why not? On the foundation Plessner has
laid so far we can see that a rational systematics is *possible*. But
is it necessary? Morphology, indeed, is, given the premise of
positionality, an a priori necessity, but that systematics is also
necessary the argument has not so far plainly exhibited. For the
moment at least, therefore, I shall just have to leave this as an
open question: why does the necessary reference to types and
therefore to a two-level reality of living things, of individuals in
relation to norms—why does this reference *entail* a structuring
into levels and a classification into "kinship" relations of these
types themselves? That such systematic comparisons are in fact
the framework of biological research and theory is clearly true;

but that is not Plessner's point. He is supposedly exhibiting a logical necessity, which in this case is, so far in his argument at least, not clear as such.

But to return to Plessner's argument. So far it runs: if living things display the relation to their boundary characterized as positionality, they must be in process, and their characteristic way of being in process is displayed in their relation to a *Gestalt*-idea or type. Correlative to the notion of type, however, is that of the *individual,* which in its existence does and does not conform to its type. Individuality does indeed empirically characterize living things, and again, in terms of Plessner's analysis, it follows necessarily from the nature of positionality that it should do so. The fact that the boundary of a living thing belongs to the thing and cuts it off from the medium, while at the same time setting it in relation to it, clearly entails the marking out of that living thing as an individual. At the same time individuality is the correlative of the *Gestalt*-idea, of the norm in relation to which it is the kind of individual it is.

Individuality expressed through process, moreover, is *development,* again an empirically listed character of living things which in this context is seen to be entailed by the concept of positionality. Development is just the orderly process in which a living thing transcends the body it is, to become—the body it is. And finally the dynamical character of living things, as developmental, necessarily entails, Plessner argues, its own rounding off, its own cessation, in aging and death. Dying is sometimes interpreted as an aspect of living: since to live is to change irreversibly and to change irreversibly is to pass away, all living is dying. This is incorrect, Plessner says, since death is not part of, but the radical other of, life, its absolute negation. But it is true, he insists, that the very nature of living things as positional entails this radical negation. The structure $B \leftarrow B \rightarrow M$ exhibits a hiatus, a cut, between body and medium. The tension between individuality and type already displays this kind of dividedness. But as development proceeds—always to a new "stage," but a new stage of the same being—it approaches the final hiatus which cuts it off irrevocably in time, as its own individuality, for all its reaching out beyond itself, has always, from its beginning, cut it out in place.

The inevitability of death, the approach of death, taken together with the whole spirallike process of development that has preceded it, show us further that living things, unlike inanimate objects, have a destiny. One can write a geological "history" of a mountain or a valley, for example; yet rocks and rivers nevertheless just are where they happen to be, even though they gradually accumulate or are thrown up by cataclysms of the earth or erode or fill up and disappear. Living individuals and only living individuals, with their Januslike direction to and from the world around them, to and from the bodies that they both are and have, are *destined* to live as they do—and to die.

Plessner's argument on death is closely tied to his critical examination of German idealist theories, and perhaps for this reason his reasoning here seems rather murky. Does the necessity of death really follow logically from the premise of positionality? The hiatus exhibited by the boundary of a living thing does indeed generate an irresoluble tension between individual and type. But why *must* growth grow toward total cessation? There is an analogy, I suppose, between the contrast: living body/medium and the contrast of life with death. But we have started, concretely, from the model of a perceptible living thing; and simply to say, "As it stops in place, so it must stop in time," seems to be, so far, stretching the model just that bit too far. And there is an empirical difficulty: if we look at the whole range of the things we do in fact call living, we find that not all of them die. Only those that exhibit sexual reproduction undergo death in the proper sense. Germ cells are potentially "immortal"; so are protozoa like paramecium which multiply by fission. The daughter cells, to be sure, are not identical with the mother animalcule, but there is no "corpse" left over. Such organisms *can* perish, but they do not die: their destiny does not necessarily include mortality, as ours does. That positionality is a good criterion of life is confirmed, Plessner points out in the Preface to the second edition of *Stufen*, by some of the discussion of modern theorists on the origin of life. But the very primitive organisms which they have in view in their discussions, though characterized by the kind of boundary structure that Plessner had described, are not characterized by the inevitability of death. This fact, though not a philosophical argument, confirms the reader's uneasiness, at this point, about the argument itself. Again we may leave this question open for the moment.

At the same time Plessner's introduction of the concepts of death and destiny at this point, in a book published in 1928, presents an interesting contrast with Heidegger's treatment of the same themes in *Sein und Zeit*. Whether or not Plessner's argument at this stage is formally valid, what is important is that he sees these concepts as essential over a much broader range than Heidegger does. For Heidegger only the rare authentic human individual has a destiny; for Plessner destiny is coterminous with life itself. And Being-to-Death, though not, as for Heidegger, the only meaning of human life, is one essential theme, in Plessner's view, of organic, not only of human, development. Thanks to this broader basis, Plessner's book lacks the dramatic urgency which made the publication of Heidegger's magnum opus so overwhelming a philosophical event. But it can also lead to more fruitful, and more balanced, philosophical consequences than have emerged, in the later pronouncements of Heidegger's "quest for being," from *Sein und Zeit*. Indeed, where Heidegger's concept of being-in-the-world has proved most fruitful—as in Merleau-Ponty's work, for example—it has been, if only indirectly, fused with Plessner's, more broadly based argument. *Human* being and Being can be harmoniously and truly interpreted only through the mediation of an adequate philosophy of *life*.

2b

The treatment of death and destiny completes Plessner's argument on the dynamics of living things. Now for their "statics." Let us start once more from the character of positionality. The body in the relation B←B→M to its surroundings has its boundary as part of itself. There is, as there is not for inanimate objects, a cut between body and medium, but more than this: the body takes up a relation to its own configuration, to its boundary. It stops, as Plessner puts it, before it comes to an end and sets its boundary beyond itself as its own limiting area. It is tempting to translate this rather enigmatic statement into visible and zoological terms and say, the living body has a skin between itself and its environment—a skin which is one of its organs and therefore a part of it, yet not "it." But this, Plessner warns, would be misleading. It is true, of course, that the development of a patterned outer layer, especially in higher animals, becomes an important organ not only of self-maintenance and survival but of expression, of what Portmann calls display. And it is also true that Portmann's "display"—which he takes as an ultimate and irreducible character of living things—is by Plessner shown to follow from positionality as a fundamental concept. But what he is arguing at this stage is not that display follows from positionality—though it does do so—but rather that Portmann's other fundamental criterion of life, "centricity," is entailed by the positional character of organisms. (I am reversing history here, for Portmann's treatment of display, through the past twenty years, has in fact been influenced by Plessner's argument of 1928.)

The body which has the property of positionality, we have

seen, assumes with this property a two-way relation to that body: it is directed both into the body and away from the body. In his argument up to this point Plessner has avoided the reflexive form of statement: he talks of the relation of the body to "it," not to it*self*. But he now makes explicit the reflexive character which we do indeed, both in common sense and science, constantly attribute to organic beings. Taken in terms of structure rather than process, positionality means that the body has an inner *core* out of which it has its parts and an outer aspect which is the aspect of that core. Its parts are peripheral relative to its center, and the center is the point of reference that makes the parts its parts. But neither core nor periphery in this context is simply spatial. Spatial depth and externality can be studied by the instrumentalities of physics and precise measurement, but the distinction Plessner is making is not touched by such analysis—though on the other hand he is not suggesting, as Driesch had done, that physical analysis of living things must somewhere call a halt. Positionality and the core-periphery relation it carries with it are irrelevant to and unaffected by physical and microbiological techniques, which can however proceed indefinitely to illuminate the conditions necessary to the existence of the entity exhibiting that quality.

This seems paradoxical. Plessner started from the perceptible difference between living things and inanimate objects and took positionality, hypothetically, as a clue to that perceptible difference. Now he says the relation of inner and outer in the living body is not a measurable, spatial relation. How then is it perceptible or entailed in what is perceptible? The answer (which Plessner had elaborated in great detail in his earlier book) is that perceptibility is by no means exhausted by what can be precisely specified in physically intelligible spatial terms. The aspect of our perceptions amenable to precise measurement and hence to physicochemical analysis is only one dimension, so to speak, of perception in a richer sense. We perceive, directly and immediately, much that is not reducible to such precise terms. All qualities, as we have already seen, resist such reduction: the physicist tells us how colors are produced, but he does not thereby exhaust or destroy the qualities of color as perceived. Similarly, the neurophysicist tells us about the deep-lying structures of the central nervous system which is the inner controlling agent of the organism's outward behavior, but he has not thereby explained, let alone explained away, the quality of tension between inner and outer, the quality of being peripheral expressions of an inner core, that characterizes life. A living body is indeed a body; it occupies space; but its center is nevertheless not a spatial center, it is a core which transcends spatiality and at the same time controls the spatiality of the body whose core it is. Relatively to the body which is its body, it is nowhere and everywhere. And it is this relation of core to periphery which we perceive when we perceive a living body, even though it is not a "perception" that we can exhaustively specify in the spatiotemporal terms of classical, or even of modern, physics. It is this relation, in short, that we are referring to when we speak of living things as *subjects having* such and such properties or parts.

It is extremely important that we understand this statement in the full generality with which it is intended. To be a subject having properties or parts is *not* to be a conscious subject. The quality of consciousness simply does not come into the present argument at all. There are biologists and philosophers who resist the allure of a one-level ontology, the temptation to reduce organic phenomena to "nothing but" physics and chemistry, because and only because they feel that the quality of consciousness which they know from their experience, and on which the very existence of their scientific disciplines as knowledge depends, is left unexplained by this kind of one-level ontology. So far they are right; physics cannot "explain" consciousness, and if it were so expanded that it could do so, it would no longer be what we call physics. And they are right also to this extent: that we do feel a kinship with anything we perceive to be alive, especially anything that we feel exhibits self-motion and animal life; and since our way of being alive is best expressed through reference to consciousness we feel also that "something like" consciousness is present here. It was this road that we followed in looking at Portmann's concept of centricity: extrapolating gently down a slope of diminishing awareness from our self-conscious awareness of our own awareness to more distant, and, we cannot help believing, "dimmer" centers of experience.

But consciousness alone is too narrow a concept to carry either the problem here or its solution. Even our own mental life is, as we well know, by no means wholly conscious; consciousness is one specialized expression of a much more broadly occurring phenomenon. To see the problem solely in terms of physics versus introspection, of space-time co-ordinates versus conscious feeling, is to see it still in terms of the Cartesian alternative which is just what we are trying to overcome—which we *must* overcome if we are to do justice to our perceived, direct, undeniable experience of the quality of life. True, consciousness is one of the forms of life, one of the expressions of the general subject-having character Plessner is describing, and indeed an adequate theory of consciousness can be developed only in these or similar terms. But at the present stage of his argument Plessner is a long way from any reference to consciousness. He is not introducing a ghost into the living machine, because he has not started from the living body as a machine. He has started from the living body as positional, in its unique relation to its own boundary, and this relation is now seen to entail the property of being a subject which both is the body that it is and has that body as its body. There is absolutely no reference here to an "inner" something in a ghostly, secret, Cartesian sense; what Plessner is describing is in its fullest range the quality that perceptibly characterizes all the bodies we call "living," from the simplest to the most complex.

It is this quality of being a subject having properties or parts, which is at the same time the body had by that subject—it is this quality which makes the living thing in fact a "harmonious equipotential system." This phrase, introduced by Driesch in conjunction with his concept of entelechy, in fact needs no such antimechanical concept for its support. What it refers to is covered by the character of positionality and its structural consequences.

The relation of subject-having to body-had, moreover, carries with it that most striking character of living things: organization. The relation of organs to organism is close to, indeed, to be equated with, the relation of periphery to core. This statement has again at first sight a paradoxical air. For even if we take the relation of core to periphery, as we must do, conceptually rather than spatially, some organs seem to be "central" not only spatially but in the sense that they are indispensable to life, while others are peripheral not only in being at the physical boundary of the organism—limbs, for instance, as against heart or liver—but insofar as life can go on without them. This distinction, however, Plessner insists, is an empirical one, which does not affect the fundamental relation which holds for all organs. An animal *has* a heart; it is not to be identified with its heart, even though it cannot live without it. The organism is, universally, the subject which possesses all its organs, however much it depends on their totality for being the organism it is.

At the same time each organ is what it is in relation to the whole, not simply as whole but as subject. Each organ is not only a part, as the windows or roof are parts of a house; each organ is part of the whole as *representing* the whole. It stands *for* the whole in relation to the "outside" and to the organism itself. *Mediation* is essential to organization. Now, the concept of mediation will sound to philosophical readers suspiciously Hegelian. Is the argument after all a fantasy, spinning our philosophical daydreams with these familiar nonsensical threads? No: mediation here is a concept clearly derived from the perceptible boundary structure from which we began. A body having positionality is a body delimited from its medium by a boundary which it *has*, a boundary which turns back on itself as part of itself and which it nevertheless transcends—goes beyond—in its relation to its medium and in its relation to itself. Its relation to its medium, its living in its medium, is necessarily mediated by and through the boundary, and out of this arises an essential mediation of its parts to itself. Plessner has generalized, as we have seen, the intuited relation of body to boundary to the relation of core to periphery, and it is this relation in turn which shows us the essential role of mediation in the structure of living things. To be a living thing is on one level to be a thing like any other, but at the same time to be a living thing is to be more than the physical thing it is. It is to be through the mediation of the parts—the periphery—which, as core, it *has*, and yet which, as body, it *is*. That is why a principle of life separate from body is inconceivable; yet at the same time life is not reducible to physical terms. A living body is, precisely, a body which as a subject is represented by the parts which in their totality are itself as object, and its relation to its medium (in biological terms, to its environment) is in turn necessarily mediated by this internal relation of subject-aspect to object-aspect of the living thing itself.

It is in this aspect of organization that the traditional means-end character of living things becomes apparent. The teleology that is involved here, however, must be carefully distinguished from the kind of teleology that seems to demand a reference to a supernatural "maker" of organic beings. It is an inner teleology, where each part of organ possessed by the subject is means to the end of—the subject itself. Nor, a fortiori, is there here a question of a conscious subject, "wanting" to see, or digest, or cool off, or whatever it "does with" the organ or organ system in question. It is still a question of an organized body which has as parts the organs which in their totality it is. As I said earlier, the dialectic of materialism versus supernaturalism which seems to follow from a means-end treatment of living things results from the failure to see the teleological character of organisms in subordination to their intrinsic significance. This acknowledgment of the intrinsic meaningfulness of life as a unique resonance of being and having, in the sense in which Plessner has been describing it, and only this acknowledgment, can rescue our conception of living things from the twin unintelligibilities of mechanism and the will of God.

The inner dialectic of organic means-end relations, on the other hand, can be better understood for what it is if it is described, as Plessner proceeds to do, in terms of powers. Once more an Aristotelian concept—dynamis—potency or power, proves itself, within limits, naturally suited to biological philosophy. An organ is an instrument, that is, something by means of which something can be done; a hand is the power to grasp, an ear the possibility of hearing, and so on. And the subject itself—this is an un-Aristotelian insight—is the central power of all these performances. Inanimate objects, even the most sophisticated machines, do not "have" their powers in the same sense as organisms, for their specific "capacities" are not held together by the core-capacity which is the living subject.

Let me turn back here a moment to an earlier difficulty. Now that Plessner has explicitly introduced the concept of organization, we can perhaps see more clearly how in his view the possibility of systematics arises. For, given the relation of organs and organ systems to an organism, we can extrapolate to arrange organisms themselves according to the levels of complexity of their organization. This is still a *possibility* of systematics, however, as I said earlier, not a necessity.

Plessner himself too turns the argument back at this point to reinforce an earlier stage. It is in its temporal structure, he reiterates here, that organisms most centrally display their uniqueness. This reference "back" to the dynamic of living things arises inevitably from a consideration of organs and potencies. For a potency is essentially in reference to the future. Just as Heidegger did for existential time, so Plessner here shows that organic time is essentially future-directed. Only this forward pull transforms the simply flowing passage of change into process and produces a true present which *is now* its possibility of becoming other, anticipating *in posse* what it is not yet. In this context, moreover, the inevitability of death becomes more intelligible than in its earlier introduction. The living thing is a nexus of finite possibilities. As each develops, it is gone; and when all the possibilities which in their totality are the organism have been exhausted, that is natural death. This is the limit of natural time, its absolute measure; as natural place, its place in its environment, is its limit for the living thing, its measure in relation to space. Only in living things, moreover, are place and time wholly at one: development is the organism's way of taking its place in nature, and natural place is the inevitable expression of the rhythm of organic process, of organic time.

2c

So far the theory of organic modals has demonstrated that, if we take positionality as our starting point, a number of the properties which are in fact ascribed to living bodies follow from this basic quality. Development; essential relation to type; individuality; aging and death; the centered relation of a subject to the properties and parts it both has and is; organization—all these follow from the postulate of positionality as the criterion of life. All these properties have to do primarily with the internal structure and individual destiny of living things. The distinction from which Plessner had started, however, was a distinction between the ways in which bodies can be delimited from their surrounding media. What is most striking, both in experience and as the principle of the present argument, is the way living bodies set themselves over against a surrounding medium—cut off in independence of it, yet living in and through communication with it. The living body is directed both beyond itself to the environment and from it back into itself. Positionality thus generates a relation between the organism, on the one hand, and, on the other, a *positional field* which is the environment in the broadest sense: internal as well as external, organic as well as inorganic. It is indeed the whole opposition to itself, otherness of itself, which positionality entails. Organism and positional field in fact appear as contrary poles of a structured rhythm of life, of what Plessner calls the *Lebenskreis*. To put such a term literally into English—"circle of life"—makes it sound mystical or gnostic. "Life cycle," or perhaps an invented term, "biocycle," might be preferable. For what is in question is no mystery, but a perfectly plain and inescapable character of living process, as Plessner's examples show. The first is the rhythm of assimilation and dissimilation, that is, of metabolism, through which the organism turns the environment into itself and breaks down again into the stuff of the environment. The second is the rhythm of adaptation and adaptability. Plessner stresses, as I mentioned earlier, the need to take into account the organism itself which *can* adapt itself as one pole of this balanced rhythm. The active and passive aspects of adaptive phenomena, emphasized in mutual exclusion by Lamarckian and Darwinian theories, respectively, are in fact equally and inextricably involved in the dynamic interaction of organism and environment. When we take the biocycle to its logical conclusion, further, we have again the opposition of death to life, and, through it, the balance back toward life again in heredity and reproduction.

Again, however, it must be emphasized, Plessner is not arguing that the forms empirically discovered to express these general properties of life can be deduced a priori from the concept of positionality. On the contrary, positionality *entails* contingency—entails the possibility of one or another type of itself as a general principle. For it is just the flexibility of form— freedom of form—as we saw at the outset, that this concept is meant to express. Life, Plessner argues further, entails *selection:* the exclusion of some possibilities in favor of others. And this leads us to discriminate, within the general pattern of positionality, certain essential variants: the forms of positionality represented, first, by plants as against animals, then by animals in general as against men in particular.

The two possibilities realized in plant and animal life Plessner characterizes as those of *open* and *closed* form, respectively. In plant life the biocycle flows smoothly in the same direction as the environment. Growth is additive: stage *n* may be simply tacked onto stages *a–m*, which still remain visibly present. From this relatively simple and directly integrated relation to its medium the basic properties of plant life follow. First, plants can, by photosynthesis, live directly from the nonliving. Second, they do not possess true locomotion, nor, third, sensorimotor functions. Indeed, so little does a plant exhibit the individuality characteristic of animal life that it might be called, a botanist has suggested, not an "individuum," but a "dividuum."

Animal form, in contrast, is *closed*. It displays, in the relation between body and medium, two contrary rhythms: one unidirectional with, the other opposed to, the environment. By this opposition it cuts itself off more sharply from the environment, stands over against it, yet is also, as an individual, exposed to it. From this variant of positionality, again, there follow the basic properties of animal life. First, there is no photosynthesis; animals can live only from life. Second, animals have developed sensorimotor functions. There is here a more complex biocycle, a rhythm which displays a gap between the receptive and the motor phases. Third, the closed form of animal existence generates an *open* positional field. In the light of the concept of positionality, that is the meaning of *drives*. Animal life is closed back in itself, but as *against* the positional field, always *wanting*, always essentially unfulfilled.

If it is objected that the distinction between plants and animals is not always so sharp as Plessner makes it, he answers: empirically, of course not. Why should it be? It is a question of two *types* which are ideally opposed to one another. Whether a given organism conforms or fails to conform, and to what extent, to one pattern or the other is a matter for the empirical investigator to ponder. But just as positionality marks off the type of living thing as such from the inorganic—even though we may be in doubt, or indeed mistaken, about the precise place to draw the line in a given case—so the ideas of open and closed form divide off, ideally, plant from animal as forms of life.

This distinction once given, moreover, much that is the case about the animal kingdom can be seen to follow logically from the principle of closed form. Positionality, we have seen, is a boundary structure such that the body both has its body and is it. This principle is relatively submerged in the open-formed life of plants. In animals, thanks to their closed form, it is much sharper and more explicit. Indeed, the difference is one not just of degree but of *level*. Where there is closed form, the body becomes what Merleau-Ponty would call a lived body, a *Leib*, possessed by a subject, as distinct from the physical body which it nevertheless is. We have already noticed, in dealing with organization, this subject-having relation. It is stabilized and made explicit in animal life through the *mediation* of a central organ which carries the sensorimotor functions and thus makes *action* possible. Not that the central nervous system, or its more primitive equivalent in lower animals, *is* the subject or is identical with the core which we have already contrasted with the periphery of the organism. But the nervous system *represents* the center, the subject, and mediates between it, its body *as* its body, and the environment as external, as all that is *not* "itself." Through this new level of mediation—which is animal organization, sensorimotor organization, as well as organization simply—through this new level the animal achieves *self*-hood. It becomes a *me*—though not, Plessner is careful to emphasize, an *I*. It *has* a body and *is* a self, but does not yet *have* a self, to which in turn it can take a stand in reflective awareness. Indeed, there is no question here, Plessner insists, of introducing into the argument a foreign and mysterious factor of "subjectivity." It is simply a question of a variant of positionality, but one by which its structure brings to the argument a new level of existence—a level which we might describe in language other than Plessner's as that of true individuality, but not yet that of personhood.

This level in turn can take two forms: either decentralized existence, where the subject is in effect eliminated, or the centralized form, which is exemplified in a series of ascending levels of animal life. For both, but most clearly for the centralized variant, some of the most striking properties of animal life once more follow logically from the characteristic form. First, the rhythm of development, in its animal form, is drawn, as we have seen, into a center, but a center which is wholly absorbed into the *here and now*. Animal life, however much directed by its future potentialities and transformed by its past, is assimilated without residue to its present. There are for it its own body and the open field of the external world—of all it needs and notices—and into this presence it is wholly absorbed. That is why—and how—animal individuality is the individuality of the *me*, but not the *I*.

In its absolute here-now, however, as the body it has—over against the environment which both threatens it and presents to it opportunities for living—in this situation, the animal displays *spontaneity:* it *acts.* It has, as against plants, a new dimension of freedom. And as agent it confronts the world: it exhibits what Plessner calls *frontality.* It takes not only a place but a *stand.*

Characteristic of this new level of existence, Plessner has already said, is the *empty center* which mediates between the sensory and motor phases of the functional cycle distinctive for animal life. In higher animals, the sensory phase becomes more marked, and in particular we can distinguish higher from lower animals—as we have seen in studying Portmann's concept of centricity—by the degree to which the body schema, their awareness of their own body, is developed. The gap is wider, the *having* of the body more clearly over against the subject.

Never, however, Plessner insists, do animals in their perception evade the intrinsic relation of perception to movement. Animals perceive *things,* he says, but not *objects.* "Things" are what they are relative to drives, to uses: they are threats, lures, playthings, friends, enemies, not objectified entities understood in and for themselves. There is indeed a gap between thing and organism, a hiatus represented by the self, by the power of perception which both exposes the animal to reality and protects it against reality. But this hiatus is never, radically never, adequate to the understanding of objects as such. Why not? Once more, because of the way in which the animal self is assimilated to the here and now. Animals, Plessner points out, have no sense of *negativity.* Higher animals do make generalizations of a sort: they abstract similarities from similar situations; learning experiments, as well as everyday experience of animal behavior, make this quite plain. On animal inference, Hume is certainly in the right as against Descartes. And this kind of abstraction does even involve in a way a grasp of generalities. Do animals then understand "universals"? Yes and no: they are, many of them, capable of experience, ordering their perceptions along rather general lines, but only because for them particulars are no more fully particular than universals are fully universal. The distinction arises in its full significance only for us who have put, as we shall see, a second hiatus, a new kind of distance, between ourselves and the world. It is this radical distancing of which animals other than man are wholly, structurally incapable. Negativity is the price we pay for being each of us an I, not only a "me."

To be sure, higher animals are capable also of insight, but again only into concrete situations. Moreover, they retain their past, not only as the product of growth and development but as a living residue in memory. And they retain such residues, further, only in relation to drives, that is, not automatically, but as the correlate of anticipations, of needs. All living things are related to their past through the mediation of development; but for animals, especially higher animals, the past can be present, yet present only insofar as the anticipated future has made it memorable, has built the past into a pattern of experience. With memory and learning Plessner contrasts instinct, which, prior to memory, belongs to the cycle of adaptation. Both instinct and learning, however, he insists, are always, in all animals, relentlessly oriented to the concrete needs of *action*.

The importance of Plessner's account of animal existence should, I hope, be obvious. In the philosophical tradition we have had, on the problem of animal intelligence, as on so many questions, only a few equally unpalatable alternatives before us. In this case there have appeared to be three possibilities. Either sentience, memory, experience, learning, characterize men only (Descartes), or there is no such thing (behaviorism), or there is a kind of brute, irrational animal inference and nothing else (Hume). The second alternative is nonsense (though still potent nonsense), denying the plain facts of our own experience. The first denies the equally plain facts of animal existence; no one who has ever known "personally" a single animal could seriously accept the Cartesian theory. And the third, though it allows us a kind of bastard reasoning—a "wonderful and unintelligible instinct in our souls"—can make nothing of the problem of standards, of truth and falsity, right and wrong, beauty and ugliness. Plessner's schema for animal life, his account of the closed form of positionality with its corresponding open positional field, his deduction of the me-body-environment structure of animal experience, brilliantly and with absolute cogency, it seems to me, sets off animal from plant life on the one hand, and on the other human from animal. There is here, as he rightly says, *no* introduction of a secret subjective factor, no *metabasis eis allo genos,* but simply a restructuring of positionality, an introduction of a second level of opposition and mediation between core and periphery, inner and outer. And again, be it noted, these are not "inner" and "outer" separable in Cartesian fashion from one another, but an ineradicably two-sided pair. The body, though beyond the center, is nevertheless within, as against the outside world. And the self, the center, is wholly absorbed in its directedness to what lies beyond. But at the same time this ambiguity, mediated through the sensorimotor cycle and its representatives, the organs of the nervous system, is a more intricate ambiguity, a more deeply leveled complex, than that of positionality simply and in general. Yet it is still lacking the further complication which, as we shall see, is constitutive for the achievement of humanity.

Two further brief comments before I go on to the final chapter of *Stufen* and the unique positionality of man. I questioned earlier how the necessity of levels in organization could arise from Plessner's argument. But at this point, it seems to me, he *has* shown how between plant and animal, and between animals at lower and higher levels, advances in organization are correlated with, and expressive of, new complexities in the property of positionality itself. What seemed earlier only a logical possibility is now filled in by the further development of the argument and appears, not indeed as, in itself, a logical necessity—for all that is proved necessary is *some* specification of positionality as a general theme—but as the concrete realization of a possibility, as a logically grounded reality, so to speak. Indeed, the distinction I have just been emphasizing between mere mechanism, plantlike subsistence, animal life including animal intelligence, with its powers of generalization and insight, yet bound irrevocably to the here and now, and finally— what we have still to come to—the unique format of human life: this series of distinctions, which takes us with firm steps beyond the Cartesian-Humean-behaviorist trilemma, is in itself worth all the difficulty of the long argument that has led up to it. Freed of an untenable dualism or an absurd reductivism, we stand at last, within the animal kingdom yet other than it, on firm and even ground.

And finally, I cannot forgo one more comparison with existentialist philosophy. The central importance of negativity in human life is, again, a familiar and a haunting existentialist theme. As Merleau-Ponty uses it in particular in *The Phenomenology of Perception*, it is endlessly illuminating. But still not so simply, nor so firmly so, as here. That animals lack true concepts because they lack a sense of negativity will be, to anyone who has been practically concerned with animals, a true and illuminating statement; but that this is so *because* of the character of animal positionality, *because* of the radical absorption of the animal self into the absolute here-now—this thesis ties down an otherwise strange contingency, a sheer fact that mysteriously confronts us, and puts it in its place in the ordered yet complex range of organic phenomena—in its place as one variant of positionality, one variant on an ordered, intelligible scale of styles of life.

3a

There remains the next and last level, which is our own.

Animals live in*to* a center and out *from* a center, but not *as* a center: the center of their experience, as we have seen, is absorbed without residue into the here and now. Men are animals; they still live, and experience, out of and into the center of their bodily lives. But they *are* also the center itself: or better, life out of the center has, in the human case, become reflexive, has set itself to itself as its own. Man cannot free himself from his own centered, animal existence; yet he has placed himself over against it. This structure Plessner calls *eccentric positionality*. A living thing exhibiting this new level of positionality is still bound by his animal nature, yet detached from it, free of it. His life has its natural place, as all animal existence has, yet is at the very same time detached from locality, is everywhere and nowhere. Nor is there any new entity which comes from somewhere—like Aristotelian nous—to create this situation: there is only a new hiatus, a break in nature, which produces a new unity. Plessner writes:

> Positionality there is a threefold situation: the living thing is body, is in its body (as inner life) and outside the body as the point of view from which it is both (body and inner life). An individual which is characterized positionally by this threefold structure is called a *person*. It is the subject of its experience, of its perceptions and its actions, of its initiative. It knows and it wills.[11]

And he concludes: "Seine Existenz ist wahrhaft auf Nichts gestellt." ("Its existence is literally based on nothing.")[12] For what produces humanity is not a new type of organization, as the closed form over against the open constitutes animal life as against plants. We are still animals, but animals at a double distance from their own bodies. We have not only an inner life distinct from, though not separable from, our physical existence; we stand over against both these, holding them apart from each other and yet together. It is our eccentric positionality that gives to our existence the ambiguity—of necessity and freedom, brute contingency and significance—which it characteristically displays.

The world constituted by this structure (*Welt,* as against the *Umwelt* of other animals) has three aspects. It is an outer world, an inner world, and a shared world (*Mitwelt*). The nature of the person is constituted by the relation to all three. Each of these aspects displays its own variety of ambiguity, its own double aspect; we have come far indeed from the simple Cartesian alternative.

First, the external world. We live as animals in an environment, of which our body is the center. But at the same time, in setting that center for ourselves, we place ourselves as physical bodies, as things, at a measurable point in a uniform space and time. We place ourselves, and everything, in the empty forms of space and time through which we constitute our world as external. Plessner is not here taking any special stand on the metaphysical problem of space and time, but outlining the consequences of our special type of positionality: interpret them as you will.

The inner world, secondly, has its own ambiguity. There is the flow of experience, of sensations, feelings, "mental" events which go on whether we are aware of them or not, whether we like it or not, and which are ourselves despite ourselves. And there are the acts of perceiving, noticing, recalling which we can—but by no means always do—enact in respect to our experience as passive. Again, the ultimate and indissoluble two-in-one character of these two aspects of our inner world follows logically from the structure of eccentric positionality as such. I am the center of my lived experience; yet, as an I, I stand apart from it. Plessner's analysis not only leaves room, as neither empiricist nor rationalist philosophies can, for the vast range of unconscious mental life. It exhibits at one stroke the inevitability, and the significance, of that strange but central fact of our inner lives which most philosophers neglect: the fact that, for all my actions, even the most considered or the most self-consciously responsible of them, I never really know whether it is *I* who perform them or something in me that is not "really" I. Many writers, especially in the existentialist tradition, have argued *that* we are always both passive and active, both bound and free. Plessner has shown *why* this is so. This is just the ambiguity produced by a centered positionality that has turned back on itself, that holds its bodily and experienced aspects together by splitting them apart. The "problem" of freedom and determinism is not a pseudo problem, but it is an insoluble problem because, as living things exhibiting the structure of eccentric positionality, this is the problem that we *are*.

But there is more to come. Psychologists, sociologists, philosophers, all have told us that each of us needs the others: that we cannot become fully human except in and through human fellowship. Plessner's theory of organic modals derives this patent truth from the nature of our positionality. To be an I or a person is to stand at a distance from one's own physical existence and one's own passive experience. All my experience is mine only, as an animal's is; my own position in space and time is nontransferable, as anybody's is. But as an I, I am both irrevocably myself, not you, *and* universally an I as such, an I in general. The detachment, the very nothingness, that constitutes a person *is* the power he has of putting himself in the place of any other person, indeed, of any other living thing. The first step in primitive, and in childish, thought is to people the world with personalities. Only a more mature humanity learns to use the category of the *in*animate; the first and essential step beyond the positionality of animal life is to see eccentricity, to see personhood, everywhere. Where there is one person, Plessner says, there is every person. And conversely, there can be one person only where there is the possibility of every person: where there is a shared world (a *Mitwelt*). Communion is constitutive of the person. Animals, too, have social lives, which serve in intricate ways to maintain and to enrich their existence. And we too, of course, being animals, have social lives rooted in a biological foundation. But beyond our animal needs and satisfactions we are persons. And it is, Plessner argues, constitutive of a person to be both I and we, to be I through being we. Nor is the "we" entailed here any particular empirical we, not even that of mother and child or husband and wife. It is communion as such that constitutes the person: as a member of the shared world, each man stands where the other stands. Only as the product of such sharing, moreover, is there *mind* (*Geist*) and its product, objectivity. The opposition of I to it, the understanding that what confronts me is capable of being elsewhere or anywhere—in other words, the grasp of true universals which makes scientific knowledge possible—this understanding is not something on its own over against our personal lives. It is constituted, as the sphere of mind, of *im*personal judgment, by the radical togetherness that is the very being of the person as such.

Again, in his description of the *Mitwelt*, Plessner has taken a simple yet revolutionary step. What existentialists call the problem of the "other," what empiricists call the problem of the "knowledge of other minds," may be, as a matter of fact, a genuine puzzle to particular people in particular situations of isolation and misunderstanding. Philosophically, however, it is a pseudo problem. For persons are persons, *by definition,* only insofar as they take a stand, in its nature general or generalizable, over against themselves as living individuals. To be an I, no matter how egocentrically, is to be able, on principle, to take such a stand. To be myself is, on principle, to be capable of putting myself in the place of others. My own particular being, in my own limited, parochial situation, is a concretion, as every particular human being is, of this generality. That is what is true in *both* rationalist and empiricist ethics. Kant's categorical imperative, the maxim of my will generalizable to a universal law, is an abstract statement of this truth, which neglects its necessary embodiment in a particular living thing. For the universality of the person is not detachable from the living individual: as a person I take a stand over against the living body in which I am and which I am, and as a person I am all these at once, my body, in my body, and over against my body. On the other hand, Hume's moral sense, "a certain calm determination of the passions, combined with a distant view or reflection," represents empirically the condition of the concrete self engaged in moral judgment, exercising personhood. But Hume's empirical description is philosophically self-denying since for him there is no self. Its factual correctness can be justified only if it is shown, as Plessner shows it, to follow from, to be the concretion of, the power of universalization which *is* the Kantian moral law. Later empiricist ethics also, like Mead's or Dewey's, which emphasize but fail to justify sociality, are made intelligible by Plessner's analysis.

Not that this is an "ethic": it is much more. For the "person" Plessner is describing, the person that we are, is not a merely moral agent. The being of the person unites all three Kantian questions: he is the agent as such, whether of knowing, of doing, or of hoping. The separation of these aspects of human aspiration is consequent to the structure of personhood as such. Again, the unity of knowing and doing emphasized by such philosophies as pragmatism and existentialism is here given, cleanly and plainly, its phenomenological root. Only as a member of the shared world, the *Mitwelt*, am I a person; only as a person can I submit myself to universal standards, whether for the objectification of perceptual experience that makes the external world knowable or for the universalization of inner experience that generates moral law.

3b

From the structure of eccentric positionality, finally, Plessner derives what he calls the fundamental laws of anthropology, that is, laws of human existence as such. The first, to which I have had occasion to refer earlier in this book, is the law of *natural artificiality.* By his constitution, by his position over against the contraposition of his body and himself as having this body, man is homeless. He is not reabsorbed into nature as other animals are. "As an eccentrically organized being," therefore, "he must make himself into what he already is." [13] "Man lives only insofar as he *leads* a life." [14]

This pathos of human destiny, over against the narrower yet securer living of other creatures, is expressed in the myth of man's nakedness. Beasts

> exist directly, without knowing about themselves and about things, they do not see their nakedness—and yet the heavenly father feeds them. Man on the other hand has with his knowledge lost that directness, he sees his nakedness, is ashamed of his bareness and must therefore live deviously, through the mediation of artifacts. [15]

This myth, Plessner argues, conveys a profound truth:

> Since man is forced through his type of existence to lead the life that he lives, to fashion what he is—because he *is* only insofar as he achieves—he needs a complement of a non-natural, nonorganic kind. He is therefore naturally, because of his form of existence, contrived (*künstlich*). As an eccentric being without equilibrium, standing out of place and time in nothingness, constitutionally homeless, he must "become something" and create his equilibrium. And he creates it with the help of non-natural things which arise from his creative action. [16]

But the things he thus creates must themselves be "real" enough to counterbalance his own neediness:

> In other words, he creates such an equilibrium only if the results of his action are set free from this their (human) origin in virtue of their own inner weight, on the basis of which man must recognize that he has not been their creator but that they have been realized *on the occasion of* his actions. If the results of human action do not acquire a weight of their own, if they do not become separable from the process of creation, then their ultimate meaning, the production of equilibrium, existence as it were in a second nature, repose in a second naïveté, has not been achieved. Man strives to escape the insupportable eccentricity of his being; he strives to compensate for the divisiveness of his own form of life, and he can achieve this only with things which are substantial enough to counterbalance the weight of his own existence.[17]

Thus, he continues:

> The eccentric form of life and the need for completion constitute one and the same state of affairs. But "need" must not be interpreted here in a subjective or psychological sense. This need is presupposed in all actual needs, in every impulse, every drive, every tendency, every volition of man. In this neediness or nakedness lies the motive of all specifically human activity, that is, activity directed to the unreal, and working with technical means. In it lies the ultimate ground for the *tool* and for that which it serves, to wit, culture.[18]

The need for balance holds, moreover, not only in the obvious need for *things* made to give ballast to our emptiness; it is expressed not only in tools, houses, cities, satellites, but in standards, in moral laws, and the authority of civic institutions:

> In virtue of the eccentricity of his positional form, man is a being who makes demands on himself. He "is" not simply and doesn't simply go on living, but is *worth* something and has value *as* something (*sondern gilt etwas und als etwas*). He is moral (*sitt-*

sam) by nature, an organism which tames itself by making demands on itself, which domesticates itself. He cannot exist without mores, without allegiance to unreal norms which have in themselves sufficient weight to demand recognition. . . . Thus the essential fact of his positionality becomes what is called conscience, the source from which ethical life and concrete moral existence flow.[19]

In conscience, then, in the responsible submission of himself to man-made yet compelling standards, man expresses both his otherness than nature and his second nature. He is both alienated from nature, from his own nature, and turned to a higher nature, a contrived nature, in which he becomes himself, in which he is at home. Nor is this just a "compensation" for his natural neediness; in culture man has transcended, or, better, continually transcends, the more pervasive teleology of animal needs. The root of culture is not pragmatic. As Plato put it, we seek the completion of ourselves, half-beings as we are, not simply through the assuagement of desire but through aspiration to the good.

Yet we never quite achieve the goods we seek. The ambiguous, indeed, the paradoxical in-between situation of man is expressed in Plessner's second law, which he calls *the law of indirect directness*. To invent, he argues, is also to discover: the inventions of culture both make and reveal a world. So it is with all our knowing and all our doing. We know objects: we hold things over against ourselves as stable, classifiable, real; yet at the same time we have, and know that we have, only their appearances to go by. Yet, again, these are appearances of reality, not floating phenomena. But at the same time they *are* also data of our consciousness. The tensions of appearance and reality, of immanence in consciousness and transcendence toward reality, express, therefore, not arbitrary philosophical quarrels, but the essence of our situation as knowers. There is in human nature, Plessner holds, a permanent possibility of solipsism, but on the other hand, he argues, against an errant idealism, we must understand *"the subject's situation as immanent in consciousness as the necessary condition for his contact with reality."* [20] "The subject is confined within himself and imprisoned within his own consciousness, and thus stands at a double distance from his bodily senses";[21] precisely for this reason, Plessner argues, we are able to hold reality at that distance from ourselves which enables us to perceive it *as* reality. It is our double distance from the world that affords us the cognitive space, the *Spielraum*, in which alone reality can be phenomenally presented, that is, as appearance, indeed, but as appearance of an objective world.

Immanence, then, displays transcendence. And a similar paradox holds in our affective lives. In action, in artistic creation, we "express" our inner aspirations: but "expression" is necessarily "realization, objectification of mind." [22] Yet never completely: what we strive for can always fail of achievement and always in some sense does. The very form through which our aim fulfills itself measures the distance of that fulfillment from our intended goal. All determination is, if not negation, at least compromise. Thus, Plessner holds,

> what, as technicians and artists, scholars and teachers, politicians, and doctors, merchants and lawyers, we call compromises with reality: all this is a necessary consequence of that original compromise in the world which we are and which surrounds us, the compromise between our personal center and reality in itself, on which the possibility of true fulfillment rests.[23]

Compromise, then, is our way of being; yet no compromise is good enough: there is always a discrepancy between what we aim at and what we achieve. And it is just this discrepancy, Plessner argues, which constitutes an *event,* the cold aftermath, the "shell" of an aspiration, from which we must begin again. And this is *history:* the process in which man has his essential life "is a continuum of discontinuously deposited, crystallized events." [24]

Finally, all these aspects of indirect directness, eccentricity as such, immanence together with directedness to transcendent reality, the paradox of expressivity—all these coalesce in the phenomenon of language and of meaning. "Language, an expression to the second power, is the true demonstration of the position of man: standing at the center of his own life and therefore beyond it, outside time and place." [25] And at the same time the existence of languages, the story of Babel, exhibits the essential multiplicity, the contingency, of realized expression. "Realization and fulfillment of an intention," Plessner argues, means the "refraction" of its original direction "in a foreign medium." [26] Such refraction cannot be calculated in advance; that the intention is not destroyed by it, is not shattered, but only rerouted, indicates its maturity, its fitness to meet reality. "A language—could say nothing." [27] The diversification of intentions, their elasticity, which is in this case, according to Plessner, the reason for the differentiation of meanings into a variety of languages, is also the token of their power to represent the real world and to achieve their own diverse but ordered reality.

Yet there is another aspect also of our eccentricity. If compromise, plurality, historicity, are the essential style of our existence, there is at the same time an all-or-none character to it which eludes such ambiguous expression. The third law which Plessner formulates is that of the utopian position. Man stands outside himself; he can do so totally, in the realization of his own nothingness or of the nothingness of the world. In his social relations, for example, the very fact of community displays his nothingness; for he, the individual, is replaceable by his fellow. Indeed, to be a person, we have seen, *is* to be so replaceable, to know one is replaceable. *One* stands for *all*. But that is to deny that one is oneself; and yet one is oneself. This paradox, Plessner suggests, underlies our social institutions: we are not born into clear, viable relations with others; we have to make them.

From the awareness of our own contingency, of our nothingness and the world's, moreover, springs the sense of religion. We must find an ultimate meaning, a world-all to worship, a God who can transform our calamities into sacrifice. Thus religion, as the escape from eccentricity, Plessner argues, is the enemy of culture. We seek to clothe our nakedness, to find an ultimate counterweight for our imbalance: but to find a perfect equilibrium is to cease to be human. Faith is at home in a self-contained world-all. Mind breaks this self-containment; its element is not eternity, but the future through which and toward which it aspires.

3c

Let me look briefly, in conclusion, at Plessner's account of a particular human phenomenon founded in his conception of eccentric positionality: his well-known study of *Laughter and Tears*.[28] Plessner, together with Buytendijk, it should be noted first, has constantly insisted that we should distinguish, within the general category of behavior, between actions, which are directed to goals, and expressive movements, which have their significance in themselves. Both these types of behavior, of course, can be studied in animals as well as men. But, given this distinction, we can look at human behavior also in terms of either concept: we are not restricted in our investigations to the goal-directed actions which form but one sector of behavior in general. I shall return to this matter later on, in connection with Buytendijk's work; the point here is that within the wide range of expressive movements—bodily attitudes as well as facial expressions—Plessner argues that laughing and crying constitute a pair of special cases which reveal especially strikingly the structure of personhood.

Plessner's argument includes a criticism of previous theories of laughter and, so far as there have been any, of crying and an analysis of the typical occasions of laughter (tickling, the comic, jokes, embarrassment) and of tears. But I think his conclusion is intelligible in itself and illustrative of the kind of illumination of the human condition which this type of philosophy permits.

That laughter and tears are uniquely human needs no argument. And it is obvious too that they form a pair. In what sense? In the sense, a utilitarian would answer, that they correspond to the twin ends of action: pleasure and pain. But this answer is inadequate; witness the fact that we can weep for joy—or for that matter, laugh out of embarrassment, which is unpleasant. What, then, is the source of the contrast? Plessner replies: the character of both *as reactions to a crisis of human behavior as such.* To be a person, we have seen, is to *be* a body, to *have* a body, *and* to take a stand over against both these and the relation between them. Animal life is absorbed without remainder into the circumstances, the ongoings, of the living body in its environment. It is our want of such absorption, our distance from ourselves and from things, that makes us human: we can take things as objects, ourselves as responsible agents, and so constitute a world. All such "takings," however, depend on our control of, our easy handling of, the relation between the body that I have, and am, and myself as agent constituting that relation. There is no Cartesian "thinking substance" to carry on this handling; I as person *am* its accomplishment. But sometimes it breaks down. Why? Because we face a situation to which there is no manageable, ordinary answer. Such a situation arises in one of two ways. Either the translucent, routine relations of everyday living suddenly display their essential ambiguity; or the relation collapses and the "me" and "it" seem to overpower the "I." In the first case we laugh; in the second we cry. In the first case a routine, self-enclosed relation opens out and displays itself in its shimmering multiplicity: laughter is open to others, breaks out fully only in the company of others. In the second, an ongoing relatedness collapses, turns us in upon ourselves alone, and we give way to tears. We can weep for joy as well as sorrow, because joy as sorrow can be "overwhelming."

Yet neither joy nor sorrow, neither laughter nor tears, Plessner insists, destroy the person: rather they exhibit his essential nature, his eccentric positionality in relation to the bodily life that he is, has, and normally leads. We break out in laughter, give way to sobs: the body takes over from the person. Yet the person thus expresses the limit, one or other limit, of the relation which it essentially is. A cat purrs with contentment or snarls with rage; a person can do so too. Or he can suppress the natural expression of his feelings, or even, Kantwise, the feelings themselves. *Or* knowing—and being—the relation of himself to his body, he can, when it exceeds his powers of control, *let* it take over. As person he asserts, through bodily agency, the limitations of his personhood. Somebody slipping on a banana peel is, crudely, funny. The clown on the trapeze, who looks as if he will fall but does not, is funnier. But the performance of the graceful clown, who displays awkwardness *through* and subject to the superb control of his own movements, is funniest of all. We laugh because he displays to us, and involves us in, the human predicament as such. Love and friendship, too, intensify laughter, make jokes funnier and wit wittier, because they cut open our routine lives and show us the ambiguity of our relations to others as physical, organic, and spiritual all at once. In all these cases and in many others a forgotten and hence unequivocal relation of self to living body to physical world, and of self to self, is revealed as double-edged, many-sided, unmanageably equivocal. There is no answer to this collapse of routine rationality—except to laugh. Or, if the collapse is total, if the relations constitutive of personhood break down altogether, to cry.

There is much more—for example, in the account of emotions and their relation to objectivity—in Plessner's analysis than I have been able to indicate here. And the case of laughter and tears is only one of many which can be illuminated from the perspective of Plessner's philosophy of man. We shall meet more of them in the special studies by Buytendijk of such subjects as pain or play. None of these studies, be it said in conclusion, are substitutes for physiology: there is no a priori reason why the facial muscles and tear glands should be involved just as they are in these twin expressions of our situation as persons. But physiology describes and "explains" only the *conditions* for laughing and crying, not its reasons—and similarly for other cases too. "In order to understand how something happens," Plessner says, "we must first understand what it is that is to happen." The morphology of human behavior, both active and expressive, both goal-directed and intrinsically significant, precedes, logically and philosophically, the analysis of its physical and biological conditions. We cannot analyze successfully the means through which our nature is expressed unless we first understand what that nature is. No such understanding, on the other hand, is ever final and complete: it belongs to the very ambiguity of personhood that this is so. Yet over against the main tradition of Western philosophical thought, Plessner's theory of organic modals, displaying as it does both our continuity with organic nature and our intrinsic difference from it, brings such understanding a significant step forward. Overcoming both the absurdities of reductivism and the emptiness of idealism, it can provide, at long last, a firm rational basis both for the biological sciences, in the many-leveled structure, and for the sciences of man.

NOTES

1. R. A. Fisher, "Measurement of Selective Intensity," *Proceedings of the Royal Society* B., CXXI (1936), 58–62.
2. H. Plessner, *Die Einheit der Sinne* (Bonn: Bouvier, 1965—reprint of 1922 ed.).
3. *Die Stufen des Organischen und der Mensch* (Berlin: de Gruyter, 1928, 1965).
4. Jane M. Oppenheimer, "Methods and Techniques," in B. H. Willier, P. A. Weiss, and V. Hamburger, eds., *Analysis and Development* (Philadelphia: Saunders, 1955), Section II, pp. 36–37.
5. *Stufen*, p. xxii.
6. *Ibid.*
7. Sir M. Burnet, *Enzyme Antigen and Virus* (Cambridge: Cambridge University Press, 1956), Chapter 5.
8. *Stufen*, p. 104.
9. *Ibid.*, p. 127.
10. *Kritik der Urteilskraft*, p. xxxiv.
11. *Stufen*, p. 293.
12. *Ibid.*
13. *Ibid.*, p. 309.
14. *Ibid.*, p. 310.
15. *Ibid.*
16. *Ibid.*
17. *Ibid.*, pp. 310–311.
18. *Ibid.*, p. 311.
19. *Ibid.*, p. 317.
20. *Ibid.*, pp. 330–331.
21. *Ibid.*, p. 331.
22. *Ibid.*, p. 337.
23. *Ibid.*, p. 336.
24. *Ibid.*, p. 339.
25. *Ibid.*, p. 340.
26. *Ibid.*
27. *Ibid.*, p. 341.
28. *Lachen und Weinen*, 3d ed. (Bern and Munch: Francke, 1961).

3

F. J. J. Buytendijk

1

"Behavior" is an ambiguous term. "Behaviorists" presumably mean by it a sequence of individually observable and measurable movements such as could characterize inanimate as well as animate objects. "How did the car behave on the icy road?" "How did the cat behave when the neighbor's dog got in?" "How did the boy behave on the burning deck?" All these questions, expressed by the same verb, seem to call for answers in terms of a single set of categories. When Watson coined the term "behaviorism" and insisted, for example, that thought is "verbal behavior," he was attacking the ghostly "inner" units of associationist psychology and proposing to replace them by units of observables out there: muscular movements, sounds, and so on. Hebb, in his *Organization of Behavior*, is using the

119

concept in the same way. "Behavior" in this sense is movement, in contrast to thought or feeling. In this sense, the car, the cat, and the boy all exhibit pieces of behavior. But is behavior ascribable to the car in the same way as to the cat and the boy? That there is also a difference in the way in which the cat and the boy "behave" is beside the point at present: let us concentrate for the moment on what is common to both our living subjects. The pieces of behavior inquired about in our second and third examples are performances; the so-called behavior of the first example is a series of movements. True, performances also entail movement, but they are more than mere movements.

Come now, the behaviorist will say, are you asking us to reinstate some ancient ghost in the animate machine? Certainly not. It is precisely this alternative of movement or ghost, extension or thought, that we need to overcome in order to see—literally see—what a piece of behavior is. It was a similar, indeed, in the last analysis, the same task—as I pointed out in the previous chapter, from which the argument of Plessner's *Stufen* began: that is, the task of overcoming the Cartesian alternative. Plessner introduced the concept of positionality in order to establish, in everyday, direct perception, a foundation for the whole study of living things: from morphology to anthropology. And he illustrated what he meant by "positionality" by referring to an experiment by his friend and collaborator, F. J. Buytendijk, on the perception of things as alive. It is a certain "freedom of form within form," a certain "irregular regularity," Buytendijk had discovered, that occasions the judgment, "This is alive." Such judgments, may, of course, as in the case of animated cartoons or of a shape that frightens us in the night, be mistaken; the point is simply that, quite immediately, without making any inference, we see such things as alive. On this foundation, as we have seen, Plessner developed a comprehensive theory of organic modals, a theory of the biological and social sciences in general. Buytendijk's own central interest, however, is somewhat narrower than Plessner's. He was initially a physiologist and a comparative psychologist, and his concern was to forge adequate conceptual tools for the study, not of morphology and systematics, but of behavior. This task is a difficult one, and difficult for the outsider to understand, running as it does head on into our deepest prejudices about the nature of "scientific" thought. Understanding is made more difficult for us in Buytendijk's case, moreover, by his enthusiasm, sometimes uncritical and unexplained, for phenomenology, or what he understands to be phenomenology. But I think we can find our way into his thought about these problems if we start from two articles that he published in collaboration with Plessner: one, in 1925, on the interpretation of expressive movements, and one, in 1935, on the physiological explanation of behavior.[1] The latter article, incidentally, is one to which Merleau-Ponty's argument in *The Structure of Behavior* is pervasively indebted, and it is of interest therefore historically as well as in itself.

The first of the two articles is chiefly concerned with theories of expression, such as Darwin's or Klages', and so chiefly with human subjects; we may return to it later in this connection. But it is worth looking at here insofar as it both antedates and leads up to the second paper. Two points in particular are worth stressing in the present context: first, the general approach recommended for the study of behavior; and second, the analysis which the authors present of the mechanistic tradition which they are opposing.

First, then, the approach to behavioral science. The article begins:

> In the year 1917 Buytendijk performed some experiments on the perception of food in lower animals, especially toads. A hungry toad is let into a closed space in which there are a number of small inanimate objects, such as strands of moss and match

boxes. The animal runs about without reacting in any way at all to the objects. If some genuine food is brought into the place and the toad notices it, then it hurries up to it, looks at it a moment, as the toads always do, and then swallows it with the familiar movement of its tongue. But now the behavior of the animal suddenly changes. It goes on until it comes to the neighborhood of one of the hitherto indifferent, "dead" objects, stops, approaches the object with a backward movement of its head, until it suddenly actually snaps at it—and then spits the unpalatable object out again. This game is repeated a number of times in the various experiments, with certain variations. After some time and after a number of such errors the significance of the dead objects declines again, until they are finally as indifferent as they had been at the beginning. Thus the dead objects undergo a change of meaning. If the true prey consists of a piece of worm, then it is the match box pieces which acquire a new phenomenal value for the animal's perception. If the prey was a spider, then it is the strands of moss [that are transformed].[2]

Now, it would be just silly to try to "explain" the toad's behavior through the principles of analytical psychology, whether of the associationist or neurophysiological variety. By association—or by the establishment of neural pathways—the toad *should* react to the bits of moss or matchboxes from the start as if they were edible: they both partly resemble some kind of natural food. But they have no such effect; the "constant conjunction" that *should* work does not. Yet if the toad is once offered the kind of food the objects in the cage do resemble, then he does attend to them—that is, the particular sort involved—in a, so to speak, "associative" spirit. What is happening here then? Clearly something about the whole patterned situation brings the toad to attention in a particular way: he is activated, not as an aggregate of unconnected responses to unconnected stimuli, but as an animal attuned to an environment. Such proneness to action, or its absence, can be understood, Buytendijk and Plessner argue, not analytically, but only *on the level of behavior*. We need neither to record a series of measurable movements which would never add up even to describing what is happening here, let alone to making some kind of sense of it, nor to infer some kind of thinking or feeling "inside" the toad, but *to see what is going on as a piece of behavior*. This is the same kind of seeing, the authors argue, that takes place when I see a piece of human expressive behavior as angry or hesitant or embarrassed. I am neither looking at mere movements nor inferring something secret and psychical behind them, but understanding a whole stance, a whole way of carrying oneself, of distorting one's countenance, and so on, in the intrinsic significance that it has in its typical context. If I assert, "The man is angry," I may be wrong, but the behavior has its significance, so to speak, on its face.

There is nothing mysterious or esoteric about such understanding: it is just its ordinariness that makes it so inaccessible, at first sight, to the scientifically trained mind. But if we are to study behavior fruitfully it is just this kind of ordinary attitude that we must cultivate. For we do perceive men and animals in the first instance as acting in certain ways, and not merely as moving:

> That the cat is running away from me, can be objectively represented in mere movements; that it is running away from me in a fright, is given me over and above this in these movements, as a unitary character. That the dog jumps up at me can be objectively ascertained; that it greets me joyously is clear to me as a directive form in his behavior. It is only because this is so that we are repeatedly tempted into anthropomorphic interpretations of behavior and project our experience into other creatures. Nevertheless it would be an inadmissible limitation of our ordinary perceived world, were we simply to deny this level of order in organic movements, in order once for all to avoid the temptations of a crypto-psychology. . . . This level of order is simply there and is perceived by everyone, whenever he apprehends an organism not as merely moving, but as *behaving*.[3]

Buytendijk and Plessner are not suggesting, however, that we abandon the scientific study of behavior in favor of something more like ordinary experience; they are suggesting that *in* the scientific study of behavior, whether of men or of animals, it is important not to violate the insights which our ordinary experience offers us to begin from. We should follow, they say, four principles:

1. We should not let our physiological knowledge of the kinematics of living bodies cloud our straightforward vision of the forms of movement of the body as perceptually given.

2. The body and its forms of movement, different for each biological species, form a unity of which one can neither say that it is physical nor that it is mental. It lies on neither of these two planes of reality, but is not therefore less real. This antithesis is no more applicable to such a unity, than, for example, the exact physical factors and constants of thermodynamic potential, or entropy, or energy are to the contrast of force and matter. The physicist in his researches does not concern himself with the question, whether the various phenomena and factors he is studying are reducible to certain opposed substances, whose existence he may not deny. In the same way the biologist should at long last place himself beyond the contrast of physical and mental, through which he has always been prevented from paying attention to realities like those just mentioned and studying them in their own lawfulness. Worthy though it is, it is not enough to emphasize the uniqueness of biological laws negatively, as Driesch, v. Uexküll, Haldane, W. Stern have done. On the contrary, the investigation of life so far adumbrated can be brought further, to a richer development, only if these levels of reality (necessarily sacrificed in physiology to reduction to the physical body) are discovered positively bit by bit through painstaking work, and then investigated step by step.

3. The forms of (animal) movement are forms of behavior, since they carry visibly in themselves and "delineate" the relation of the body to the environment and conversely of the environment to the body.

4. On the level of behavior there is an original identity of perceptibility and intelligibility on the basis of the character of the forms of movement. For although there are realities which are perceptible without being intelligible, such as colors and

figures, and realities which are intelligible without being perceptible, such as mathematical and logical relations, we believe that we have here singled out a level, behavior, on which, strictly speaking, perceptibility and intelligibility are given inseparably from one another, so that behavior cannot be perceived without at the same time being (although possibly wrongly) interpreted.[4]

Only in music, the authors suggest, does a similar unity obtain. That is why analogies from music are especially useful in clarifying organic, and in particular, behavioral events. See for instance, Uexküll's concept "melody of movement" (*Bewegungsmelodie*).

In terms of these principles, the authors conclude, we must treat behavior as lying outside two of our current scientific or philosophical pairs of categories. First, behavior is indifferent to the distinction between the physical and the mental; this is especially important for Buytendijk's work. Second, behavior is indifferent to the distinction between image and sense, or between sign and signified. Though, indeed, open to misinterpretation, it carries its "normal" meaning on its face. An angry gesture does not signify anger as the word "cat" signifies a cat or "fire" a fire; it is, given its natural context, in itself that kind of gesture. We "read" it as we read a face, not looking from it to something behind it, but seeing its expression in itself. The study of behavior is, to begin with, physiognostic rather than analytical.

This is true especially of the class of behavior which Buytendijk and Plessner call *expressive movements,* as distinct from actions. Eating, for example, is an action, smiling an expressive movement. The same movement may, indeed, depending on the context, form part of either type: for instance, the movement of the lips as in biting something hard may be either part of the action of eating or an aspect of the expression of "distaste." But the context shows clearly which it is. In general, one may take temporal structure as a criterion of the difference between these two types of behavior. An action is the sort of behavior which stretches through a finite time span to its fitting conclusion; an expressive movement, on the other hand, endures; during any section of its duration it is completely the expression that it is.

It is exclusive attention to the former class, moreover, which has made it possible for the study of behavior to be "behavioristic." For to reduce the series of steps constituting an action to mere motions, it is only necessary, or so it looks at first glance, to put the seeming goal of the action at the beginning as a "drive" or "motive." In contrast to actions, however, expressive movements, if one really pays attention to them, resist such maneuvering. They demand, on their face, that we *see* them as they are.

Such a physiognostic approach, however, is more easily described than carried through. For it does, as I have said already, run head on against very deep-lying prejudices about the phenomena susceptible of scientific study. Even theories of expression, Buytendijk and Plessner point out, up to the time at which they are writing, have been of a kind to reduce expression to action and so make it susceptible of mechanistic explanation. In order to develop a more adequate theory of expressive movement in its own right, therefore, they suggest, it is necessary to examine the structure of the previous theories and to bring their prejudgments in favor of mechanism into the open. Without going into their detailed criticism of these theories—chiefly those of Darwin, Wundt, and Klages—let us look here, secondly, at their account of the nature of mechanistic explanation in general. In both biology and psychology, they point out, mechanistic explanation—which has been taken to be the only kind of explanation—entails from the outset certain "prejudgments." [5] This has been often said, of course; yet Buytendijk and Plessner's restatement of an old story is both unusually clear and important for their analysis of conditioned reflex theory, which we shall presently examine. The principle of mechanistic explanation, they write, "is the reduction of all phenomena, of whatever type . . . , to the model of movement by impact or collision." [6] The colliding entities "are permitted to have only such properties as are absolutely necessary for the exercise of pushing and pulling. Only such a minimum of properties is allowed." [7] It makes no difference, they point out, whether in the course of its operation, mechanical explanation arrives at a complete dissolution of the "matter" of its points of impact; they may be thought of purely as centers of energy, and the mechanistic model still holds. What is essential is simply that the scientist's data must be conceived as "the effects of uniform ultimate units ('atoms') related to one another by uniform actions differing only in direction and velocity." [8] To practice science is, on this view, to produce such a uniform, reductive interpretation, and no other. But the world must consist of only one kind of entity and one kind of event: in these terms "every difference in kind necessarily becomes a difference in degree." [9] To the extent to which we do not find the phenomena themselves in fact changing purely in terms of push-and-pull relations, we assume, therefore, that the changes we observe are simply the effects of such relations.

This model, of course, lends itself particularly well to use in handling external, perceptible phenomena: we can see it and feel it in the real world. So, our authors point out, as long as science is dealing with the external world, the temptation to invoke this kind of explanation is likely to outweigh any theoretical objections to it. Turned inward, it seems at first more artificial. Yet even here,

> psychology has succeeded in working with it, and achieving results. Alongside physical atomism there appeared a psychological atomism, which introduced, between sensations and between ideas, the push-and-pull effect of association. Thus mental life takes place in an inner space, in such a way that its complete

one-to-one correspondence with brain (processes) guarantees
the unity of the mechanistic world view.[10]

What has given this single model of explanation its power over
our minds? Not simply its conceptual plausibility, the authors
suggest:

> It is rather the immediate translatability (of mechanistic ex-
> planation) into practice, and our increasing ability to control
> the world through it, which lends it such strength. But since the
> practical applicability of a theory assists, not so much itself, as
> mankind, who achieve through it a higher productive efficiency,
> the mechanistic type of knowledge appears, whatever its cogni-
> tive value, as the true ferment of human progress. Technical
> achievements can be compared in terms of the extent of their
> practical effects. We have here, then, a hierarchy of achieve-
> ments, which corresponds throughout to a constantly increasing
> development of mechanical knowledge, so that to this extent the
> mechanistically thinking intellect becomes the measure of human
> development—but a development, of course, of practical results.
> The meaning of life is exhausted, according to this theory, in the
> meaning of the machine: in the production of work.[11]

In the 1925 paper, Buytendijk and Plessner are concerned
with the effects of this concept of life on theories of expression.
Their summary of mechanistic explanation, however, serves also as background for their paper of 1935, on "The Physiological
Explanation of Behavior," where they examine the conceptual
structure of Pavlov's conditioned reflex theory.

Physiology sets out to explain animal function. By analytical
methods it investigates the functioning of parts of organisms;
yet it is the "functioning" of the whole that needs, ultimately, to
be explained. In some way the whole has to be reconstructed
out of the parts. For this purpose physiology needed a model,
and it chose the reflex, a unit which it treated not simply as a
model but as a reality. There were several advantages in building from the reflex as a basic unit. First, physiology was bent

on applying mechanical cause-and-effect thinking to the study of organisms, and reflexes do proceed in this mechanical way; they fit easily with the demands of "exact" thought. Second, reflexes are found in the various systems through which the organism enters into relations with the environment, so that stimulus-and-response situations are easy to construct and to measure. Third, reflexes are conducted through nervous tissue, and there is no question of invoking "consciousness." And finally, the structure of the reflex arc lends itself easily to the concept of a chain of reflexes in which the first effect acts as cause of the next and so on. Thus, it looks as if the whole could be reconstructed out of these simple units.

How does this reconstruction work in a particular case? For example:

> Somebody goes for a walk, comes home, hangs his hat on the hook and sits down at his desk. As seen by himself and also by others, his behavior appears as motivated, and therefore intelligible, conduct. He wanted to get some fresh air before settling down to work. But the physiologist can do nothing with this motivation, because it doesn't explain for him the actual succession of bodily processes of which the conduct in question is composed. Therefore, as soon as the physiologist, true to the principles of natural science, renounces the subjective aspect of motivation and confines himself to what is objectively given in the bodily process, he must apply a different principle of explanation. If, in doing this, he relies on the reflex and the possibility of reflex chains, then the conduct as a whole appears to him as a chain reflex, a mosaic of reflexes, which produces automatically the concatenation of stimulus and effect.[12]

We may leave out of consideration, Buytendijk and Plessner write, the fundamental question whether the man is free in the sense that he might have acted differently in spite of certain initial conditions. But, they ask, what about the initial conditions themselves? Will science ever be able to specify them, or will it just have to impose its causal description on an arbitrarily selected segment of behavior starting from indeterminate beginnings? To this the reflex physiologist may reply that all scientific inquiries have to begin in this way; and besides, so much of our behavior is routine and in a sense "reflex" that the "image of the reflex chain does really begin to seem more than an image." [13]

There is a further serious difficulty, however. The reflex has been chosen as the building block of physiology because of its fixity; it is an inborn, invariable unit. Yet behavior *changes*. As a substitute for—or addition to—the inborn reflex it was necessary to build a superstructure of *associations* and to assume, underlying these, corresponding mechanisms in the central nervous system. It was these "genuine, but acquired," reflexes which Pavlov, with infinite care and experimental precision, set out to study.[14]

The results, as Buytendijk and Plessner demonstrate by careful documentation from Pavlov's work (both in general, and in particular on animals under hypnosis), was a rigorous interpretation of the phenomena in terms of C-R theory, but in such a way that the artificial complexities of the theory—with its balancing of conditioning and inhibition, irradiation and restriction—are read into the phenomena themselves:

> For as long as we observe behavior through the spectacles of reflex-mechanics, we will not recognize as such the distortions produced by those spectacles in the phenomena we are observing. So we shall always believe that the complicated problems which the phenomena pose for us lie only in the phenomena themselves, and not in our spectacles. While in reality what we ought to do is to take off our glasses and look at conduct with our natural eyes, in order to describe and understand it without prejudice. Our interest in a physiological, and particularly in a neurophysiological, causal analysis should not be allowed to endanger our attention to this duty. And it is endangered, if even in a simple description we dissect the behavior and conduct of a living organism, according to the desired explanatory scheme

of reflex machinery, as if it were the phenomena themselves that spoke a neurological language, and not the reflexologist who is talking about them.[15]

Indeed, all that he has added is a name:

Thus: in Pavlov's basic experiment a conditioned reflex: bell ringing—salivation, was established with the help of an unconditioned reflex: appearance and smell of food—salivation. It is a presupposition for this procedure that eating can follow the presentation of food. But the only evidence for the fact that "a" conditioned reflex has really been established, is, every time, the onset of salivation when the conditioned stimulus (bell ringing) occurs. There is no other criterion for the real existence of such a conditioned reflex. In other words, the phenomenon, repeatable within certain limits, of salivation following on bell ringing receives a name (C.R.), which in effect claims to be able to prescribe the reason or the cause for the repeatability of the phenomenon, that is, for what it is naming—although the cause is something different from the phenomenon so named. And this claim, to be more than a name and a designation, the name in question has no way of fulfilling. Like Molière's *vis dormitiva!*

Admittedly, a great many combinations of salivation with conditioned reflexes can be experimentally produced. Instead of a bell one can make something else into a conditioned stimulus, one can substitute growling noises, gurgling noises, tapping sounds, clanging sounds, colors or shapes. This variability on the side of the conditioned stimulus, with a constant end result, does doubtless justify the choice of a common name for these phenomena in view of their similarity and their kinship. But what is dangerous is to give the name the appearance of a designation for a process underlying the phenomenon, since in that case every one will be seduced into believing that we have at the same time achieved the knowledge of something responsible for the phenomenon. Moreover, this misconception is bound to become totally misleading, through the fact that a further thesis is connected with the chosen term "reflex," namely, the thesis that the process underlying the phenomenon is a process in the nervous system. The "nervous system" is a morphological concept, and it is a problem in itself to determine whether and how far even the simplest functions (for example, excitation) can be described on a morphological level, without the loss of their essential criteria. If we said, for example, that excitation "is" change of the surface tension of a nerve cell, not only would nothing be gained thereby for the understanding of the phenomena themselves, but we should have lost sight of excitation itself as a physiological phenomenon. It is just the same as with the definition of a tone as a vibration: this definition does indeed make physical acoustics possible, but it bars the way to immediacy and therewith to the theory of music.[16]

We have absolutely no knowledge whether the brain processes "behind" the observed phenomena are in fact of the nature of reflexes. And even if we *should* acquire such knowledge, what would it give us?

We should have achieved only the analysis of the means with the help of which a certain behavior of the organism is realized. But the behavior itself does not have its seat in the nervous centers, by which—though surely not exclusively—it is controlled. For this kind of control does not proceed in the manner of direct transmission as in a ship or an automobile, where the position of the rudder or the steering wheel determines the direction of the course. To the efforts of Pavlov and his school, therefore, to translate the fluctuations of behavior into a purely conjectural language of cerebral events, on the principle of direct, or at any rate uniform transmission, . . . we can allow no other value than that of a translation of actual observations into an imaginary picture language: a picture language which has become dangerous, because words like excitation, inhibition and release have lost their original vital meaning—in connection also with the anatomical model of localization and the physico-chemical tendencies of the older physiology. . . . The brain with its tracts of fibers and central areas, its cortex richly divided into fields, offers to the imagination an ideal basis for sketching out events which spread from point to point ($=$ cell to cell) on the connecting pathways ($=$ neural processes). What is more obvious, then, than to choose for these events words which are adapted as closely as possible to their physico-chemical nature; words which represent a directive to future research, without themselves saying too much? [17]

Such hypothetical constructions, moreover, not only fail to illuminate the phenomena they claim to explain; they keep us from *seeing* them:

> The trouble is that they already burden and obstruct the description of what we see, and, further, that they restrict observation itself by prejudicing it. Since the explanation consists in reducing the full behavior to processes of a single kind, and since this reduction is necessarily associated with a limitation, a homogenization and thus an impoverishment in the descriptive expressions, it acts not only as a compulsion to use a telegraphic code, but as a screen before the eyes of the observer.[18]

Take dissociation, for example:

> What do we experience of the so-called dissociation of the secretory and motor regions, which are correlated with certain definite forms of behavior and are indeed an expression of this behavior? Only the "dissociation" itself. Why? Because in the last analysis Pavlov only wants to find out "whether the secretory and motor part of the . . . conditioned reflex depends on the same parts of the cortex, or whether there is a difference in the relation of these parts." [19]

Such explanations, the authors maintain, are translations into an artificial language on the basis of three assumptions:

> 1. of the central "localization" of all the manifestations of life which determine behavior. This localization would be in itself an important principle, if it did not mean an uncritical displacement of the function in question into cell groups of the brain. Pavlov thinks of localization as preformation of function and takes no account of the essential circumstance that every so-called function is itself a process, the course and limitation of which are controlled by the particular situation in which they take place.

2. of the complete correspondence between changes in behavior and changes in the central distribution of forces. This correspondence, too, would be a correct principle, if it were not governed by the idea that the knowledge of brain processes could finally supplant the knowledge of functional relations. In truth, the contrary is the case. If two functions occur together, such as, for example, the contraction of the agonist and antagonist, then we can infer from this cooperation a structure in the nervous system which establishes it. Such a connection (in the nervous system) however, does not determine whether the muscles work together in the same or opposite directions.

3. of the complete correspondence between this distribution of forces and the anatomical structure of the brain. Through this assumption physiological analysis is especially burdened. It stands from the start not only under a neurological perspective, but under the compulsion of a definite neurological model patterned on cellular structure.[20]

For example:

The dog eats the food, but there is no salivation for ten or twenty seconds. "Reason": an unusual inhibition in the cortex. From the "points" of the artificially conditioned stimulus it spreads over the subcortical nutritional center as well as over the corresponding part of the cortical motor analyzer. In this condition there is no salivation, but neither does the dog eat. This condition "appears" only in its first half (and is thus wholly hypothetical). Now—after the conditioned stimulus—the food is offered. From the "points" of stronger, natural conditioned stimuli an excitation of the nutritive section of the motor analyzer follows quickly, since it posseses greater mobility than the subcortical nutritive center. (This greater mobility is introduced *propter eventum*.) The inhibition in the nutritive center for salivation, on the other hand, is overcome only after continuing application of unconditioned stimuli—that is, by the meat.[21]

Does this explanation provide anything, the authors ask, except "a re-writing of a process, in itself problematic, in a much more problematic language"?

Why, then, do such "explanations" work? They do so, Buytendijk and Plessner conclude, because of the ambiguity of the terms, which can in fact be interpreted *either* mechanically *or* in terms of behavior properly so called:

Is it not in reality so tempting to use words like excitation, inhibition, release, facilitation, just because they are equivocal and can be used for mechanical processes as well as for types of behavior? There is inhibited and stimulated behavior, there are inhibited and stimulated processes. The same words mislead us into blurring the fine and yet fundamental differences between processes and behavior, and lend support to the insinuation of mechanico-physical symbols. But once the reductive tendency is established, and at the same time the idea of the basic machinery in the brain, then the construction of a certain behavior in pseudo-analytical terminology is nothing more than a repetition of observed events or a re-description of them through imaginary processes.[22]

In contrast, the authors argue (as they had done also in their earlier article), the only approach to behavior which avoids such forced and imaginary construction is one which begins from the *physiognostic understanding* of behavior itself. It is plain to see, they write, that the questions asked by the student of behavior are determined by his experimental approach and thus, in effect, by the kind of answer he is looking for:

For that reason the greatest caution is needed here, especially when we begin to introduce explanations, and in particular neurological explanations. The plasticity and reactivity of behavior makes almost insurmountable difficulties for the analytical scientist, because he binds the living object to himself, instead of leaving it to itself with the least possible interference; yet it also provides a certain counterbalance for this difficulty through its physiognostic intelligibility. We are bad physiologists if we ignore this physiognostic face of living behavior. The description of events is itself an art and demands the right physiognostic tact. As in every science, it is the foundation for everything else and it has the very highest significance for physiology, the significance of a constant corrective, since behavior in the experiment is altered by the experiment itself, not only in certain organs or in certain parts of the behavior, but in its whole character.[23]

But such understanding entails the recognition that behavior is always an *answer* of the organism to, and within, its environment:

> Behavior is response (*Antworten*), and we find the responses intelligible if we look at the animal in the context of the situation which forces its questions upon it. A physiologist who believes that he need not linger with these ostensibly merely descriptive matters, and who presses straight on to explanations, offends against the basic principle of all exact science—whatever one may think of the value of his explanations. After all he is in the first instance a physiologist, he has living material under his hands, and its observation and description demand a total view of the natural articulation of behavior in connection with a situation. That is the starting point and the constant corrective for all further analysis.[24]

Where this starting point is not respected, the physiologist makes behavior *un*intelligible through his analysis and then tries to reconstruct it out of the parts he has "discovered" through his own ingenuity. And even though classical conditioned reflex theory is no longer at the center of physiological research, the authors' concluding warning is still apposite to the current mechanistic thinking of cyberneticists and their disciples:

> In the present stage of physiological analysis it is not a question of putting a new explanatory model in the place of older ones, but of ascertaining whether what we extract from the organism in the laboratory, under extremely contrived conditions, is also present in the organism under the normal circumstances of its life. Nowhere must this principle be more carefully heeded than

in the investigation of behavior, which is of immediate significance for diagnostic, and especially for neurological-psychiatric
diagnostic. For this purpose observation in the so-called animal
psychology experiment has its special value, if it really remains
within the bounds of experience and does not sacrifice experience and the understanding appropriate to it for the love of an
explanatory schema.[25]

Buytendijk's critique of exclusively analytical methods in the
study of behavior is once more expressed in a much more recent article in which he collaborates with P. Christian to compare cybernetics with Weizsäcker's *Gestaltkreis* as explanatory
principles in the study of behavior.[26] Without making a detour
into the argument of Weizsäcker's book, I may perhaps best
conclude this introductory section by referring to the critical
aspect of this paper: the points on which, these authors tell us,
the cybernetical approach, like earlier analytical methods,
proves inadequate to explain behavior. First, the concepts of
cybernetics are unable to take account of the temporal structure of actions. Actions are directed to achievements; and so
are machines. Hence the plausibility of cybernetical models.
But in fact the principles of cybernetics, like those of classical
behaviorism, once more reduce actions to mechanistically conceived causal chains in a monolithic time series. Organic time,
however, is structured in reference to natural goals: a point
familiar to us, in somewhat different form, from Portmann and
Plessner. Second, the "learning" of learning machines is only a
pseudo learning: a machine that plays a game, for instance, is
programed to avoid the wrong moves. But a person who learns
to play a game stores up information in such a way as *to be
able* to make, flexibly, a variety of moves. Machine-learning
eliminates potentialities, but does not, as true learning does,
create them. Related to this contrast are two further points:
machines always work in a complete yes-no fashion. There is
always a pair of alternatives, one of which is avoided. But liv-

ing things display what Weizsäcker has called a principle of "anti-logic": that is, they respond to situations in self-qualifying ways with a "yes-and-no" of which no machine—or at least no digital computer—is capable. (Whether analog computers practice "anti-logic" is another question; since, however, it seems to be agreed that any analog computer can be paralleled by a corresponding machine of the digital type, the answer to it is irrelevant.) And finally, they can do this because their relation to their environment, their way of being in and over against it, always involves, so long as they are alive, openness and restriction at one and the same time. Machine-learning is restrictive, in organisms as in computers; but in living things even processes in themselves restrictive—such as homeostasis, for example—act in the service of a complementary principle: they serve to sustain a field of action for the organism (*Spielraum*). For any adequate handling of behavior, the complementarity of these two aspects is fundamental.

2

Given, then, that neither the reflex model nor the cybernetical model of behavior is adequate, how is the student of behavior to proceed? Is Buytendijk proposing an alternative model, which he finds more adequate? No. He is proposing, first, that the student of behavior return, in a sense, to the older conception of biology as a *descriptive* science. True, exact or analytical science needs to rely on models. It has taken off, on the wings of mathematics, from the concrete look and feel of experience, and it needs some mechanism to channel its flight through the attenuated spaces of the intellect and to control its landing again somewhere in contact with some diminished aspect of the actual inhabited world. But it is a mere matter of prejudice to assert that only such analytical, model-manipulating "science" is science. As C. F. A. Pantin has recently pointed out, not only the biological sciences but geology, too, must rely for its operation on much broader and more various contacts with our ordinary environment than mathematical physics permits itself.[27] Pantin calls all these, therefore, "unrestricted" sciences, as distinct from the restricted sciences, of which physics is typical. But no one can seriously deny the impressive body of knowledge accumulated by these less restricted techniques or forbid their inclusion among the established sciences. In rejecting the reflex or cybernetical model of behavior, therefore, we are free to reject also the narrow model of science itself on which they rely and to claim for behavioral science the prerogative of scientific *description* prior to hypothesis and model-building.

But, of course, not all description is scientific. Once we leave the tidy framework of mechanistic model-building, how shall we know a "better" description from a worse? Buytendijk's answer is that phenomenology offers us such a criterion. Phenomenology takes an individual instance, and, "bracketing" its spatiotemporal existence, describes its *essential* character—that character without which it would be impossible for it to be the *kind* of thing it is. This is the sort of thing, Buytendijk says, that Plessner was doing in constructing his theory of organic modals. As we have seen, he took a simple account of the kind of quality of a visual object which makes us call it alive, and from this quality he deduced other characters which we do in fact ascribe to living things as such, and further, to living things of different types: notably plants versus animals, animals versus men. These are not empirical generalizations, but distinctions of type, which we can make in thought, even though some of the examples we meet in experience may only partly conform to them. As distinct from "rational biology," which operates solely with the concepts of function, survival, and means-end relations, Buytendijk calls this sort of discipline "ideal biology."

We shall see shortly how Buytendijk applies this conception

meantime we may perhaps find a clue to what
older and more ontological model of biological
omenology suspends ascriptions of existence
descriptions of essence, but the first pre-
ently biological philosopher, Aristotle, found the essential
forms of living things *in* the existent individuals representative
of each species. Every beginning student of biology does in fact
proceed in this way: he learns about *the* nervous system of *the*
dogfish, *the* circulatory system of *the* cat, by dissecting one, or
at most a few specimens. He does *not* proceed by the "inductive" method: all observed cats have four-chambered hearts;
therefore all cats have four-chambered hearts. Indeed, even in
the exact sciences an experiment has to be repeated once, or
perhaps several times, but not hundreds of times. Moreover,
discovery sometimes proceeds, not by "induction" and experiment at all, but by the apperception of some new order explica-
tive of "facts" already known, as was the case with Newton's
discovery of gravitation or Einstein's of relativity. Similarly, in
biological science of the kind Buytendijk is thinking of, it is not
so much a question of new "facts" as of seeing a pattern in the
facts. Indeed, in biology as distinct from the exact sciences, the
order to be found is not only "behind" the phenomena but also,
more concretely, *in* them, in the individual which exhibits the
structure or the behavior that *is* the object of the biologist's
research. He has to *see* the order *in* the individual, the species
in the specimen. And this is true for behavioral as well as morphological investigation.

If this is what Buytendijk is doing, however—if, for example,
he is examining *the* behavior of *the* toad as the beginning student dissects the circulatory system of the dogfish—why does
he not say so? Why not admit that he is attending to the *real*
situation before him, as he and Plessner have in fact declared
one should do in the study of expression? Why have recourse to
the phenomenological claim that he is *not* talking about exist-

ences, but only about some *ideal* forms which are discovered by "bracketing" existence?

The answer may be to say that Buytendijk's ideal biology *is* ideal in the sense that he is establishing *norms* of animal behavior and animal existence, just as Plessner did in his theory of organic modals. Plessner distinguished, for example, open and closed positionality as forms, independently of the empirical question whether, for example, *Euglena viridis* is "really" a plant or an animal. Against this it may be said, however, there would be no purpose in establishing such a distinction if there were in concrete experience *no* cases to conform to it. It is the norm of, and in, existence that one is seeking. So, for example, in the experiment with the toad from which we started, and in the other examples of Buytendijk's work which we shall presently examine, he is, of course, working, not with ideals or essences, but with existing individual experimental subjects. In this sense, therefore, he *is* doing what Aristotle did: finding the type *in the individual*.

Yet Buytendijk is not an "Aristotelian" biologist. There is, as I have said, an analogy between his "ideal" biology and Aristotle's study of essence, of the being-what-it-is of each kind of thing. But there are important differences. For one thing, Aristotle had no conception of experimental method. One would surmise that any modern scientist, reared in an experimental tradition, would look at nature in a different perspective from the classical Aristotelian. I shall leave this question aside here, however, and concentrate on a second essential difference, as it seems to me, between the Aristotelian biologist and any modern worker: that is, the transformation of the modern world view through the theory of evolution. Aristotle's world was a finite and eternal one of fixed and eternal species. No modern biologist can think in these terms. True, none of the thinkers I am concerned with in this book is an "evolutionist"; yet all would admit the fact of evolution, and, this fact admitted, an

Aristotelian grounding of biology becomes impossible. For this reason also, therefore, Buytendijk cannot, in rejecting a mechanistic model for the study of behavior, turn back to the Aristotelian conception for support of his work.

Moreover, I suspect, the mechanistic model of explanation may be compelling, or at least limiting, even for those who reject it. Taken at its broadest, without reference to any principle of underlying physical atomism, it becomes the Humean model of constant conjunction. And on this model, *existence* can be dealt with only by empirical generalization. To talk about existence is to predict future constant conjunctions from hypotheses conceived as generalizations of the constant conjunction type. Now, the animal psychologist running a Skinner box experiment and counting, say, the number of times his rats jump right or left when confronted with a given stimulus may perhaps fancy that both the phenomenon he is studying and his study of it can be dealt with in constant conjunction terms. But in Buytendijk's experiments neither the phenomena studied nor the scientist's approach to them can be reasonably interpreted in this way. Buytendijk as behavioral scientist is not trying to reach inductive empirical generalizations nor to predict results from causal hypotheses. He is trying to construct experimental situations such that the behavior of his individual subject can be seen in its intrinsic significance: this is a general significance, to be sure, but a general significance presented on the face of it in the individual, structured case. Thus in an experiment which Buytendijk reports in *Wege zum Verständnis der Tiere,* for example, the following behavior is observed:

A rat climbed up on the narrow edge of a water-filled lead container and looked over at a wooden block standing in the water, on which there was a piece of meat. The block was in an eccentric position, and the animal was on the far side of the container. After it had taken a look, the rat jumped down to the ground, ran straight to the place nearest the block and tried to climb from there onto the rim of the vessel. (The rat could not see the block in the water from the floor since the rim was 20 cm. high.) Here it got up on its hind legs with its forepaws supported on the wall, but apparently could not get up. At once it turned, ran back to the first on the wall (which was more easily accessible because of a wooden box standing in the sand) and climbed again onto the narrow rim of the container. Then it ran slowly and with great care along the edge of the vessel till it came to the place nearest the block and jumped from there onto the block, where it devoured the meat.[28]

Admittedly, this happened several times; if it had happened only once it might conceivably have been counted an anomaly. But the point is that in any one case, the rat's behavior shows on its face a number of interesting traits. Buytendijk lists five of these:

1. The "good error" in its running around to the apparently nearest place to its goal.
2. The definite directedness of the rat to the goal, which lasts for some time, not only when the goal is visibly present.
3. The visual estimate which brings the rat exactly to the place under the wall corresponding to the block.
4. Experimentation, when the first attempt is not successful, its return to the old path.
5. The exact apprehension of "the nearest distance," from which the rat at first tried to jump onto the block.[29]

None of these points, be it noted, is an *explanation* of the rat's behavior. Nor is Buytendijk here attempting to explain. He is merely trying to understand the behavior in its natural form. This is a different kind of performance from that of the Skinnerian psychologist, just as Buytendijk's rat's performance is of a different kind from that of Skinner's rat. How is one to express this double difference? If, in terms of modern methodology, existence can be handled only through empirical generalizations of the Humean type, then what Buytendijk is doing in his kind of experiment must not be directed to existence. The alternative is that it is directed to form as such, conceived as apart from existence; in other words, that his method is phenomenological. Or to put it a little differently, in reacting against reductivism in psychology, he turned to the principal antireductivist school of thought in Europe, phenomenology, even though this means pretending to separate forms from existence in a fashion in fact incompatible with his own practice. His descriptions are normative, indeed: they aim at *typical* behavior, at *patterns* of living, but they are descriptions, as any experimentalist's must be, of what he sees—and of what he sees in the context of his own contriving of an experimental situation.

It should be added, however, that Buytendijk himself, in some of his later writings, has rejected, at least by implication, the allegation that phenomenology, whether in its pure philosophical form or in its applications to comparative psychology, does entail a separation of essence from existence. Husserl's stress on the "life world" in his later work may be interpreted as an effort to do just what I have been describing Buytendijk as doing: that is, to try to assess correctly the structure *of* experienced order. Reduction so interpreted remains within existence, but seeks essences in it, even the essence of it. Merleau-Ponty, in *The Phenomenology of Perception,* interprets the phenomenological method in this sense, and Buytendijk in his essay on "The Human in Human Movement" states a similar view. The slogan "Back to the things themselves" should be understood, he writes, "as the rehabilitation of the freedom of western science, which is founded on our trust in our rootedness in the life world." [30] "Back to the things themselves means . . . an ever renewed participation in the phenomenal world, our world with its rich structure of significance. This must be a participation without practical aims or theoretical presuppositions—that is the path which the best investigators of animal and human behavior have always followed." The world of the research worker, in other words, however objectivized, is still our world, the human world. We can only look for structures within it, not turn away from it.[31]

But the quarrel as to what is and is not "phenomenology" is an endless and sterile one. We can agree in any event that Buytendijk's ideal biology is founded on the demand for comprehensive and accurate description. Experiments are so contrived as to give the animal scope to display, not simple variables abstracted by human ingenuity, but its own natural behavior patterns in their full concrete existence. And the experimenter's aim is to *see* these patterns intelligently, to comprehend them as accurately as possible.

Such description, however, has also its effect on theory. If we look at the phenomena more concretely, we can—indeed, we must—admit into biological knowledge dimensions which more rigid experimentalists have endeavored to ignore. Thus Buytendijk, like Portmann, insists on a quality of life transcending the functional. Life exhibits, he insists, *demonstrativen Seinswert:* literally, "evident ontic value." What he is referring to, in effect, is the conjunction of Portmann's "display" and "centricity," the basic characters of organic phenomena insofar as they resist reduction to the purely functional, to "survival value." Michael Polanyi, in *Personal Knowledge,* speaks of the "intrinsic interest" of living things over against dead nature. This suggests a certain subjectivity: we, being alive, have an interest in life. Perhaps the phrase "intrinsic worth" would be more appropriate. Again, as in Portmann's case, this is not an explanatory principle. It is a descriptive-normative principle which permits the fuller recognition of organic phenomena in their own right.

Such an approach permits, in particular, the admission into biological discourse, without pretense or apology, of judgments of rank. Functional biologists, too, of course, speak of "levels of organization" in living things. Yet all these must be ultimately "explained" in terms, on the one hand, of physicochemical regularities and, on the other, of survival value. The concepts of "higher" and "lower" are either impermissible or temporary steppingstones on the road to ultimate one-level explanation. Buytendijk's "ideal biology," in contrast, puts unashamedly at the heart of biological study predications of rank. Thus he ranks higher and lower forms, in his *Traité de Psychologie Animale*, by means of four criteria.[32] Lower animals, first, have "no true youth": they develop, like insects, for example, through discrete stages. Only higher forms exhibit the full pattern of growth and maturation, from the newborn through the youthful to the adult form. Higher animals, secondly, show a more marked contrast of *inner* and *outer* aspects than do lower forms. This distinction, thirdly, is mediated through the nervous system: the expression, Buytendijk argues, following Plessner, of the idea of *closed positionality*. The same closed form of life, fourthly, is expressed in the development of epidermal organs. Again, Buytendijk is here applying the same criteria as Portmann: his second and third criteria refer to "centricity" and its primary organic embodiment, and the fourth to *display*—or at least to the chief system through which display as a basic character of living things has come to be expressed. (It is not necessary here to sort out the historical priorities: Portmann acknowledges indebtedness to Buytendijk, whose work in the main is earlier; but what is important for our purpose is simply the convergence of their ideas.)

Now, again, as in the case of Portmann, mechanistically minded biologists would probably accuse Buytendijk of "teleological" thinking. It is important to recognize, as he himself stresses—and as I emphasized also at the beginning of the preceding chapter—that there is here *no* question of "ends" or "purposes" of nature. What Buytendijk is sketching in the *Traité* is *not* a series of differentiated ends, but a series of diverse—and progressively richer—*realizations* of the *idea,* the type, of animal life. He is following through, in his own way, Plessner's conception of closed positionality as the form of animal life and of an ordered series of expressions of this basic form. Such an approach to biological work does, indeed, entail a nonreductive, non-Galilean ontology. It entails an acknowledgment not only of methodological levels but of levels of reality. But it does *not* entail an "anthropomorphic" reading into animal life or into nature as a whole of the concept of "plan" or "purpose" as we find it in our subjective lives. As I have already argued, both in this book and elsewhere, these are false alternatives. Indeed, it is just that simple-minded dichotomy which I hope that this introduction to the work of scientists like Portmann and Buytendijk may help the reader to revise.

3

Buytendijk's early work was in physiology; the experiments I have referred to in the preceding sections belong to the field of comparative psychology. His best-known writings range over a wide area in this general field, including studies of special topics, such as rest, play, or movement. With the qualification I have just been discussing, these can be described as phenomenological studies, often comparative of men and animals, sometimes dealing with uniquely human phenomena. Two partly overlapping books on animal psychology, for example, *Wege zum Verständnis der Tiere* (1938) and *Traité de Psychologie Animale* (1953), are matched by a recent collection, *Das Menschliche, Wege zu seinem Verständnis* (1958). Of works available in English there are one on *The Mind of the Dog* and one on *Pain*—the latter comparative of the phenomenon of pain in animal and human life.[33] I shall consider here as a characteristic example the work *Das Spiel bei Mensch und Tier* (1933).[34]

It is only a theory, Buytendijk asserts, that psychological and physiological problems can be studied in separation. It is with the whole life of animals that he is concerned. We should treat them, he says, like boxes to which we do not necessarily have the key: an image which recalls Wittgenstein's rejection of the "beetle in the box" theory of perception. In terms of traditional empiricism, the "box" was on principle never opened by anyone but its owner. Since communication, however, is always *between* owners—in effect, between boxes—we might as well, the modern philosophical therapist argues, abandon the "box" metaphor altogether: take the effective, working "outside" as the whole. Now we can do this, if we will, for human beings, just because each of us *is* after all inside his own "box," and we take it, whether the philosopher will or no, that the other person has an "inside," too, to which we seek to penetrate through the key of speech and gesture. With animals this pretense is both easier and more absurd. It is easier because we cannot, on principle, ever open the box. To use Portmann's metaphor, animal behavior is like a play in an unknown language. We see that something is going on and can partly interpret it, but we could never enact that play ourselves. So it is easy to pretend that the whole is a meaningless sequence of movements, that there is no "inside" to this box. And yet at the same time the pretense of pure objectivism is here even more absurd than in the human case, just because we do not have the immediate awareness of what it is to be inside, on which the behaviorist of human speech or action implicitly relies while pretending to deny it. So we must rely wholly on guesswork; we *must* grope for the key. Yet we never, of course, do get inside. Buytendijk suggests another metaphor: looking at an organism's behavior, he says, is like looking down into a brook at the bottom of a cliff. We see it remotely; yet we do see it and can try to describe meaningfully what we see. And, keeping our distance, we can manipulate our vision in a number of meaningful ways.

The first clue Buytendijk uses to the meaning of play is again reminiscent of Wittgensteinian philosophy: he looks at the meaning of the words (chiefly in Dutch and old Dutch) and finds that "play" connotes a limited freedom of movement, or movement in limited space. More far-reaching in significance for him, however, are visual criteria, and indeed, systematic visual criteria. Actions, he insists, like structures, display a pattern which can be experimentally investigated and scientifically described. It is not directly, however, the pattern of play as such which he now proceeds to describe, but the pattern of *youthfulness*. His first major thesis is that play can be understood only as following necessarily from youthfulness. So it is the systematic visual criteria of the "youthful" that he is seeking to describe. This does not mean, be it noted, the "essence of youth": we may find, especially in human beings, occasional "youthful" characters in an older individual. But where they are, there is play too.

What, then, are the characters of youthfulness? First: want of direction (*Ungerichtetheit*). Youthful activity springs from an indeterminate cause and moves in no particular direction. In this respect, Buytendijk writes, "childish dynamic is a hybrid between expression and action." [35] There is a readiness to change direction, as in a baby's head movements. There is a lack of direct adaptation to the environment, yet not the kind of nonadaptation that marks stupidity. Further, youthful undirectedness expresses a preponderance of "fullness" over form (note: Guardini's distinction), a want of moderation (*Mass*), and a lack of co-ordination between phases. Even a static youthful body, Buytendijk holds, shows this lack of over-all directedness.

A second characteristic of youthful behavior is the drive to movement (*Bewegungsdrang*). Buytendijk refers to Coghill's thesis—in contradiction of S-R principles—that "the organism acts first on the environment." [36] The conjunction of undirectedness and the drive to movement produces an instability which is only later to be replaced by fixed reactions. Limited movement also develops later; in youthful activity there is a more diffuse mobility, what Buytendijk calls *Mitbewegungen*, accompanying or initiating movements.

In view of these two characters, thirdly, youthful behavior is characteristically *pathic*. Buytendijk is here applying a distinction introduced by Erwin Straus between the *pathic* and *gnostic* modes of spatiality (see Chapter 4, below). The pathic mode is more primitive and pervasive; it characterizes the animal's original sensing of the qualities of his environment. The gnostic mode is directed to the *what* of the environment; it develops through the elaboration of perception, in its cognitive aspect, into knowledge. The pathic is directed to the *how*: the immediate tones, feelings, appearances of environmental happenings as they meet the organism in its dawning awareness. Does the pathic, then, Buytendijk asks, result simply from inexperience? Not alone, he answers, since a "newborn" insect is not youthful. It is not inexperience, but nondirectedness, that produces the pathic mode of being: "youth does not yet live with the environment, is not yet directed to it." [37] There is a certain nonfunctional, unorganized quality about it. Thus youthfulness includes the sensitivity to bright colors, to certain qualia in the outside world, quite apart from their "pragmatic" or cognitive significance.

Other characteristics follow from the predominance of the pathic in the youthful organism: ease of distraction, suggestibility, the tendency to follow and imitate the movements of live and inanimate objects. Negatively, also, the nongnostic relation to things is naïve. As Straus has pointed out, the inclination to dance, in particular, is an expression of pathic spatiality. "We walk *through* a space," he writes, but "we dance *in* a space." [38] Note, for example, that it is difficult to walk backward, but not to dance backward. Accordingly, children have as yet no gnostic fear of space: they can even run backward. "Youth lives," in short, "in a different space from adults." [39]

A fourth youthful property is *shyness,* an ambiguity of the to and fro. Shyness is different from fear, Buytendijk argues. In a way he follows Freud here, in deriving this character from the phenomenon of birth. The child both strives back to the familiar, to the mother, and forward, to the individuality of his own being. But this is not, Buytendijk believes, a "trauma" that will govern the individual's whole life. It is a phenomenon of youthfulness, which fades away in the developed organism. To understand the opposing tendencies implicit in shyness, he argues, we must notice, first, that all living is living together; second, that every disturbance of communal living invokes two responses: an activity to restore what has been broken, and formation of a new community. At a primordial level, both these tendencies are already present in organic life; for instance, in wound healing and in embryonic development. Accordingly, when the new, developed relation between organism and environment has been established, shyness disappears. Moreover, where the original ambiguity is lacking, shyness is also absent. There is no such phenomenon, for example, in nidifugous young or in adult animals. We may leave open, Buytendijk remarks finally, the question to what extent these two tendencies are reconciled consciously or unconsciously.

These four qualities, then—undirectedness, mobility, pathic attitude, and shyness—define youthfulness as the area of play. But we have to locate and define play itself within this area. Play is a hedonic activity (*lustbetont*), but it is not coextensive with hedonic activity as such. How shall we determine its proper extent? We can take a lead here again from the use of language. We say, for instance, that light plays on the water, that the wind plays with the dust: these expressions refer to the same dynamic, the same directionless to-and-fro quality as characterizes "real" play. And, of course, there is the aspect of

play in art, reflected in the phrase to "play" a musical instrument. Of all the "playful" activities we observe, we may ask,
then, are only some of them "really" play? Or are very different
activities equally appropriately called play? Let us follow language again, and ask, of what animals do we normally say that
they "play"? Midges "dance" in the sun, but do not play. Dol-
phins play, perhaps fishes, certainly mammals. The spread of
play, we may conjecture from this series of examples, seems to
be connected with the difference in the relation of the animal
to its environment. Carnivores hunting on land (though not
bats!) play. Herbivores play little, Buytendijk says, except for
apes. One wonders here, it must be admitted, about the gam-
boling of young lambs and kids, and surely foals are playful as
well as squirrels or rabbits. There may be a difference here
between the use of the verb "play" in Dutch and English. In
any case, Buytendijk is confident that the animals to whom we
apply this term most properly are apes and hunters. Apes, he
says, play most of any animals, and they have the best-
developed grasping appendage, the hand. Hunters, too, in contrast to herbivores, have a better-developed relation to individual things. Herbivores, he points out, have a more generalized
field of interest: thus a rabbit may be interested in one pasture
rather than another, but not, in the same way as a carnivore, in
an individual entity. Herbivores are flight animals, with a generalized need of water, warmth, shelter, and so on. Hunters
and apes, on the other hand, are thing-approaching-animals
(*Dingannäherungstiere*). Herbivores usually live in herds or
groups and find their mates easily. Hunters and apes exhibit a
differentiated relation to individual objects in their environment. Moreover, they are "distrustful" of much, the hunter because he seeks a living prey, the ape because grasping with the
hand is dangerous. This tendency to approach individual things
evokes play more readily and also more complex behavior at
the adult stage.

In view of this correlation between play and thing-relatedness, Buytendijk concludes, "Play is always playing with something." [40] This relation to a "plaything" develops, moreover, but with surprises (an aspect most systematically realized in "games of chance"). Further, the relation of player to plaything is reciprocal: play is with something, but something must also play with the player. And the *kind* of thing we play with, again, must be susceptible of such development and reciprocity. Both animals and men, Buytendijk says, play with images: with objects belonging to the in-between sphere of "fancy," the pathic half-light of the known and unknown. Finally, all play needs a "playground" (*Spielfeld*), an area defined by rules, such as to allow flexibility, a certain indeterminacy, within their confines. In sport these rules become *intellectual* norms: hence animals other than man, though they play, do not organize games. They have no sport.

The amplitude of the "playground," moreover, is important. Play demands a certain rhythm of tension and relaxation. If the area is too small, we have something less than play, as in dancing. If it is too great, we move on to action in earnest. Admittedly, Buytendijk writes, we cannot distinguish simply between play and earnest: children may play in earnest. (Love-play, too, it should be said, is serious.) Nor is the distinction between work and play a simple and exhaustive one: going for a walk, for instance, is neither work nor play. But we *can* say that in general the playful tends, when too much amplified, to become serious reality. Thus playing with a ball develops into sport, love-play into the sexual act, mock battle into battle. In the change from play to sport, however, Buytendijk believes, there is a sexual difference. Girls, he notices, play—in the pure sense—more than boys, who turn sooner to sport. This, he thinks, reflects a masculine development to the rhythm of work and relaxation, while the more feminine character develops the pattern of a more pervasive "concern"

(*Sorge*). On the other hand, human beings are the only animals, he insists, who do in some form retain play behavior even in adult life—though here some cat and dog owners will register a protest.

The relation of play to intelligence is complicated. Clever children often play "more," but meditative children (even if very clever) not much, because they are not interested in *things*. In a strange environment or where there is a new and striking impression, play stops, because the undirected, youthful course of events is suddenly fixed. Similarly, play extends less far in mature existence because more is fixed. In the adult, too, however, the pathic is "the firm ground" on which the inexhaustible movement of play takes place.[41]

It is important, moreover, Buytendijk believes, to see this pathic communion, which characterizes the vital level of existence, in its true relation to the growth of our intellectual and spiritual lives. Pathic communion, he believes, gives way to the life of the mind, not, as Klages thought, through the action of a drive opposed to life, but through the emergence of what he calls a "desire-free love," a love which is at the root of all objective behavior. "Everything," he writes, "that we admire, recognize or obey, that is, everything with which we come into contact through this desire-free love," is beyond the proper sphere of play.[42] It is a different form of communion that we enter into here, one in which "the existence, and still more, the value of the object are sought and found." [43] This new dimension depends for its being on our transcendence of the animal's rootedness in his specific environment. It begins in the child with his free-roving "curiosity" and moves on to the highest reaches of mental life. Such love, however, is an emergent from life, not its enemy.

At the same time, admittedly, there is an analogue of play, also, in mental life, but only where there is youthfulness. Fundamentally, Buytendijk believes, the attitude of maturity is gnostic; it has transcended the "how" of experience in favor of the "what." But then, on the other hand, our mental life, for all its greater earnest, is also, it must be noted, the only development of animal life that exhibits the phenomenon of *humor*. Animals are curious and playful, but they do not *joke*. This is the reverse side, perhaps, of the ambiguity of the intellect.

Both the growth of intellectual life, then, and the persistence of playful activities in the adult are characteristically human. What is it in our institutions, or our natures, Buytendijk asks, that encourages these persistent youthful activities? Wealth: we can play after our needs are satisfied. Fatigue: this can both prevent and encourage play, depending on the kind of fatigue in question. Climate: light, heat, and so on influence the desire to play. Finally the decrease of the sense of our own body, especially in urban life, increases the need for play.

Buytendijk next considers the relation of play to drives: first to the special drive toward movement, then to drives in general.

Play entails movement, if not real, then virtual, as, for example, in chess. Often also there are accompanying movements, expressive or symbolic movements. Spectators also "virtually" move, or follow the movements of the players. Yet movement itself is not identical with play: it must be accompanied by *spontaneity*. To understand play, therefore, we need to investigate spontaneous as distinct from reactive movement. Buytendijk refers again to the work of Coghill, who has exhibited spontaneous movement in amblystoma larvae before the development of motoric or sensory nerve cells.[44] Similarly, Graham Brown has shown that a dog makes "walking" movements after the spinal column has been cut.[45] The best example, however, Buytendijk writes, is breathing. With Adrian, he has demonstrated that breathing persists in fish after the removal of the nervous system.[46] This is, therefore, a spontaneous movement, compelled from within. The drive to movement thus exhibited, he declares, should be distinguished equally from necessitated, purely reactive movement, as in the knee jerk, and from voluntary motion. It is this drive to spontaneous motion that play exemplifies.

But we still have to specify further. Not all spontaneous movement is play: for instance, skipping. Play movements are goalless, undirected. They are circular, capable of repetition, and hence rhythmical. We see this in the rhythmic movements of infants, which are produced in circumstances of boredom, impatience, or pain—wherever there is a situation of confinement, of "unfreedom." What is in question here, Buytendijk argues, is a spontaneous drive to movement in the youthful organism: in the last analysis, a drive to freedom. Such a drive is, he believes, an ultimate and irreducible force, which goes back to the beginning of cultural history. If you hold a puppy still even without hurting it, it tries to move, as does the baby in its crib: "The child or the puppy would like to get free; but the impulse to free themselves leads to a host of meaningless movements, which *represent* the adult's attempts to free himself." [47] Thus, in Buytendijk's view, the action of the youthful organism is an *image* of a rational act of liberation. In other words, it is a structure which represents the meaning of the rational act, without being it. The drive to freedom is a constant, but the puppy or the baby, in its inexperience and want of objective direction, can express it only in a series of rhythmical or circular movements without a definite end in view. Such movement has expressive value, as, for example, in fidgeting. It also has its effect in turn on the organism itself, so that a functional cycle is established. In the consequent rhythm of tension and relaxation, the sense of "a promise that's kept," we get the essential dynamic of play.

All this, of course, Buytendijk notes, occurs only in animals, not plants, since only animals live in the mode of closed positionality and move themselves from and into an environment.

Thus hedonic movement in general (not only play) expresses most fully the significance of animal life.

How about the relation of play to drives in general? Buytendijk has already suggested the general nature of his theory in referring to a drive for freedom: this very generalized drive is, in his view, both genetically and logically primary. Even hunger and thirst are related to this primary urge, since the feeling of constriction, of being hemmed in, is relieved through eating and drinking. In contrast to this urge for liberation, on the other hand, is the equally basic drive to union: the lure of environment. We wish both to free ourselves *and* to lose ourselves: the child throwing himself at the ball loses himself. "Desire in every form," Buytendijk writes, "is basically surrender, the striving for binding, for unfreedom." [48] This view is, of course, a generalization of Freud's: "It is not hunger and love, not love and death, that govern animal existence, but freedom and bondage, or if you like, freedom and death." [49] It is true, however, as Freud saw, that desire, seeking in a sense the loss of one's own existence, is the image of death. Again, Buytendijk finds this ultimate duality even in the simple example of breathing. If you hold your breath, you *have* to breathe, yet you do so "with rapture." Similarly, drinking when thirsty exhibits the union of both drives: we satisfy our need, but also lose ourselves, in union, in surrender. Think, for example, of the experience of drinking at a brook after a long walk on a hot day. Sometimes one of the two tendencies is dominant, but in normal activities both are present. This is especially clear in sexual activity, which seeks both liberation from need and union. Indeed, love-play, Buytendijk holds, is the purest example of play. But we must always remember both aspects in interpreting play. Thus, for example, the tendency to destroy in play follows on the one hand from the drive to union: the urge is to destroy one's own existence *and* the object. But the drive to liberation also entails the urge to destroy obstacles to liberty.

The child destroys an object because it offers resistance *and* because he wants to be united with it.

Play always involves repetition, but this does not represent a special drive. Nor does the tendency to imitate demand such a special cause. On the contrary: imitation is a special case of the replication of movement. It is replication through participating movement (*Mitbewegung*), which copies a perceived movement (not one's own). It is explained by the unity of perception and movement, combined with the openness and undirectedness of the youthful. Replication, indeed, is a basic property of the nervous system, a fundamental phenomenon of life. The relation of play to drives, in turn, is founded on all three essential criteria of animal existence: the drives to freedom, to union, and to replication—three themes which "underlie all the concrete activities of animals." [50]

Human play, however, as we have already noticed, also involves much that is not bound to the vital processes that characterize all animal life. In virtue of what Plessner has called his "eccentricity," man takes a stand over against both his own vital processes and the external world. His mental life, therefore, is marked, as we have already seen, by *Sachlichkeit*, respect for standards, for the objectivity of context and evidence, which transcends the medium of play and playfulness. Adolescence is the transition from a play-oriented milieu to the "real" world; hence much of its misery, and also its fresh hopefulness. But at the same time, man, in learning to live "in earnest" as citizen, professional, craftsman, or what you will, also carries the play world with him: it is only among men, in Buytendijk's view, as we have already noticed, that the mature animal continues to have a life of play. There is intellectual play; and above all, there is the analogy—indeed, the more than analogy—between play and art.

Buytendijk touches briefly on this familiar theme, suggesting that the key to the kinship may lie in man's development of a "play ethic." To play well is to remain in the play world, to suspend goals. But since play is so often with images, this maturer play entails the respect for images in their own right: and this is pre-eminently the insight of the artist. In Buytendijk's own terms, moreover, I think one could say a little more. The drive that carries the life of the mind, Buytendijk has argued, is a "desire-free love" which transcends the demands of appetite. Our "serious" work, therefore, the proper fulfillment of our humanity, lies not in the technical know-how directed to biological ends, but in understanding *beyond* techniques, in the more-than-useful, in what Aristotle called the contemplative life. "Goal-free" understanding is indeed the aim of pure science, but equally and even more evidently of art. Yet at the same time art retains the goal-free attitude of play, imbuing it with earnestness. In art the play world is transmuted, through desire-free love, into the world of serious intent. To say this, of course, is still to say very little. Sport, when practiced or followed by adults, for example, might be said to exhibit the same structure; yet this is clearly not the case. Still, an analysis along some such lines might be undertaken in the terms which Buytendijk's theory of play suggests.

Buytendijk's book on play antedates Huizinga's classic *Homo Ludens*, which in fact contains one reference to it.[51] Huizinga's work, of course, is narrower in scope, concerning itself only with the play element in culture. Yet they are worth comparing on a number of points. To begin with, Huizinga relates play to a drive for freedom only, not to the opposed impulses toward freedom and surrender. Second, unlike his compatriot, he ranks play higher than seriousness. Seriousness, he argues, seeks to exclude play, while play *can* tolerate seriousness. Yet surely in art, as Buytendijk suggests, play and earnest are mutually interpenetrating. Even Huizinga admits, indeed, the role of "illusion," the play with images, in the artist's conception of his work; yet he insists that (except for music) play is excluded both from the artist's execution and from the aesthetic experience of the spectator. Surely he is mistaken on both these counts. As William Bossart argues, in an article on "Form and Meaning in the Visual Arts": "It is inconceivable that an artist could create without any free *play* of the imagination. Even within the strictest artistic conventions—in the sculpture of Africa, for example—we find evidence of individual style." [52] (My italics.) Further, Bossart argues, art essentially entails a playing of artist with spectator. He writes:

> Huizinga overlooks the fact that no matter how carefully the artist conceives his work beforehand, the process of execution is not one of mechanical translation. Throughout this process the artist's hand and eye are constantly alert to possible changes of direction suggested perhaps by accident or by the nature of the materials with which he is working. And if we accept the view that art is the product of a partnership between artist and viewer—of their *collusion* in the sense of "playing together"— Huizinga's conception of aesthetic enjoyment as passive must also be discarded. [53]

Finally, the separateness of art from life bears a striking resemblance to the separateness of play—the analogy, here at least, needs to be taken seriously.

> Nor is art "ordinary" or "real" life. In liberating us from the cares and desires of daily life, a work of art introduces us to a world with a structure and meaning all its own. Art is also distinct from ordinary life with regard to location and duration. The museum, the gallery and the artist's studio are places dedicated to the specialized activities of appreciation and creation. They are analogous to the playing-field, the playground, and the temple. [54]

Bossart's reference to "the temple," secondly, in following Huizinga's interpretation of ritual as play, points to another deep-seated divergence between the two Dutch thinkers. For

Buytendijk, religious life belongs almost wholly to that realm of desire-free love where seriousness takes over, and it proves itself superior to play precisely by transcending, by excluding it. Here, again, it seems to me, Buytendijk's view is the more plausible of the two. Play and ritual are both formalized activities; both follow rules, but how differently! Play proceeds with characteristic flexibility, with the to-and-fro of youthfulness, at one remove from serious intent—*this* side of practical concerns. Ritual, on the contrary, is rigid; variation destroys it. Like play, if you will, it is nonuseful, goal-free. Yet it is so, not out of lighthearted exemption from serious goals, but out of its *greater* seriousness. It lies *beyond* the practical, in the surrender of freedom to the object of worship. Of course, an element of play is present in ritual and can in time grow out of it; one need only recall the origin of drama, both Greek and medieval. Yet in themselves, I think it can be convincingly argued, the buoyancy of play and the solemnity of ritual are much more contrary than akin.

Finally, although Huizinga and Buytendijk would agree in placing morality outside the world of play (except, of course, insofar as there is, as we have noticed, an "ethic of play"), they would, I think, disagree about the relation of play to truth. Huizinga explicitly divides them from each other:[55] knowing and playing coalesce, it would seem, in his view, only insofar as knowing is *not* directed to truth. And there are, of course, philosophers—and scientists—who believe, not only that we can never *know* we have found the truth, but that we never even seek it: that knowing is *wholly* a game—"only for fun." This is not the place to refute this theory, and although its adherents may find comfort from his argument, I doubt if Huizinga himself seriously meant to sponsor it. But I do think we should notice that, at least insofar as art is, or entails, a form of play, and insofar as art conveys truth, there is an area where truth-seeking and playfulness meet and coalesce.

4

So far we have been considering Buytendijk's study of phenomena which range over animal and human life. Let us look,
in conclusion, at an essay on a specifically human phenomenon:
meeting or encounter (*Begegnung*).

In an address delivered at the *Eranostagung* in 1951 ("Zur
Phänomenologie der Begegnung"), Buytendijk presents, to begin with, an unusually clear statement of his method.[56] To
study encounter as a phenomenon characteristic of human societies demands, he writes, a methodological decision. We have
to abandon the position of the objectivist who would take encounter as one item among others in the indifferent catalogue
of spatiotemporally perceived objects. As a mode of being-in-
the-world it can be understood only if we share it, if we ourselves *live* encounters with others and so approach our subject
through participation as well as observation. This is not, be it
noted, a subjective *Verstehen* set alongside, let alone substi-
tuted for, empirical observation. It is, Buytendijk insists, the
necessary ground for empirical work in any field of psychology.
He quotes Sartre's remark: "If we want to found a psychology,
we must mount higher than the psychological, higher than the
situation of man in the world, to the source of man, of the
world and of the psychological." [57] In this case we have to
work back to the source of encounter as a way of being in the
world: that is, to *Mitsein*, "togetherness," the ultimate sociality
of human being, as the ground of every meeting. Within this
fundamental perspective we can work empirically; we can
study in detail the particular variants of the phenomenon of
encounter; but without the foundation in our own being, our
own existential participation in encountering others, we should
have no access to the phenomenon we have set out to investigate. Indeed, it is in general the want of such initial insight, I

believe, which generates the endless squabble about "facts and values" in the social sciences. Buytendijk's aim, it must be emphasized, is to keep his empirical study clearly distinct from its initial existential foundation; yet without that foundation it would be impossible to undertake it or to carry it through to any fruitful conclusion.

At the same time, he makes it quite plain that this is no floating a priorism: the fundamental existential insight from which we proceed in such studies is not only the starting point of empirical protocols but is essentially related to them throughout. Every person chooses his way of being in the world; he makes his world the world it is by his projection of it. But at the same time every such choice is concretely historical in two senses: it is the upsurge of *this* person as history, and it is one expression of the social history of the community out of which and within which the individual person's project arises. Further, the externally given, what is objectively present, is a necessary point of reference within the structure of being in the world. In the case of encounter, all three of these aspects must be kept in mind: the individual chooses to meet another, he does so in the style of his society, and he can do so only if he finds the other person already there, inviting encounter. The other person comes into view as pre-existent, as a *question expecting an answer.*

On this methodological basis, then, Buytendijk proceeds to examine a number of questions about the phenomenon of encounter: the questions of its most elementary form, its genesis, its essential nature.

It seems obvious that we *meet* only other people, or, at most, other living individuals. Things are simply there. They may offer themselves, so to speak, as instruments or as obstacles to our projects; or they may just *be*—inert *res extensae* defined by their space-time co-ordinates. Walking through a wood, for example, I do not encounter a rock or a river in the same way that I might encounter a snake or a stranger. Encounter demands a certain reciprocity. Perception, therefore—the awareness, through sense, of objects in general—seems at first sight to fall wholly outside our present theme.

Yet there is, Buytendijk believes, at least an analogue of true encounter in our perceptual awareness. He follows here Weizsäcker's theory of the *Gestaltkreis*, which stresses the mutuality of active and receptive factors in organism-environment relations.[58] Irritability and motility are not radically separate "faculties," but aspects of a two-way, indeed, a cyclical, rhythm in which we go out to meet a world that equally comes to meet us: "In the concreteness of existence, every objective perception, in its indissoluble union with intentional movement, is produced only out of a *productive encounter* of man with his environment." [59] Man in the world, therefore, is not so much *conscience témoin* as *conscience engagée:*

> Man perceives, insofar as he at-tends, takes notice, . . . and he perceives not first and foremost colors or sounds, nor things and objects, but surprises (*Auffälligkeiten*), like the railroad crossing's being blocked, the piano's sounding out of tune, the appearance of a light in the dark, the coming of evening over the fields, a key's not fitting, an increase in prices.[60]

These examples illustrate, Buytendijk says, the dictum of Merleau-Ponty that "in order to perceive things, we have to live them." [61]

In this active life with the world, then, things "show themselves, withdraw, approach, play games with us—and so are able to encounter us." [62] Thus the immediate perception of events takes place beyond—or before—the conceptual differentiation of the inert environment from the social world. Indeed, as Merleau-Ponty has described it, perception is "the original faith which binds us to a world as to our fatherland; perceived being is the antepredicative being toward which our whole existence is polarized." "The thing," he writes, "offers itself to perceptive communication like a familiar face whose expression we immediately understand." [63] This expression, Buytendijk comments, is "the language of things" and the reason why they speak to and encounter us.[64]

The continuous interplay of sense and motility which generates this primordial encounter is common to all animals; in a stricter sense, however, human encounter arises out of this foundation through the recurrent divisions from and reunions with the world that constitute a human life. Both for the pervasive give-and-take of perception and movement and for the human rhythm of division and renewed communion, Buytendijk points to the analogy of the dance: dancing partners function only in interrelation as partners; yet they move also through separation and reunion.

How does specifically human encounter originate? We can see its beginning foreshadowed, Buytendijk suggests, in the child's first play activity—his playing with his mother's breast:

Already in the first play of the nursing infant and in all later variants of this play with elastic, swinging objects, there is a condition of being moved while moving oneself and of moving oneself while being moved. This double activity in play is, as in every authentic human encounter, the expression of a twofold intentionality; that is, we do something, reach out to the other in a grasping gesture, and surrender ourselves in such a way that something can be done to us—we choose activity and at the same time passivity. In this ambiguity of existence, in which doing and suffering, grasping and being grasped rise up out of the unambiguous nature of unconscious life, the child enters into the sphere of ambiguous human behavior and into an ambiguous world. Thus we already meet the ambiguous structure of genuine encounter, in a shadowy and elementary form, in the first erotic play of the moving, touching lips, tongue and hands of the nursing infant.[65]

There is here, as there will be in true encounter, a double movement, *with* and *against* the object—or later, with and against the other person. The first, the movement of fondling, which will be preserved in erotic encounter, seeks surrender to the quality and *Gestalt* of the other (object or person). The second, aggressive movement seeks to overcome the resistance of the other as obstacle or antagonist:

> The baby playing with his rattle displays a mixture of adaptive and aggressive dynamic, and his encounters with his toy prefigure our encounter with persons, in evoking tension and relaxation, expectation and surprise, grasping and being grasped, movement with and against, watching and showing oneself, listening and making oneself heard, surrender and liberation.[66]

The first true encounter, however, has moved beyond its tentative anticipation in the infant's play. It is impossible to tell exactly at what moment the child first enters definitively into the human world. He is fascinated by faces looking at him; he looks back. To animals, too, Buytendijk points out, the head of another animal has special interest. And animals, too, can be fascinated by the gaze of another of their own or another species; they respond, as we do, to expressive gestures. In their case, however, such encounters are transitory: they are completely reassimilated into the biological situation which constitutes them. But with human encounter, in contrast, there is a surplus over and above the "natural" foundation of animal life. In the human case there is not only meeting of things, lures, or threats, within the world; there is also something essentially different: *loving encounter* of person with person.

We can follow Buytendijk here only if we take account of one of the basic distinctions of existential analysis, which he borrows from Binswanger. As most people understand existentialism—and indeed, if they take Sartre and Heidegger as typical, as they have every right to understand it—this is a philosophy concerned with the lonely individual, thrown into a threatening world, free to make that world his own, yet never succeeding, falling forever tragically short of the world-

creation and self-creation at which he aims. It is a philosophy
of isolation, alienation, and despair. For Heidegger, *Mitsein* is
chiefly an aspect of forfeiture, of inauthentic existence. For
Sartre, each *pour-soi* is forever alienated from every other:
"groups" are constructed indirectly through need, seriality, and
the *pratico-inerte;* but there is, and can be, no "we." Binswanger, however, starting from Heidegger's *Daseinsanalyse,* distinguishes between two modes of human existence, the second of
which Heidegger almost altogether ignores. He distinguishes
existence, as the *singular* being of the questioner, from *Dasein*
(human being) as *dual* being, as "loving communion"
(*liebende Wirheit*), a way of being which dispenses with puz-
zlement and with fear. ("Existieren . . . als fragendes, das
Sein als endlich-fragliches ansprechendes und in diesem
Fragen stehendes singulares Sein und Dasein als 'liebende
Wirheit,' als ein 'fragloses, seinssicheres und in diesem Sinne
. . . wesen-einbildendes duales Sein zum Grunde fragend
furchtloses duales Stehen im Dasein.'") [67] This is (in Plessner's
terms, for example) to separate on the one hand the relation of
the inner to the outer world and on the other the shared world.
Buytendijk has already observed that we have to take the "risk
of knowing Dasein" (*das Wagnis der Daseinserkenntnis*) if we
are to study such a phenomenon as encounter; but it seems
now that we have to take a double risk: to acknowledge the
being of the individual existent as questioner *and* of the real
relation of two individuals in mutual question and response.
Man is a questioning being, the only being, as Heidegger has
argued, for whom Being is in question. But he is also the only
being whose questions can be put to rest through participation
in the world of the mind—a world constituted by the union of
persons in mutual understanding of the more than personal.

The external mark of such a world's existence is speech; but
prior to the acquisition of language the infant must have
learned to *be* with others in loving encounter. Indeed, without

such encounter there could be no discourse. Plato held that the necessary condition of rational discourse was the separate existence of the Forms; but he held also that this nontransient Being could be approached only through dialectic, that is, through dialogue. It takes two to make a language: speaker and hearer, questioner and answerer. The child's first immense step toward humanity, therefore, consists, prior to his first words or his first steps, in his first true encounter with another human being.

The sign of this encounter is the *smile*. With its ambiguity of approach and withdrawal, openness and secrecy, the smile marks the child's entry into the intellectual world. Not that the infant with his first smile grasps intellectual concepts, but he has come to the threshold of such understanding. Smiling, Plessner has said, is the "miming of mind" (*die Mimik des Geistes*).[68] It expresses that distance from natural being and at the same time identification with a new, yet alien being, which constitutes humanity. To the smiling infant the other is not a threat, but an invitation—an invitation to find himself in the other, to reach out beyond himself and be restored to himself at a new level of reality, the level of being human. I am not saying, of course, that the child distinguishes "consciously" or even "unconsciously" himself from the other. That is just what he does not do. The point is rather that he comes *to* himself, hesitantly and shyly, *through* the other, in the loving reciprocity which he expresses by giving smile for smile. Buytendijk writes:

> Thus the smile is the expression of an unstable threshold situation, a standing at the entrance of a new world, of disclosing and advancing, yet hesitant positionality, filled with an anticipating and transcending joy which breaks through embarrassment, and with an immanent well-being. As can be demonstrated, that "moderate excitation" and "ready reaction" which call forth the motoric pattern of the smile are prepared for in the child's bodily make-up, in the physiological unconsciousness of his nature.

This motor pattern, however, can fulfill its meaning only when the temporal physiological process is transcended in the timeless being of freely chosen, loving encounter.[69]

Here the phenomena of social life common to men and animals —both recognition of strangers and response to expressive gestures—are supplemented, and transmuted, by the emergence of a new level of being: the child enters into a relation of communion, a common being of man with man. On this ground of mutuality, and only on this ground, the life of the mind, with its impersonal, "objective" content, can take root.

What part has imitation in the child's first encounter and in his developing relation to the world? The importance and variety of *manners* make it plain that imitation is an essential ingredient in our ways of meeting one another. We can understand its human function best, Buytendijk suggests, if we compare imitative movements in animals and men:

> The animal can imitate movements, because the perception of movement is always already a *participation* in the movement that is heard or felt. We can observe very beautifully this functional transfer of movement as induced movement with or against another, in play, in courtship and in combat, or in the common attack or common flight of animals. The pseudo-encounters of animals display a coherent dynamic unity similar to that of our hands in the execution of a complicated movement, such as untying a knot.[70]

Such participation in movement, Buytendijk argues, is only apparently imitative: the animal can indeed grasp the expressive significance of movements and share in them, but not imitate them properly as even a small child can do. He cites an example given by Merleau-Ponty: "A fifteen months' old child opens his mouth if I playfully take one of his fingers between my teeth and pretend to bite it." [71] Here, Buytendijk comments, we have genuine imitation, and indeed in the medium of encounter, not only a reaction to a particular state of affairs and to a given expressive content, but "the act of biting has immediately an intersubjective meaning," and such a meaning is possible, Buytendijk observes, only where there is encounter. Only in encounter do we have that relation which (in Merleau-Ponty's words) "makes the other appear as the completion of the system. The certainty of the other is possible only because I am not transparent to myself and because my subjectivity draws its body in its wake." [72] If we understand this statement aright, Buytendijk writes, "we have the key which opens for us the dwelling place of human existence and hence of its encounters and its relations to rituals in the most comprehensive sense." [73] My own awareness is never wholly univocal (*eindeutig*), because it is rooted in my bodily being, which it presupposes but which is never wholly and completely absorbed into it. It is this incompleteness which is completed by the person I encounter, and that person is in turn directly and certainly present to me in our shared world through his completion of my being: "In encounter—and the imitation of another is, like smiling-at, looking-at, talking-to, only its consolidation—I not only *am* my body, but I *have* my body and have it in its ensouled nature as *in*complete. The other is the complement of my being, its 'completion,' and this ontic relation makes itself felt in the experienced ambiguity of our own existence." [74] Thus the presupposition of imitation is the reciprocity of the body-image: my glance, invisible to myself, is completed by the other's glance which meets it. [75] In the case of true encounter, moreover, this mutuality of gaze, which animals too perform, is supplemented by touch and voice, "for these too can produce communication with the being of another which is, like our own, open to the world, and which presents itself therefore in all the objects of our environment." [76]

And so, finally, the child comes to discover the presence of his fellow man, first in direct encounter, and then indirectly in signals, noises, events, and all the cultural objects that surround him. His own world develops, in its differentiation and its inwardness, as the world, at the same time, of other human beings: his awareness of "coexistence" and existence, of the being of others and of his being himself, develops as a unity. This reciprocal development, of course, is confirmed and maintained, once the child speaks, through dialogue. At the same time, however, the child's sense of the mystery of an alien subjectivity develops, too:

> Encounters first become pronounced in dialogue and are reinforced through thoughts, moods, feelings, evaluations, convictions. But these acts or dispositions are never identical with the other in his being. Every human being has his own world and his own subjectivity and as he develops the child experiences the completely *unknown* quality of "the presence of another to himself." In every encounter the maturing individual experiences—and more deeply so, the further he leaves behind the thoughtlessness of the age of play and hesitates, as an adolescent, uncertain and unresolved, at the threshold of the adult world—the secret of the present absence and the absent presence of the other.[77]

These paradoxes are essential:

> The uncertainty in familiarity, estrangement in presence, concealment in revelation, emptiness in fullness, which can be felt in encounters, are not "subjective" feelings, residues of earlier impressions, fusions of memories with present contents. They are noticeable in the first place because every human being is never simply and univocally there, like a thing, a plant or an animal, but his bodily being—as mediator of his being in the world and as the situation of his own existence—meets, and projects, and, in this projection of its body, comes to present itself for others and for itself.[78]

So far Buytendijk has been describing the origin of encounter. To focus on its essential nature is more difficult. Somehow, encounter produces—or rather, is—a unity of two individual beings who nevertheless are *two* individuals, not one: "The individual becomes aware of himself in unity with the other." [79] But how? What *is* a meeting of true minds? When we ask this question on the level of philosophical reflection, we find nothing but impediments. Both idealism and empiricism have proved their inability to deal with the problem. It is the stumbling block, also, of Husserl's phenomenology.

Buytendijk gives the core of his answer in four pages of unparalleled lucidity and elegance. Unfortunately, they resist any nearly literal rendering into even tolerably lucid or elegant English. As so often happens in German philosophy, the heart of the matter is a pun—and worse still, a Heideggerian pun (in the essay "Der Ursprung des Kunstwerks")—of the very same kind as the notorious "nothing noths." [80] In these circumstances it seems wise to make a slight detour and approach what Buytendijk is trying to say by considering first a related phenomenon perhaps more accessible to description in our unmetaphysical tongue.

Buytendijk leans heavily, not only in this essay, but in much of his writing, on the work of Merleau-Ponty, and I think that what he says here about the nature of encounter bears a close kinship to Merleau-Ponty's account of *bodily spatiality*. Admittedly, encounter is of two persons, and *one* person has, or is, his own spatiality. But it is on the bodily presence of two to one another that encounter depends. It is the person's way of being present (to . . .) that the concept of bodily spatiality helps us to understand. And an encounter, in turn, is a reciprocal pair of such presences.

Let us look first, then, at the phenomenon of bodily spatiality. A map of the United States, for example, shows the Sierra Nevadas between California and Nevada; they are located by longitude and latitude at a certain place on the globe. A map showing population will also specify the number of inhabitants of California, and on any given day a fair number of these will also be found, geographically, within the borders of the state. Similarly, to have been born in the state means that the town containing the building containing the room where one first drew breath can be unequivocally located on such a map. Now, since (as Plessner has emphasized) we both *are* and *have* bodies, such geographical location is indeed a necessary condition for the existence of human beings. But it is neither a sufficient condition, nor indeed is it the *primary* way, in which persons are related to space. Uniform, measurable, geographical space, the infinite container which Kant believed to be the pure a priori form of all our perceptions, is an abstraction from a more primordial spatiality: not a prior "concept" of space, nor even a prior "form" in the Kantian sense, but a prior mode of spatial experience. Every organism, or at any rate every animal, we have seen, takes its place within, toward, against an environment. A human being, as he achieves humanity, takes his place not only in an environment but in a world. He takes a place defined not so much by geography as by roles, responsibilities, institutions. All his life, his existence as a person is constituted by such "place-taking."

It may be objected that I am, first, confusing "space" with "place" and, secondly, playing with a literal versus a metaphorical meaning of the latter: to take one's place on the stage is not the same as to take one's place in society. The answer to the first objection is to assert that indeed place *is* prior to space. This is not a confusion, but a recognition of the priority, in experience, of the concrete to the abstract. The child's dawning awareness of his body as *his* and of its localization at the center of things and events moving identifiably around it—it is this primary spatialization, so to speak, which underlies all spatial concepts, physical, geographical, mathematical, or what you will. As to the second point, again, yes, there are "places" (as measurable portions of space) and "places" (as roles—like "one's place" as one is said to "know" it in stratified societies). But the metaphorical meaning in this case is not an arbitrary parallel; rather it expresses the continuity between bodily and cultural "location." Geographical orientation, moreover, is one subclass of cultural location; it is by no means automatic or universal. ("Is Congo in Belgium?" the Irish asked when they sent U.N. troops there in 1960.) The point here is that all orientation, in a job, a society, a friendship, a landscape, is rooted in the primordial, lived spatiality of my body as the instrument through which and the medium in which I reach out to the world. And conversely, culture at every level of abstraction and sophistication is an articulation of lived spatiality.

Consider a person entering a room: his manner of entrance transforms the room through his way of being in it. A very timorous person once came to call on my mother, carrying under her arm a very small brown paper parcel. "Do you mind, Mrs. Glicksman," she said, "if I bring this package into your house?" Compare, in terms of bodily spatiality, her being-in-the-world with Madeline Vesey's, who demanded to be carried into the ballroom on her sofa, specially designed for the direction in which she could turn most gracefully. It is not that Madeline, having, in some hidden way, a domineering and selfish disposition, "had" the resulting character of being a *femme fatale*— and a social nuisance. Her way of spatializing, of locating herself, preferably in Italy, if need be in dull old Barchester, *was* that demand. That is how she *presented herself*.

To meet such a presentation with and through one's own lived spatiality, one's own bodily being in, and being open to, the world: such mutual presentation constitutes an encounter.

Consider Yeats's lines:

> O heart! O heart! If she'd but turn her head,
> You'd know the folly of being comforted.

Such "presence" is not the flat "Here!" of an answer to a roll call: it is not simply physical nonabsence. Nor is the person, as present, *identifiable* with his actions or even with his words: he presents himself *in* and *through* them, but not *as* them. But neither does he "display" itemizable characters or qualities A, B, and C, while "concealing" D, E, and F. He presents *himself*. That, in reflection on our encounter with him, we may find we were deceived, that we learn to know him well or remain ignorant of his "real" character: all this belongs on a level of criticism and conjecture, removed in two contrary ways from the phenomenon of encounter. On the level of cognitive reflection, of my "knowledge" of other people, I abandon both the *immediacy* of our mutual presentation and the *mediation* of that presence through the body. Encounter, on the contrary, is the mutual presence of two persons to one another; and such presence is bodily, that is, I present myself to another in and through the body which I both am and have. Encounter is *confrontation*.

While we are in this punning mood, we may return to Buytendijk's account—which, though deviously, I have in effect been paraphrasing—and look at the use he makes of Heidegger's "Kunstwerk" essay. Heidegger, speaking of a Greek temple, writes: "Durch den Tempel, west der Gott im Tempel an." Following my description of a person as "presenting himself," I may render this: "Through the temple, the God presents himself in the temple." Admittedly, like Richardson's rendering of Heidegger's neologism as "to come-to-presence," [81] my version of *anwesen*, "to present oneself," misses wholly the other side of the pun. *Anwesend* is the German for "Present" in answer to a roll call; *Anwesenheit* is presence also in a more personal sense; but *Wesen* is, further, that term for *essence* of which Hegel himself made such ponderous use and on which Heidegger is playing here. To "present oneself" is to bring into presence one's very nature. It is to appear through one's bodily presence *as* what one is. Now, of course, to say that "essence esses" sounds at least as ludicrous as to say that "nothing noths." And I agree, for that matter, with soberer Anglo-Saxon philosophers that most of Heidegger's—as of Hegel's—arguments through punning (especially when, in Heidegger's case, they involve forced and fantastic etymologies) are arbitrary and obfuscating in the extreme. Yet this one, with a very simple turn of phrase, hits on something which reams of ranting against "black boxes" leaves quite untouched. When I "present myself," it is I, the whole person, my very nature, that opens out to confront another person in his world.

Well, then: "Through the temple, the God presents himself in the temple." By analogy, Buytendijk wants to say, "Through the body, the person presents himself in the body." True, the two cases are significantly different; indeed, it is the examination of the differences that brings out clearly the uniqueness of the human "presentation." A builder has built the temple; it has been consecrated, so that, for believers, the god is encountered there. The human being, first, is his own builder: through living his body he makes it the vehicle of personhood, the instrument of encounter. A human body is not put together out of pieces of stuff by an external agency and *then* used for the purpose of communication. Qua human body it *is* the self-presenting of a person. Second, while the god comes, in the house of God, to encounter only those who believe in him, no such "belief" is needed to produce the mutuality of human encounter. We do not add to our perceptions a "faith" in others' existence; they meet us directly by their very being, as we meet them:

> Every human encounter is in some way reciprocal. We don't *believe* we are encountering some one, any more than in perception we "believe" in the thing-character of objects. Only if I do not present myself in my body, is the other unable to present himself in his. In that case all encounter fails and what remains is at best the perception of a thing which I call a man. Reciprocity is the condition of *real* encounter.[82]

Admittedly, such reciprocity is seldom complete; and when it is so, Buytendijk remarks, it is "no longer intended, but is the mystery of a gift and a revelation." [83] Indeed, for most encounters some inequality is a condition, as it is between mother and child, doctor and patient, husband and wife. Yet reciprocity is always there as well, or there is no encounter.

Buytendijk proceeds to touch on the role of speech—and of silence—in encounter, to stress the ambivalence always inherent in every occasion "when two freedoms meet" and the multiplicity of styles of meeting that constitute a human life:

> One only needs to read a novel, say Dostoyevsky's *The Idiot,* to be convinced of the way in which all of human life is caught in a net of encounters, how many forms of bodily presentations can occur and how the slightest alteration of behavior, . . . gesture, words, syntax and tone of voice alters the character of an encounter.[84]

And it is through the infinite variety of such meetings that we become human. The reciprocity of the gaze, of friendly gestures, of the smile, or, on the contrary, of contemptuous, supercilious, or hostile grimaces and postures: these are the media in which, in embodied question and answer, human beings come to full awareness of their existence in the world. This awakening, Buytendijk says, is the process of taking on humanity, "for existence is actualized only in communication." [85]

The central argument of the essay concludes with a reference to Michelangelo's "Creation of Adam," which represents so superbly the achievements of humanity through the body's taking on of a spiritual life:

> In the encounter in which the dreamlike, earthly nature of man is transformed from the determinateness and limitation of mere life to that of a living mind—to the free initiative of an indeterminate and unlimited transcendence—in this encounter God presents himself in the lightly touching movement of his hand. And at the same time man presents himself in his own hand, and its helpessness is transformed into a grasping toward the world

and into bodily participation in creative power. But the existence (*Dasein*) of the man as the power of the hand, with its skill and its concern, is already shared existence (*Mit-sein*), for out of the dark shadows the first woman is watching this awakening, rapt as if in the expectation of her own existence in the humanity of care for others. Timeless, because beyond the world, is the encounter, eternally recurring in time, of man with the ground of his transcendence *and* the meeting of man and woman.[86]

Starting from Buytendijk's program for psychological methodology, I have tried to illustrate the kind of experimental and phenomenological study that has resulted from the application of his method. The concepts he uses, and many of his detailed insights, are largely drawn from the work of others, for example, Plessner, Weizsäcker, Merleau-Ponty, Straus. But, eclectic though they are, his expositions of a wide variety of subjects show the fruitfulness of this kind of approach for the study of behavior. For the most part it is not, indeed, *theories* that he produces; but he does make us *look* at phenomena which classical experimental methods can only assist us to ignore. In this sense studies like those I have been discussing, of play or of encounter, give concrete body to Plessner's philosophical theory as well as to Portmann's account of the characters of living things and of the biological uniqueness of man.

NOTES

1. F. J. J. Buytendijk and H. Plessner, "Die Deutung des mimischen Ausdrucks," *Philosophischer Anzeiger*, I (Bern: Francke Verlag, 1925), 72–126; "Die physiologische Erklärung des Verhaltens," *Acta Biotheoretica*, I (1935), 151–171.
2. "Deutung," pp. 72–73.
3. *Ibid.*, p. 83.
4. *Ibid.*, pp. 83–84.

5. Some of these are logical, some determined by the peculiar character of living things or of mental life when approached in the spirit of mechanism.
6. *Ibid.*, p. 94.
7. *Ibid.*
8. *Ibid.*
9. *Ibid.*, p. 95.
10. *Ibid.*
11. *Ibid.*
12. "Erklärung," pp. 154–155.
13. *Ibid.*, p. 156.
14. *Ibid.*, p. 157.
15. *Ibid.*, p. 160.
16. *Ibid.*, pp. 162–163.
17. *Ibid.*, pp. 163–164.
18. *Ibid.*, pp. 164–165.
19. *Ibid.*
20. *Ibid.*, p. 165.
21. *Ibid.*, pp. 165–166.
22. *Ibid.*, p. 166.
23. *Ibid.*, p. 168.
24. *Ibid.*, pp. 169–170.
25. *Ibid.*, p. 170.
26. F. J. J. Buytendijk and P. Christian, "Kybernetik und Gestaltkreis als Erklärungsprinzipien des Verhaltens," *Der Nervenarzt*, XXXIV (1963), 97–104.
27. C. F. A. Pantin, *Science and Education* (Cardiff: University of Wales Press, 1963); "Organism and Environment," in *The Anatomy of Knowledge* (Amherst: University of Massachusetts Press, 1968).
28. *Wege zum Verständnis der Tiere* (Zurich: Niehans, 1938), pp. 220–221.
29. *Ibid.*
30. *Das Menschliche, Wege zu seinem Verständnis* (Stuttgart: Köhler, 1958), p. 173.
31. *Ibid.* For a fuller account of Buytendijk's relation to phenomenology, see his "Husserl's Phenomenology and Its Significance for Contemporary Psychology," in D. O'Connor and N. Lawrence, eds., *Readings in Existential Phenomenology* (Englewood Cliffs: Prentice-Hall, 1967), pp. 352–364; translated from "Die Bedeutung Husserls für die Psychologie der Gegenwart," in *Husserl et la Pensée Moderne* (The Hague: Nijhoff, 1959).
32. *Traité de Psychologie Animale* (Paris: Presses Universitaires de France, 1952), Chapter 2.
33. *Pain*, trans. by E. O'Shiel (London: Hutchinson, 1961); *The Mind*

of the Dog, trans. by L. A. Clare (Boston and New York: Houghton Mifflin, 1936).

34. *Das Spiel bei Mensch und Tier* (Berlin: Kurt Wolff, 1933). Cf. the essay "Der Spieler" in *Das Menschliche* on play (or better, gaming) in man.
35. *Spiel*, p. 25.
36. *Ibid.*, p. 28.
37. *Ibid.*, pp. 30–31.
38. Quoted in *ibid.*, p. 33. Cf. Chapter 4, below.
39. *Ibid.*
40. *Ibid.*, p. 44.
41. *Ibid.*, p. 51.
42. *Ibid.*, p. 52.
43. *Ibid.*, pp. 109–110.
44. *Ibid.*, p. 63.
45. *Ibid.*, p. 64.
46. *Ibid.*, p. 65.
47. *Spiel*, p. 73. (My italics.)
48. *Ibid.*, p. 103.
49. *Ibid.*, p. 104.
50. *Ibid.*, p. 113.
51. J. Huizinga, *Homo Ludens* (Boston: Beacon, 1955).
52. W. H. Bossart, "Form and Meaning in the Visual Arts," *British Journal of Aesthetics*, VI (1966), p. 266. (My italics.)
53. *Ibid.*
54. *Ibid.*
55. *Op. cit.*, p. 158.
56. *Das Menschliche*, pp. 60–100.
57. *Ibid.*, p. 62.
58. V. F. von Weizsäcker, *Der Gestaltkreis* (Leipzig: G. Thieme, 1943).
59. *Ibid.*, p. 70.
60. *Ibid.*
61. M. Merleau-Ponty, *Phénoménologie de la Perception* (Paris: Gallimard, 1945), p. 376.
62. *Das Menschliche*, p. 71.
63. *Phénoménologie de la Perception*, p. 372.
64. *Das Menschliche*, p. 72.
65. *Ibid.*, pp. 74–75.
66. *Ibid.*, p. 75.
67. *Ibid.*, p. 78; quoted from L. Binswanger, *Grundformen und Erkenntnis menschlichen Daseins* (Zurich: Niehans, 1942).
68. H. Plessner, "Das Lächeln," in *Zwischen Philosophie und Gesellschaft* (Bern: Francke, 1953), p. 201.
69. *Das Menschliche*, pp. 79–80.

70. *Ibid.*, pp. 80–81.
71. *Op. cit.*, p. 404.
72. *Ibid.*, p. 405.
73. *Das Menschliche*, p. 81.
74. *Ibid.*, pp. 81–83.
75. See H. Plessner, "Zur Anthropologie der Nachahmung," *Mélanges Philosophique* (Amsterdam, 1948), p. 103.
76. *Das Menschliche*, p. 82.
77. *Ibid.*, pp. 82–83.
78. *Ibid.*, p. 83.
79. *Ibid.*, p. 84; quoted from P. Häberlin, *Der Mensch* (Zurich: Schweizer Spiegelverlag, 1941), p. 80.
80. M. Heidegger, *Holzwege* (Frankfurt: Klostermann, 1950), p. 31.
81. W. J. Richardson, *Heidegger: From Phenomenology to Thought* (The Hague: Nijhoff, 1963), p. 698.
82. *Das Menschliche*, p. 88.
83. *Ibid.*
84. *Ibid.*, p. 92.
85. *Ibid.*, p. 93.
86. *Ibid.*, pp. 93–94.

4

Erwin W. Straus

1

Straus's *Vom Sinn der Sinne* was published in 1935, Kurt Goldstein's *Der Aufbau des Organismus* had been published the
previous year, E. Minkowski's *Le Temps Vécu* in 1933,
Helmuth Plessner's *Die Stufen des Organischen und der
Mensch* in 1928. In the European literature of philosophical
anthropology and, more broadly, of philosophical biology, all
these works have exerted a profound influence. In particular,
when one reads this literature, the phrase "das schöne Buch
von E. Straus" becomes almost a fixed epithet like "swift-footed
Achilles" or "the incomparable Mr. Newton." Even Buytendijk,
who takes issue with Straus's theory of sensing, pays tribute
to—and borrows a great deal from—particular Strausian
themes.

Yet, on the whole, the influence of all these writers outside Europe has been negligible, if it exists at all (and this despite the fact that two of them, Goldstein and Straus, have been active in this country since the thirties). True, their work is now beginning to bear philosophical fruit, indirectly, through the influence of Merleau-Ponty, who in turn—also in part indirectly—owed much to their conceptual reforms, and, beyond philosophy, in some branches of psychotherapy. Yet outside a small circle their work is still ignored. This is doubtless due in part to problems of semantics. Minkowski and Plessner are still untranslated; Goldstein's major work, which is really quite unintelligible in its English version, remains, understandably, unread. A similar fate seems so far to have overtaken Straus's book. A second German edition appeared in 1956, and this was published under the unfortunate (and ungrammatical) title, *The Primary World of Senses*, in 1963.[1] It is by no means an adequate translation, but that hardly justifies its total neglect. It is to be hoped that the more recent collection of essays, *Phenomenological Psychology*,[2] will find a readier reception and will thus call attention to the earlier, and basic, work.

Linguistic difficulties, however, are not, I believe, the major obstacle to the acceptance of these authors in America and England. As Straus himself emphasizes, the chief hurdle is metaphysical. The scientific study of behavior has been hamstrung since its inception by its Cartesian heritage: a thesis which not only Plessner, Buytendijk, Merleau-Ponty, and others have argued, but which Straus himself defends in a detailed study of the presuppositions of and contradictions inherent in C-R theory in particular and objectivist psychology in general. Putting Ryle's "ghost in the machine" in other words— and supporting his accusation with a detailed critique both of Pavlov's original work and of its later sequels—he refers to the "one-and-a-halfism" of psychological theory, in which an impotent epiphenomenal consciousness floats over the allegedly

effective, and purely mechanical, neurological processes which
are thought wholly to determine the course of action.

Admittedly, there has been of late, a widespread movement
among philosophers of empiricist cast to rectify the Humean-
Pavlovian "causal"-associative theory of action. See, for example, among many others, such writers as Melden, McIntyre, or
Hart. They share with Straus the aim of diverting attention
from a misleadingly abstract "scientific" construct to the massive facts of action as we perform, and hence pragmatically
"know," it. But there are two major differences between their
approach and that of Straus which make their arguments, in
my view, the close of a tradition and a rejection of philosophizing, a caution, like Hume's "to live at ease ever after," and
Straus's, in contrast, a beginning of a novel tradition and a
Wegweiser to a new and more fruitful style of philosophical
thought. The first is that Straus's reflections are founded, as I
have already said, massively and concretely in a critique of the
opposing theory, not only in a general and philosophical vein
but through a particular examination of the paradoxes to which
experimental psychology itself gives rise.[3] Second, and much
more fundamentally, Straus tries to lead us, not to complacent
games of backgammon, but to critical and constructive reflection on the nature and presuppositions of action and, more
generally, of what it means to be, both in perception *and* motility, in sensing *and* performing, "an experiencing being." His
aim, in short, is, as he says, to vindicate "the unwritten constitution of everyday life."[4]

Perhaps Melden, for example, might protest that in *Free Action* he has done the same. But look at the climax of his argument. Rejecting the causal theory and yet denying that one can
seek the characteristics of a person or of an action as such, he
remarks: "One can say that one wants to know what these are,
but one can also bark at the moon."[5]

This is, as Austin, Ryle, and others also habitually do, laboriously to approach a philosophical problem, only to turn one's back on it when it comes plainly into view. "Don't shoot when you do see the whites of their eyes!" seems to be these writers' tactics. Not only do some of us, however—driven by the motives to speculation which Kant has told us are inescapable, though hopeless, drives of the human mind—want to bark at the moon. We believe that, in view of the conceptual and moral inadequacies of the still powerful alternative behaviorist position, we ought to undertake this (to empiricists) seemingly fruitless task: that we ought to seek, in fundamental reflection, to renew speculative daring and to justify the fundamental beliefs about man and nature which, outside the psychological laboratory—and, as Straus demonstrates, even inside it—we still, and irresistibly, hold. We believe, in short, in line with Burtt's critique of Strawson, that metaphysics should set itself not only a descriptive but a revisionary task.[6]

Straus's work furnishes, not such a metaphysic, but a solid, sound, and richly fruitful prolegomenon to it. There are, as we shall see, metaphysical (and epistemological) issues on which he takes an ambiguous and even inconsistent stand, but he does raise basic problems and suggests, at least, lines along which some of them may be answered.

The range of Straus's insights I cannot hope to exhaust in such an introductory essay. My principal hope is an exhortatory one: that I may persuade some already sympathetic readers, that is, readers already unhappy about the philosophical implications of orthodox theories of mind and already open to the possibility of speculative thought, to read his work. I shall try to implement this aim here: first, by indicating the basic distinctions underlying Straus's phenomenology of experience; second, by referring to some of his detailed studies, where, as seldom happens, the experience of a clinical psychiatrist and the reflections of a philosophical mind meet to open new conceptual avenues to otherwise neglected problems; and third, by

suggesting, in the course of this exposition, some of the philosophical perspectives which, on the one hand, his analysis
opens up and which, on the other, it sometimes seems to blur.

2

As a psychiatrist, Straus starts from a critique of psychological
theory, and in particular of Pavlov. His argument in many
ways parallels that of Buytendijk and Plessner. Both for that
reason and because it is now available in English, I shall not go
into detail in reporting it here. Its general theme is: that in its
underlying metaphysic, C-R theory is still Cartesian, and that
in particular it still rests on the time-atomism which cuts off
Cartesian thought from the original structure of experienced
time. (Charles Taylor has described the way in which a seeming threat to this concept of time from Thorndike's Law of
Effect was happily assimilated by psychologists to their official
view.[7]) I shall return to some of these metaphysical implications of psychology later; but the distinction I want to start with
is the one to which Straus frequently returns, between *stimuli*
and *objects*. This distinction entails a fundamental change in
epistemology and, through it, in metaphysics.

Within the tradition of empiricism it has been held that we
must penetrate to the ultimate units of experience as presented: sensa, atomic facts, or whatever we call them. Everything else has been held to be superstructure upon these primary givens. Straus reverses this fundamental conception: it is
objects that are primary and "stimuli," the "scientific" equivalents of atomic facts, that are abstracted from them. True, the
ur-empiricists Berkeley and Hume were looking for presented,
not constructed, data. Berkeley really thought he could find a
minimal visible, a minimal audible, and that it was judgment
which, with the help of God, built objects out of them. Hume
too, *pace* the missing shade of blue, thought he had found such

minimal givens. But we can see now that this search was dictated, even for Berkeley, by an epistemological, if not a metaphysical, atomism: by the acceptance of a reduced and purely passive Cartesian *simple* which *must* be the isolable unit of knowledge, the building brick out of which an aggregate equivalent to "experience" could be constructed. With the further reduction of mind to ghost or less, however, these singulars of "experience" have become the presumably separate impacts of isolable physical events upon separate nerve endings. The physiological model of action takes over. So, says Boring, "to understand man the doer, we must understand his nervous system, for upon it his actions depend." [8] But if no one has ever discovered Berkeleian minimum sensibles or Wittgensteinian atomic facts, so much the less can an observer discover in his own experience their presumed physiological equivalents.

To begin with, stimuli exist only as pure physical events, "unstained by any secondary qualities": they are neither audible, tangible, nor visible.[9] Indeed, they have no existence independently of the nervous system that has received them. But the objects with which we deal in our ordinary experience are not of this refined and reduced character. "The wall over there, the writing pad, the pen and ink": these are things I confront, but they are not "stimuli." True, Straus admits, the light, once reflected from the wall or the paper, might be described as a stimulus, but only after it has reached the optical receptors, a process which I may postulate, but have never experienced. And the experimenter, for all his alleged sophistication, is in no different situation in confronting his rats, Skinner boxes, or what you will. How can he set out to work, not with rats and apparatuses, but with the hidden, hypothetical events of which, on his own theory, his own behavior consists? Indeed, he cannot—for the temporal relation between objects and the experimenter's action upon them is precisely the converse of that between stimuli and responses: "Because stimulation precedes response, nobody can handle, nobody can manipulate, stimuli; they are out of reach. I as an experiencing being may stretch my hand toward the pen on my desk; a motor response cannot be directed to optical stimuli already received in the past." [10] Thus "stimuli" can be neither *observed* or *manipulated*.[11] Nor, since they are, by definition, events *in* the receiving organism, can they be shared, in a psychological experiment, between "subject" and experimenter: "Those stimuli which provoke responses in the experimental animal never reach the eyes or ears of the observer. Stimuli cannot be shared by two organisms." [12] On all these grounds, then, it appears that "stimulus" and "object" are by no means synonymous terms: "stimuli are constructs, never immediate objects of experience." [13]

An experiencing being moves, on the contrary, not among stimuli, a life which even Pavlov's dogs sometimes resisted, but in a surrounding field within which things approach it and it approaches things. Its basic experience is of what Straus calls an I-Allon relation—where "allon" means not just other persons but the organized totality of objects within which the living being moves. The stimuli with which the scientific observer operates, on the contrary, are not *alla* to an experiencing being; they are not objects at all, but highly abstract constructs which split apart and render unintelligible this primary relation.

If he were consistent, therefore, the S-R theorist ought to legislate *himself* out of existence. If he too is a congeries of physical stimuli and physiological responses, he ought not to pretend that he can observe the behavior of his subjects or manipulate his apparatus. But, "spellbound by the magic of a venerated metaphysic," he neglects to notice his own inconsistency.[14] He continues, a necessary exception to his own alleged cosmology, to act as an experiencing being among objects which he can observe, manipulate, and share. Thus experimental psychology, in its classical form, rests on a fundamental inconsistency.

That is not to say, however, that causal investigation in terms of S-R theory is useless; but it should be put into its due place *within* a theory of living beings and their experience. Causal analysis investigates the necessary, but not the sufficient, conditions of sensory experience. Thus "the stimulus delimits what will be seen and determines that it will be seen." "Intentionality of vision and causality of seeing," Straus insists, "are fully reconcilable." [15] But causal analysis can operate consistently only *within* the all-embracing I-Allon relation; it cannot put Humpty Dumpty together again out of senseless fragments. Indeed, Straus argues, traditional theory has never even embarked upon its proper subject, which it has eliminated before it even begins:

> Instead, traditional theory interprets sensory experience as the result of the interaction of two bodies. The sender produces in the recipient a phantom-like perception. Such sensory data do not belong to the outside world of objects; they represent them— it remains unclear how and to whom. In any case, while they represent an object, they are cut off from the outside world; they are said to be objective; they belong to the subject. Since perceptions represent the outside world, but belong to the subject, they cannot be an object of action. Everyone, supposedly, carries in his consciousness a private gallery of such shadow images. The collector himself is not a part of his collection. He owns it; he has it; he does not belong to it. Sensory experience in classical theory does not include the experiencing being. The content of sensory experience is reduced to the appearance of a more or less distorted replica, a counterfeit of the outside world. Seeing is acknowledged as a physiological process, but not as the relation of seeing beings to things seen. The relation I-Allon is slashed. The Allon alone is left, but in a profoundly mutilated form. Perceptions are many; they follow one another in the order of objective time. They do not belong together in a meaningful context; they stick together through synaptic welding. Positivism from Hume to Skinner preaches the gospel that sense is repeated nonsense.[16]

In place of this absurd situation, Straus proposes that we abandon the myth of "sensa" or "impressions" and examine the process through which we do in fact find ourselves in contact, through sensory channels, with the world around us, a process which he calls sensing (*Empfinden*) in contrast to perception.

Sensing, Straus stated in an essay of 1930,[17] embraces both *gnostic* and *pathic* aspects, a distinction I have already referred to in connection with Buytendijk's discussion of play. "Gnostic" in Straus's usage denotes the primitive forerunner of the cognitive, and "pathic" the immediate communication we have with things on the basis of their changing mode of sensory givenness,[18] but sensing, he holds, is primarily pathic. For sensing is a way of receiving not merely atomic cues from a prompting environment (*Umgebung*) but moods, as well as lines, from fellow actors, from the stage set, from the whole ensemble within which we discover other things and persons, through cooperation with (including rebellion against and revulsion from) whom we develop our own roles as actors in a scene. My metaphor limps, for the *Umfeld* Straus is speaking of is no artifact. It is the living nature in which every animal is immersed and through contact with which it expresses its style of living and of being. From this encompassing *Allon*, we, and also to some degree other higher animals, have abstracted a perceptible world of stable, manipulable, and (for us at least) intelligible kinds of objects. But our primary, pathic sensing is the ground on which alone the chiefly gnostic achievements of perception can develop.

This, like every fundamental conceptual reform, is a difficult distinction to assimilate. I shall return later to the problems raised by Straus's cognitive theory of perception; but for the moment let me try, if I can, to elucidate the concept of sensing by making a number of comparisons with more familiar philosophical theories of experience, and in particular of sensory experience.

Straus presents his theory as a reversion from Cartesianism to the open vision of an experienced world. Let us begin, however, not with the subtly ambiguous Cartesian, but with the more crudely ambivalent Lockian position, from which, through refinement and excision, traditional empiricism has developed. The real givens of sense for Locke were single separable ideas, pieces of mental content whose originals were resident in some material, but unknown, X, and which the mind could manipulate, abstract from, and return to for its intuitive knowledge, such as it was, of a "real" world. But this was the real world of a good Newtonian, of a founding father of the Royal Society, for whom the "corpuscular philosophy" had proved a liberation from the dead tags of scholasticism and useless Latin learning. It seemed common-sense because of the nonsense it had abandoned and because of the prospects for natural philosophy which it appeared, at first sight, to permit. Yet, except for our primary experience of motion, solidity, and weight, the experienced surface of the world, its colors, smells, and sounds, were held to be but secondary: mere expressions of as yet unknown processes in those underlying X's. But are our apprehensions of color, smell, or sound, in fact less experienced, less substantive in their shaping of our ongoing experience than our apprehensions of motions and shapes and of the solid resistance of bodies to touch?

Travel from the Sacramento Valley an hour's drive into the snow country of the Sierras: this experience is not described, in its immediate quality as experience, by substituting for one congeries of "ideas of sensation" another that includes more white bits and fewer gray and red and yellow, or more "silences"—what are they in empiricist terms?—and fewer loud noises. The traveler finds himself *in* a different medium; his very being changes. Or compare, similarly, the difference between the impact on the ear—or rather on the person, through the ear—of a grating Bob Dylan ballad with the experienced effect of a well-performed baroque concerto. The first slaps at us; the second surrounds us: it places us, auditorily, in a different *landscape.* The summative plus representative plus hedonistic account of these experiences triply falsifies them. It forces us to reduce what is comprehensive to an alleged (not an experienced) atomic base, and to this it adds, on the one hand, an invented intellectual superstructure (like Helmholtz' "unconscious inference") and, on the other, a "merely subjective" feeling tone. But why must we insist that we infer, unconsciously or otherwise, the snow from the whiteness, the music from its discrete sounds? We have known since Ehrenfels that melodies are not experienced like that and since Wertheimer that neither are visual objects, let alone whole landscapes. Let us leave these cramped constructions and return, Straus exclaims with Husserl (though in a different spirit), to "the things themselves."

Not that that is easy or infallible; Straus performs no "reduction" and hence possesses, or can claim to possess, no stringent method. On the one hand, to be sure, this reviewer agrees with Straus in suspecting the overintellectual and, indeed, the presumptuous, method of phenomenological reduction. Yet admittedly, if we stay *in* the "life-world," as Straus urges us to do, rather than bracketing its existence to seek its "pure" structure, we risk substituting what are our own personally slanted descriptions, however universally we intend them, for what is truly universal.[19] But that is our condition, and we do better to face it than to substitute for the rich multidimensionality of our experience, both shared and single, some skeletal surrogate, whether in an abstract Lockian reconstruction of sensation or in the Husserlian highroad to "transcendental subjectivity." What Straus is seeking is a reinstatement of the life-world as lived, of that comprehensive horizon of earthbound experience which Descartes had distilled to a geometer's two-halved paradise: an impoverishment which is still the starting point as much of Husserl's enterprise (whose *Cartesian Meditations* are not for nothing so entitled) as of Locke's *Essay.*

The phenomenological enterprise which, in its starting point, Straus's most resembles is Heidegger's, and it may be useful, therefore, to compare his approach briefly with the *Daseinsanalyse* of *Sein und Zeit*. Straus's I-Allon relation is a variant, if you like, of Heidegger's being-in-the-world. A *Dasein* is an experiencing being, and the I-Allon description, like the first part of *Sein und Zeit*, does genuinely turn its back on the divided world of *res cogitans* and *res extensa* to plunge directly into the inspection of human being in its entirety. The differences, however, are also significant for philosophy, as well, I should guess, as for psychiatry. Two points should be mentioned. First, despite one passing reference to a possibility of authentic *Fürsorge*,[20] *Mitsein* characterizes Heideggerian *Dasein* only on the level of forfeiture. The authentic existent who emerges in the second part of Heidegger's argument is, despite the bow to national destiny later developed in the chauvinistic vision of the *Introduction to Metaphysics,* the one, rare existential hero, utterly cut off in his true being from the contemptible *das Man* from whose distracting influence the rest of us never escape. In Heidegger's authentic existence there is no Allon. Not so for Straus. As a psychiatrist, and a humane psychiatrist, he looks with equal openness at the general character of all. One is reminded, in reading his psychiatric essays, of Jaspers' adjuration to the physician, in his *General Psychopathology,* that he must confront the patient as a person. This Straus accomplishes by seeing the pathology of the individual case as a rending in one way or another of the seamless whole that constitutes the norm of everyday life. Thus the I-Allon relation stands as the paradigm which becomes, in illness, split apart or deformed. For Heidegger, on the contrary, as for his hero Nietzsche, the norm is the deformity, and only the rare soul who hates and repels the norm can be said to live authentically. Indeed, although it is, of course, an *ad hominem* argument, it is perhaps not wholly irrelevant to point out that the two geniuses Heidegger most admires, Nietzsche and Holderlin, both went mad. Not that Straus's philosophy of mind elevates philistinism or mediocrity at the expense of genius; he could interpret the I-Allon relation of an Einstein or a Goethe as well as of the rest of us; but he need not dismiss as despicable, as Heidegger contemptuously does, all that *is* ordinary.

And there is a second important difference. Heidegger's *Dasein*, like Sartre's *pour-soi*, or for that matter Jaspers' *Existenz*, is only human. Straus's "experiencing being" is human *or* animal. It is the structure of all sentient living, not only of our relatively self-conscious living, that he wishes to reinstate as the foundation of knowledge and of action. And this aim—to reinstate man in nature—is an essential one for any philosophy that would finally exorcise the persistent Cartesian ghost.

For both these reasons, it seems to me, Straus's approach is more fruitful than that of other "existential" psychiatrists, notably, for example, that of his friend Ludwig Binswanger (to whom his German collection of essays, *Psychologie der menschlichen Welt*, was dedicated).[21] Binswanger simply takes Heideggerian being-in-the-world, the very essence of which demands arrogance and hatred as the road from me to thee, and injects into it, with sublime incompatibility, a generous dose of love. But to restore a balanced vision of existence we need, both in our recognition of its positive rootedness in communion and in our recognition of the kinship of men and other animals, a broader and firmer foundation from the start.

There is one other effort to overcome the Cartesian tradition, in particular the Cartesian-empiricist theory of perception, with which one is tempted to compare Straus's proposed reform. He rejects, as we have seen, the empiricist concept of sensation in favor of a theory of sensing (*Empfinden*) as the fundamental sense-mediated road that links object with experiencing organism, and he contrasts this pervasive process with the more sophisticated and at least primarily cognitive sensory

...areness of objects in *perception*. This is obviously not the stock psychological distinction between sensation and perception,[22] but it is reminiscent, at least at first sight, of Whitehead's distinction between presentational immediacy and causal efficacy.[23] Yet, it is also, again, in some essential ways different. Whitehead is contrasting what *is* really present, what is "enjoyed," in "sensa" or "pure" givens with the opaque but powerful impact upon us of the processes beyond and around us in the world. The latter—causal efficacy—does in fact resemble Straus's "sensing." It is the constant interchange of experiencing being and surrounding field, the way in which an animal becomes the figure it is, expressing unity and contrast with its medium as ground, that they are both concerned to describe. And it is indeed this living dynamic of sensory awareness, a dynamic expressed, for example, in Aristotelian *aisthesis*, that the modern tradition has neglected and even denied. "Presentational immediacy," however, is very different from Strausian "perception." It is the illusory surface of sense experience, while for Straus "perception" is the sensory-interpretative process through which we know presented things as stable objects amenable to classification, definition, explanation, and the like.

On the other hand, if we liken Whitehead's distinction to Straus's distinction of stimuli and objects, we find that causal efficacy, which is another name for sensing, is indeed our everyday path to objects (in an ordinary, not a "scientific" sense), while stimuli are by no means the givens of presentational immediacy, but intellectual artifacts constructed by abstraction and hypostatization to suit the demands of a physicalist metaphysic. So this distinction is not quite parallel to Whitehead's either. At the same time, we should notice that the data of presentational immediacy are after all the data, detached and delusive, from which Berkeley and Hume generalized to produce their theory of ideas (or of impressions), and they are the

data which experimental psychologists have first fastened on
and then forgotten in order to build beneath them the apparently solider neurophysiological foundation with which they
suppose themselves to work. The import of the two analyses
seems to me, therefore, to be convergent, even though the distinctions used are not entirely congruent. In both cases it is the
reinstatement of experience in its concrete significance that is
at stake.

One more brief comparison. I remarked at the start of this
chapter that Buytendijk, although leaning heavily on Straus in
many contexts, differs sharply from him so far as the theory of
sensing is concerned. Their analyses are parallel, and indeed
convergent, insofar as they both follow in one way or another a
phenomenological method in the analysis of behavior and, as I
mentioned earlier, insofar as they both elaborate psychological,
methodological, and philosophical critiques of conditioned reflex theory. What Buytendijk objects to, however, is Straus's
attempt to develop a theory of animal *experience*. He prefers to
view behavior from outside and to say nothing at all about anything resembling (to borrow Uexküll's well-known term) the
Merkwelt of animals. It is a little hard to see why his objection
here is so emphatic. It is, of course, true that we can, as human
beings, say nothing, strictly speaking, about what the experience of any other sentient creature *feels* like; but by extrapolation, and, in the case of some gifted observers and trainers of
animals, by a sort of participation, we can, I should think, ap-
proximate to *some* insight into *some* aspects of the experience
at least of animals fairly close to us in the evolutionary scale.
We know what it is to be frightened or hungry, to purr with
contentment, to feel at home. Yet Buytendijk seems not simply
to reject such analogical inferences but to fear them. One can
only suppose that, on religious grounds, he wishes to emphasize
the complete, radical uniqueness of the human spirit and to
minimize the continuity of our mental life with that of our dis-

tant kin. For my present purpose, in any case, his divergence here from Straus needs only to be reported, not explained.

3

For the arbitrary models of empiricist psychology, then, Straus would substitute the conception of an experiencing being in its relation to a surrounding world. A host of philosophical themes are given new illumination by this change of ground. I have already touched on some of them, but will mention more explicitly three: the concepts of time and space, the mind-body problem, and the problem of universals.

Philosophers in the empiricist tradition, and experimental psychologists, who have depended on this tradition for their metaphysical nourishment, have taken, by and large, time and space as either objective and Newtonian or as subjective constructs equivalent to those uniform containers. But our experience of time and space is not thus uniform. Nor, in the case of time, does this assertion imply setting a Bergsonian *durée* or a literary stream of consciousness over against the uniform chronology of the "real" world. Chronology is a product of culture, which we rely on to set our alarm clocks, to meet classes or fry chicken or catch planes; but like clocks, classrooms, frying pans, and Boeings, it is an artifact which we use in order to move about *within* the richer framework of lived time. And lived time is neither Cartesian-atomic nor Newtonian-continuous. It exhibits all, and more than, the modalities that Rosalind enumerated. It is not a measure, but a medium.

The concept of lived time, of course, is by no means original with Straus. His exposition is paralleled in Minkowski, in Merleau-Ponty, or, in a different style, in Heidegger, and it is reminiscent again, in its metaphysical implications, of Whitehead's philosophy of process. What distinguishes his work, however, is its linkage to specific psychological themes: as in his demonstration of the difficulties that follow from the time-atomism of Pavlovian theory, or in his treatment of the theory of memory-traces, or of time-disturbances in endogenic depression.

Let us look at one example: his account of the phenomenon of infantile amnesia: "In organic and senile amnesias, earlier experiences prove more resistant than recent ones. Yet, infantile amnesia sets a barrier which prevents the recovery of memories from our first years." [24] What can be done with this topic in Kantian, Lockian, or any other conventional philosophical terms, or in orthodox psychological theory? In terms of Straus's phenomenology, however, it makes perfectly good sense. "The subject of remembering," Straus argues, "is a human being who forms his life history within the temporal horizon of personal time." [25] Thus within the medium of lived time I form a concept of my history which is objective and chronological:

> Human life evolves on two levels: on that of biological need and satisfaction in the circle of daily routine and on that of signal events, marked in the annals of the curriculum vitae. Corresponding to the two levels of existence, there are two modes of remembering and forgetting: one characterized by the familiar and the repeatable and the other by the new and unique.[26]

This double structure the infant still lacks; hence the baby's inability to remember. Thus this insight permits a much simpler and more adequate explanation than psychologists have been able to devise. Straus compares his own explanation, for example, with Freud's:

> In search of an explanation of this deficiency, Freud . . . assumed—in line with tradition—that, since single, stimulus-bound impressions are preserved in memory, the earliest ones would also be available to us in later years, as long as they are not kept away from consciousness by the forces of repression. If Freud was right, one should expect that a child at the age of three would still remember well the events of his first and second years.

This is not the case. Those early experiences are not preserved up to the advent of the Oedipal situation and then extinguished by repressive forces. Nothing needs to be repressed in this case, because nothing is preserved in its original form—for this reason: what is remembered is the *novum* in its particularity standing out from an invariant ground. This ground is built when the order of things (the world) is detached from the personal order. Before a child is able to remember, it has to fulfill the following conditions: (1) to detach the world from the moments of direct encountering, (2) to extend the temporal span beyond the moment, (3) to build an invariant framework into which single events can be entered, (4) to establish permanent and identifiable structures of particular things and events, and (5) to allow physiognomic changes no longer to interfere with the constancy of the invariant framework and with the identity of single events. But the baby lives from one moment to the other in the narrowness of his temporal horizon. A baby experiences the world basically in relation to himself. The early tendency to put things into his mouth is quite characteristic of his own attitude to the world. He lacks specification. There is an obvious lack of self-reflection; yet, this is what is required to sever the order of one's own existence from the order of the environment. In short, there is a lack of a stabilized preserving order, of a schema in which events are to be registered in order to be recalled in latter days. The conception of the historiological structure of memory not only states, concerning infantile amnesia, *that* it is so—which is a fact that everyone accepts—and not only explains *why* it is so—which Freud had tried to do—but, also, finally, makes evident that it *must* be so.[27]

Even more striking, because the topic is more habitually neglected, is Straus's treatment of space. This resembles, and has plainly influenced, Buytendijk's exposition, as exemplified for instance in the "Encounter" essay referred to in Chapter 3, as well as Merleau-Ponty's concept of bodily spatiality, on which, as we have seen, Buytendijk heavily relies. The first essay in *Phenomenological Psychology*, "The Forms of Spatiality," illustrates Straus's approach to this problem.[28] If we look, without metaphysical prejudice, at the phenomenal difference between color and tone, we find that while colors are "over there," "on" an object, sounds act on us from a source: they approach us or move away from us:

> Color clings (phenomenally) to the object while the tone produced by an object separates itself from it. Color is the mark of a thing, whereas tone is the effect of an activity.[29]

This is so, Straus argues, because, while color and form constitute an object, sound essentially separates itself from its source. Sounds may indeed indicate objects, but they may also, as in music, separate themselves from objects to achieve an autonomous being. Nor do these differences correspond to different judgments, unconscious inferences, or the like, superadded to differing sensory data. They express different pathic modalities, essentially diverse ways of receiving, or achieving, sensory experience. They express different forms of spatial being. Thus:

> Tone has an activity all its own; it presses in on us, surrounds, seizes, and embraces us. Only in a later phase are we able to defend ourselves against sound, only after sound has already taken possession of us, while in the visual sphere we begin to take flight before we have been prehended. The acoustical pursues us; we are at its mercy, unable to get away. Once uttered, a word is there, entering and owning us. Nor can it be rendered unspoken through any pretense or apology.[30]

But color, on the other hand,

> not only presents itself from over there, opposite to us, but also is demarcated at the same time that it demarcates, articulating space as regions, laterally and in depth. In optical space, things stand out from one another with sharply defined boundaries; the articulation of optical space is governed by contour. The optical image appears as a representative of the concept, just as

the melody serves as a natural representative of the unity of the Gestalt.[31]

Further:

> Artistic activity is dependent on the pathic moment of the optical phenomenon—reactively depended down to the tiniest details of technique. Baroque painters did everything to keep things from appearing as simply juxtaposed; to reduce the contours through representation in the plane, they manipulated such devices as the density of paint on the canvas, the distribution of light, the picture's dimensions, its frame, *chiaroscuro* modelling as in etching, and indirect representation of contour. One need only call to mind the work of Rembrandt, especially his famous landscapes.[32]

Nor are these random observations, but recordings of the lawful patterns of the pathic aspect of sensory experiences. They are essential, moreover, to the understanding of movement in its relation to sensing. Thus in dance, which is dominated by the musical, we move, not *through* a space, as in practical purposive action, but *in* a space.[33] Dance, Straus infers, expresses "the tendency of live body space to expand against surrounding space and to actualize itself symbolically." [34] Dance transforms the oriented optical space of our routine practical activities into a "presentic" acoustical space. Consider, for example, the experience of dizziness outside and inside the dance. Dizziness in climbing a ladder is purely unpleasant; dizziness in the dance exhilarates. The proprioceptive sensations in both cases are identical, yet "they are embodied in different structures of immediate experience." [35] It is worth quoting Straus's description at some length:

> The space in which we move on the merry-go-round or in dance —which we are discussing here—has lost its directional stability. Of course, it is still a space with extension and direction, but direction is no longer disposed in a certain way around a fixed

axis; rather, direction moves and turns with us as it were. The dissolution of defined direction, and, correspondingly, of topical valences, homogenizes space. In a space of such modality, it is no longer possible to act; one can only enter into it as a participant. Actually we don't live in space but in spaces, spaces somehow demarcated and stabilized by a system of fixed axes. One need only imagine a room perfectly quadratic, without windows and indirectly illuminated; in the middle of each wall is a door, while furniture and pictures are arranged in a strictly symmetrical manner so that each wall appears as a mirror image of the opposite wall. If one were to spend some time in this room and then walk back and forth several times, one would become confused about the entrance, having lost his orientation to neighboring, surrounding areas; one would be bewildered and bewitched like a person in a magic maze. To enter such a space in fantasy is sufficient to show why we make our rooms rectangular rather than square, why we prefer asymmetry—a clearly and distinctly apprehended difference between length and width, as proportions in the ratio of the Golden Mean. Action demands a system of definite, distinct directions and determining loci with valences varying in accord with their relationship to the directional system. When the spatial structure changes, as happens in dance, the immediate experience of confrontation also changes that tension between subject and object which, in ecstasy, completely dissolves. When we turn around while dancing, we are, from the very start, moving in a space completely at odds with oriented space. But this change of spatial structure occurs only in pathic participation, not in a gnostic act of thinking, contemplating, or imagining. That is to say, presentic experience actualizes itself *in* the movement; it does not produce itself *by means of* the movement. Even though a dance occupies a considerable interval in objective time, the entire movement is still integrally presentic. In itself, it does not produce any changes in immediate experience nor any changes in the external situation, as does action which must abandon its starting point to reach its goal. Every action demands that a particular condition or position be left behind in order to reach another condition, another position. This defines both direction and limits for action. When the new condition is reached, the old one belongs to the past; action is a historical process. Presentic movement, on the other hand, is free of direction or limits; it knows only waxing and waning, ebbing and flooding. It does not bring about this change; it is not a historical process. It is for just this reason that we term it "presentic," despite its duration in objective time. The dissolution of the subject-object tension, culminating in ecstasy, is not the aim of the dance; rather, the very experience of dancing originally arises within it.[36]

This general description is confirmed by a comparison of different styles of dancing, say, a minuet and a waltz:

> The dancer of the minuet performs his steps over the basic rhythm. The "filling" of space is only figuratively represented by the formation of couples, the "visits," etc. The dancer of the minuet senses the harmonizing influence of the music without yielding to it entirely; he remains an individual. . . . The different ways of life of social classes and the changes of sentiment dominating different historical periods are directly reflected in their forms of dancing. The sequence: minuet, waltz, jazz strikingly demonstrates the extent to which the individual existence has been abandoned and swallowed up by mass movements.[37]

This contrast, be it noted, moreover, does not indicate a contrast between the spatiality of dance as pathic and a gnostic, Euclidean space as our everyday medium:

> The space in which we live is as different from the schema of empty Euclidean space as the familiar world of colors differs from the concepts of physical optics. . . . As immediately experienced, space is always a filled and articulated space; it is nature or world.[38]

Thus, the difference between dancing and walking indicates a contrast, not between lived space and Euclidean space, but between two forms of lived spatiality. Our ordinary motility is the progressive one of purposive movement, and it is this that is reversed in the abandon of the dance. But purposive movement is not Euclidean, spread out in three dimensions indifferently to time; it is *historical.* It is the space of action.[39] In it we move ahead in preference to back, out from a stable *here* to the goal of our proposed action. This, not the infinite extension of geometry, is the ordinary lived spatiality which we forget in the self-abandonment of the dance. The contrast between acoustical and optical space is still a contrast within the pathic aspect of sensing.

Straus is often repetitive, often given to cryptic epigrams; for example, "Repetition is possible in the acoustical sphere, while the optical sphere is limited to reduplication [*Vervielfälti-gung*]." [40] (Cannot colors repeat themselves in a pattern or a costume?) Or: "The space that extends before us is, thus, a metaphor of the approaching future; the space that lies behind is a metaphor of the past that has receded from us. When we hear something, we have already heard it." [41] But in general his exposition is not only illuminating in itself: it can serve to rouse us from our dogmatic slumber. We take it for granted that non-Euclidean geometry has undermined the Kantian theory of spatial intuition. But why should we ever have thought that our everyday experience of space was that of the "infinite container" Kant envisaged? We could find, if we sought philosophical precedent, a more faithful rendering of our experience in Aristotle's concept of place, or we could find a corrosive critique of the empiricist conventions about sensation in Hegel's argument, in the *Phenomenology of Mind,* on the here and now. In the main, however, philosophers have failed to build on these insights; and here, moreover, we have an alternative approach tied, not to alternative philosophical systems, but to concrete psychological insights. Such an account may perhaps induce us to abandon the poverty of our usual school examples—the desk or the tree, the building across the quad—not, indeed, for irrational wallowing in "situation," but for the structured descriptions of phenomenal realities, which may serve as the coping stones of a sounder metaphysic.

4

In studies like those of the forms of spatiality or of lived movement, we have already—as I suggested earlier—emerged from
the shadows of Cartesian dualism to look at human existence in
its unitary, mental-and-embodied being. Straus has developed
such non-Cartesian thinking in many areas, but nowhere more
strikingly than in his essays on the upright posture.[42] Man's
posture, he argues, exhibits and conditions his nature both as
animal and rational: neither has priority. Language, he points
out, has long taken cognizance of this fact:

> The expression "to be upright" has two connotations: first, to rise,
> to get up, and to stand on one's own feet and, second, the moral
> implication, not to stoop to anything, to be honest and just, to
> be true to friends in danger, to stand by one's convictions, and to
> act accordingly, even at the risk of one's life. We praise an up-
> right man; we admire someone who stands up for his ideas of
> rectitude. There are good reasons to assume that the term "up-
> right" in its moral connotation is more than a mere allegory.[43]

But that is not to say that the more "basic" meaning is the
moral one. Our posture, unique among animal species, is physi-
ologically grounded in all details of our nervous, muscular, and
skeletal development:

> There is no doubt that the shape and function of the human body
> are determined in almost every detail by, and for, the upright
> posture. The skeleton of the foot; the structure of the ankle,
> knee, and hip; the curvature of the vertebral column; the propor-
> tions of the limbs—all serve the same purpose. This purpose
> could not be accomplished if the muscles and the nervous sys-
> tem were not built accordingly. While all parts contribute to the
> upright posture, upright posture in turn permits the develop-
> ment of the forelimbs into the human shoulders, arms, and hands
> and of the skull into the human skull and face.[44]

Upright posture pre-establishes our way of being-in-the-world. To begin with, it is an achievement, not of the species only, but of each individual, an achievement which every infant must realize—and glories in—for itself. "Man has to become what he is." [45] He has to learn to walk, and he has to learn to speak. Nor can his defeat of gravity ever be made definitive: we have to abandon our upright posture as part of our daily rhythm and assume it again, often reluctantly, next day. If, moreover, the young child enjoys his success in learning to stand and to walk, both child and adult enjoy the abandonment of the struggle against gravity in "reclining." Indeed, the rhythm of waking and sleeping, in its human form, is linked essentially to the rhythm of standing and lying down. To stand up is to rise to command the world in opposition to it; in sleeping, in contrast, we do not so much leave the world as give in to it, let it play upon us kaleidoscopically without giving it the order that in waking we are able to impose.

In its ever renewed attainment, then, the upright posture displays manifold significance. So, Straus argues, does the very fact of standing, once acquired. In standing, he points out, we put ourselves in three ways at a distance from the Allon: from the ground, from things, and from our fellows. The second of these brings us our confrontation with objects as objects and prepares our formal ways of handling them: "Spoon and fork," Straus remarks, "do not create distance; tools can only be invented and used where distance already exists." [46] Distance from our fellows, similarly, underlies both our formalities and our expressive relaxations of them. Such forms, of course, vary from culture to culture: yet everywhere the vertical is predominant, the vertical as presenting the aloof or the solemn; the deviation from it—"inclination"—representing the abandonment, at least in part, of such aloofness:

> There is only one vertical but many deviations from it, each one carrying a specific, expressive meaning. The sailor puts his cap

askew, and his girl understands well the cocky expression and his "leanings." King Comus at the Mardi Gras may lean backward and his crown may slip off-center. However, even the disciples of informality would be seriously concerned if, on his way to his inauguration, the President should wear his silk hat (the elongation and accentuation of the vertical) aslant. There are no teachers, no textbooks, that instruct in this field. There are no pupils, either, who need instruction. Without ever being taught, we understand the rules governing this and other areas of expression. We understand them not conceptually but, it seems, by intuition. This is true for the actor as well as the onlooker.[47]

The constancy of the vertical dimension, Straus adds, is exhibited in the fact that young children can draw a vertical or horizontal line or a square while still unable to copy the same square presented as a diamond.[48]

Walking, finally, depends, like standing, on a highly complex combination of physiological conditions, which predetermine the way in which we experience the world:

Human bipedal gait is a rhythmical movement whereby, in a sequence of steps, the whole weight of the body rests for a short time on one leg only. The center of gravity has to be swung forward. It has to be brought from a never stable equilibrium to a still less stable balance. Support will be denied to it for a moment until the leg brought forward prevents the threatening fall. Human gait is, in fact, a continuously arrested falling. Therefore, an unforeseen obstacle or a little unevenness of the ground may precipitate a fall. Human gait is an expansive motion, performed in the expectation that the leg brought forward will ultimately find solid ground. It is motion on credit. Confidence and timidity, elation and depression, and stability and insecurity are all expressed in gait.[49]

All this is entailed in the very fact of standing up and walking; but there is more. The development of hand and arm, which has so strikingly enlarged our body schema and permitted the development of so many human skills, depends on upright posture. And so does the function of the head, which liberates the "visage":

> Eyes that lead jaws and fangs to the prey are always charmed and spellbound by nearness. To eyes looking straight forward— to the gaze of upright posture—things reveal themselves in their own nature. Sight penetrates depth; sight becomes insight.[50]

The contrast with animal orientation is evident:

> Animals move in the direction of their digestive axis. Their bodies are expanded between mouth and anus as between an entrance and an exit, a beginning and an ending. The spatial orientation of the human body is different throughout. The mouth is still an inlet but no longer a beginning, the anus, an outlet but no longer the tail end. Man in upright posture, his feet on the ground and his head uplifted, does not move in the line of his digestive axis; he moves in the direction of his vision. He is surrounded by a world panorama, by a space divided into world regions joined together in the totality of the universe. Around him, the horizons retreat in an ever growing radius. Galaxy and diluvium, the infinite and the eternal, enter into the orbit of human interests.[51]

Among the many changes implicated in the transformations of the animal into the human head, that of the jaws into the mouth is of special significance as a prerequisite for the development of language. But it is only one of the many preconditions of human speech laid down in the achievements of upright posture:

> In upright posture, the ear is no longer limited to the perception of noises—rustling, crackling, hissing, bellowing, roaring—as indicators of actual events, like warnings, threats, or lures. The external ear loses its mobility. While the ear muscles are preserved, their function of adapting the ear to actuality ceases. Detached from actuality, the ear can comprehend sounds in the sounds' own shape—in their musical or phonetic pattern. This capacity to separate the acoustical Gestalt from the acoustical

material makes it possible to produce purposefully and to "re-produce" intentionally sounds articulated according to a preconceived scheme.[52]

In this "re-production" of sounds, moreover, we can already recognize the achievement of generalization or abstraction characteristic of human thinking: for "the phoneme itself is a universal." [53] Speaking is already what some philosophers like to call "rule-governed behavior":

> A spontaneous cry can never be wrong. The pronunciation of a word or the production of the phoneme is either right or wrong. The virtuosity acquired by the average person in expressing himself personally and individually in the general medium of language hides the true character of linguistic communication. It is rediscovered by reflection when disturbances of any kind interfere with the easy and prompt use of language or when the immediateness of contact does not tolerate linguistic distance, and the word dies in an angry cry, in tender babble, or in gloomy silence.[54]

Indeed, language requires, in Straus's view, all three aspects of that distance from the world which we acquire through upright posture. Distance from the ground, with the disappearance of a mobile outer ear, leaves us to receive the phoneme in its pure acoustical character. Distance from things enables us to make them the objects of discourse mutually understood. And only a distance between speaker and listener could be overcome, as it is, through the mediation of speech. In short, as Herder observed, "The upright gait of man . . . is the organization for every performance of his species and his distinguishing character." [55]

5

Such studies may appear "unphilosophical"—mere excursions into anthropology; but they are the kind of exercise we need if we are to pay more than lip service to our alleged rejection of mind-body dualism and to the conception of a "lived body" which we hope to set in its place.

At the same time, Straus's phenomenological insights are sometimes too easily won. In "The Upright Posture," for example, he contrasts the horse, who can sleep on his feet, with man, who must relinquish his conquest of gravity and lie down to sleep. But surely this example makes the contrast look sharper than it is. If one thinks of a cat, domestic or not—indeed, a tiger or leopard comes most obviously to mind—the posture of repose in contrast to the active gait, with the aura of delight in both, is at least as striking as in our case. Yet cats do not stand on two legs; even moving as "easily" as they do on four plainly demands rest as its contrary. Could it be that hunters show this contrast more clearly than grazers? Similarly, Straus contrasts the "earth-bound" animal with liberated man; but what of the air-borne vertebrates to whom we refer when we call someone "as free as a bird"? Or again, Straus analyzes "awakeness" as the mode in which persons act, and sleep, or dreaming, as the contrary state which can be judged as such only *from* the waking state. This is, I believe, a valid answer to the "Am I dreaming?" question, but again it seems falsely to make the rhythm of sleep and waking a perquisite of human life alone. Other animals, too, "act" only when waking and need the refreshment of sleep. In short, while Straus is correct both in rooting human cognition in a wider I-Allon relation of any experiencing being to its surrounding field and in seeing a deep-seated difference, inextricably linked to the physical basis of our being, between men and other animals, he sometimes makes this distinction in an aphorismic style that fails to stand up to closer analysis.

6

The same weakness infects Straus's treatment of the third problem I want to touch on—the problem of universals. Here too an illuminating account is confused by hasty, and indeed contrary, generalizations, and again just where the distinction between men and animals is concerned.

In both ancient and modern philosophy, the problem of universals has arisen from the contrast between the mere particularity of sensory givens and the generality of language or of thought. Let us start, for example, from Plato's position in the *Theaetetus*. Knowledge, to be knowledge, Plato argued, must be both *infallible* and *real*. Sensation, as the particular, immediate, *given-to-me*, is indeed infallible. But it fails the test of reality, since "existence" can be grasped, not by sense, but only, *through* the senses, by the mind alone. Sensation, therefore, cannot qualify as knowledge. It presents us with the particular, meaningless *this*; but only through the comprehension of general concepts, like existence, can we *know* that the presented datum not only presents itself but *is*.

Straus's position seems to stand in a peculiar relation of agreement and disagreement with this classic text. On the one hand, he is convinced that philosophers, from Plato and Democritus onward, have been, in the main, unfair to sensory experience. Sensing is not a delusive blooming buzz of meaningless particulars on which we must turn our backs in order to reach an intelligible world where the mind can feed on its proper objects. It is an all-inclusive road of access to the world, our means, over the varied spectrum of the five senses, of communicating with reality. It is thought, not sense, which cuts itself off, by a negation of which men alone among animals are capable, from immediate rootedness in the real, to spin out its gnostic constructions in separation—or at least in quasi separation—from the more immedite immersion in reality of sensing in its pathic mode. Such sensing, moreover, far from being a congeries of meaningless bits, is itself already general. Though limited to, or at least ranging out from and returning to, the *here* and *now*, it nevertheless grasps the presented world in its generality. The experience of generality is intrinsic to sensing and also common, therefore, Straus suggests, to men and animals:

> I maintain that animals, too, experience the general—for example, sound. They have this experience not because they think in general terms, but because the relationship of an experiencing being to the world is a general relationship, whereas the singular moment is merely a constriction of this relationship. The content of each moment is determined in part by that from which it is distinct, that is, by what it no longer is, as well as by what it is to be. How, otherwise, could animals experience signals, which are midway between an undifferentiated and a differentiated situation and which announce the transition from the one to the other? [56]

This seems to me an important insight, and one which helps us to recognize a minimal continuity at least in the styles of being-in-the-world of all sentient beings. "Generality" is not a human invention, which we have superadded to the merely patricular data that make up, Humewise, the raw givens of animal experience. It is of the very fabric of sentience itself. And it is from *within* the world of an experiencing being that we extract, as it were, the more refined universals of language and of the articulate knowledge which it enables us to acquire.

So far, so good—or so it appears. But if Straus rejects the contrast between the sensed as merely particular and the known as general, professing to find in sensory experience the full-bodied medium of all experience, even of the most refined cognition, he insists, at the same time, as strongly as did Plato, that sensory experience is *not* knowledge, is not even an "inferior" brand of knowledge, but differs radically from it, and differs precisely in this matter of generality. Thus in contrast to perception—*Wahr*nehmung—which is cognitive and grasps things in their objectivity as things, of one or another kind, sensing, *Empfinden*, after all, Straus asserts later in his argument, grasps only the here and now: "In sensory seeing the thing is for me, for me here and now in a passing moment. But after the step to the world of perception, this being-there-for-me is apprehended as a moment in a universal, general chain of events." [57] It is "only by the use of universals," he argues, "that I can describe a thing as it is for me . . . and for every one," [58] and such description, he seems to feel, is entailed in the very act of perceiving. Sensing, in contrast, permits no such generalization, no such enlargement to logic and taxonomy, to the rational use of "all" and "some." This contrast is surely Platonic, but a strange transposition of Plato's dichotomy. In the *Theaetetus* we have the contrast of *aisthesis* with knowledge; here we have a different dichotomy: sensing (=*aisthesis?*) is indeed noncognitive, and perception—which is not to be identified with sensory experience—is taken as at least the primordial level of, if not equivalent to, knowledge. "Perceiving," Straus writes, "and not sensing, is a knowing." [59] Its theme, we are told, is the factual, which is constituted—made (*factum*)— by means of a breach in sensory experience, in the singling out of some*thing* against a neutral background of objective space and time. Thus by a fundamental negation man breaks through the sensory horizon, in which he like all animals originally experiences the world, to attain the geographical space of objectivity. He never does so totally, indeed, except in illness: the melancholic is precisely he who has lost touch with the landscape; "frozen in unmoving time, . . . he looks at the world . . . in a bird's eye view." [60] But normally we live in both spaces, that of landscape and that of geography. Routinely we sense; reflectively we perceive.

Indeed, as Straus introduces the distinction of sensing and perceiving, perception seems to be the sharpening of our sense-mediated attention that arises in response to language:

We see a thing a thousand times and yet have not really seen it. A question forces us to look at it properly for the first time. The first seeing was a sensing, a participation in expression; the second seeing, however, is a perception. Questions force us into a new order of understanding. We are asked about "something" and wish to answer what and how that something is. We speak now of things or of a thing, we speak of its properties, its possible modifications. We speak of one thing which we see at this moment in front of us, or which we visualize in its particular place. We speak of one single thing, but we distinguish it with general words.[61]

So we have, if you like, generality in sensing, but "true" universals, let us say, in language-mediated perception. Thus the perception *of* speech ("The phoneme itself is a universal"—see above (p. 210) becomes the model for the perception also of events and objects, which are seen or heard as such only within the universe of discourse that language has already shaped. Can it be that the "generality" of sensing is that of the concrete universal, while perception, like all cognitive processes, depends on the more abstract universals that language enables us to understand? It may be some such dialectical solution that will enable us to reconcile the seeming contradiction.

In that case, of course, however, only language users perceive, and at one place at least Straus suggests that only language users learn.[62] Thus, starting out to put our sensory experiencing on a par with that of other animals, and to exhibit the continuity on the ground of which our unique achievements have arisen, he seems, in his doctrine of perception, to outdo even the Cartesians in his relegation of animals to outer darkness. Yet surely that animals learn and in some sense acquire knowledge is as well attested as that human knowledge is in some way unique.

Moreover, in his account of perception, even Straus's analysis of human experience is strangely contradicted. In his account of the dance, for example, we have seen that he contrasts both "presentic" or expressive and purposive or "historical" space with the uniform, infinite space of Euclid or Newton. Here, however, he contrasts the presentic space of landscape directly with the uniform space of geography and geometry, which he identifies with that of history. Thus, he points out, a "remote valley" is, geographically, on a uniform plane with my present location in this room. But the farmer living in the remote valley, he remarks, is immersed in it as his landscape. Granted: but the farmer plowing a furrow, for example, is not moving like the dancer in a space; he is advancing purposefully—and historically—through a space to reach a goal. Both these forms of spatiality are to be contrasted, as Straus himself has contrasted them, with the geographical framework, say, of an agricultural survey. It seems, therefore, that we have here not a simple dichotomy, but a many-one relation. On the side of sensing, there are diverse forms of lived spatiality; on the side of perception, there is the one geographical space accessible to objective thought. And the concept of "history" seems, if with different significance, to fall into both categories. Purposive action is historical; an expressive activity like the dance is not. But the universal framework of history entails "history" in a more refined and critical sense.

Such ambiguities need ironing out if we are to work with Straus's basic concepts and particularly, once more, when we are faced with the teasing question of the distinction between men and animals. As Straus argues in "The Upright Posture," in agreement with the comparative studies, for example, of Adolf Portmann, men differ fundamentally from animals even in their anatomical and developmental endowments as animals. But is the diversion to be seen so sharply that perception and knowledge are wholly denied to other animals? There seems to be here a radical transmutation, indeed, but of a common gift. Were not generality embedded in sentience itself, the power of language to mediate assertions with universal intent, and hence to aim, not at awareness only, but at truth: this power would remain, as it does for traditional empiricism, an unintelligible mystery.

NOTES

1. E. W. Straus, *The Primary World of Senses*, trans. by J. Needleman (New York: Free Press of Glencoe, 1963).
2. E. W. Straus, *Phenomenological Psychology*, translated in part by Erling Eng (New York: Basic Books, 1966). © 1966 by Erwin W. Straus.
3. In this respect Charles Taylor's *Explanation of Behavior* (New York: Humanities Press, 1964), which admittedly owes much to Merleau-Ponty, forms a striking exception to the general rule in recent Anglo-American thought.
4. *Phenomenological Psychology*, p. xi.
5. A. I. Melden, *Free Action* (London: Routledge, 1961), p. 198.
6. E. A. Burtt, "Descriptive Metaphysics," *Mind*, LXXII (1963), 18–39.
7. Taylor, *op. cit.*, pp. 115–120.
8. Quoted in *Phenomenological Psychology*, p. vi.
9. *Ibid.*, p. viii.
10. *Ibid.*
11. Cf. *ibid.*, pp. 269–270.
12. *Ibid.*, p. viii.
13. *Ibid.*
14. *Ibid.*
15. *Ibid.*, p. 26.
16. *Ibid.*, p. 272.
17. "The Forms of Spatiality," *Phenomenological Psychology*, pp. 3–37.
18. *Ibid.*, p. 12.
19. The concept of universal intent is derived from Michael Polanyi's *Personal Knowledge* (Chicago: University of Chicago Press, 1958).
20. M. Heidegger, *Sein und Zeit* (Halle: Niemeyer, 1927), p. 122.
21. *Psychologie der menschlichen Welt* (Berlin: Springer, 1960).
22. See, for example, D. Hamlyn, *Sensation and Perception* (New York: Humanities Press, 1961).
23. A. N. Whitehead, *Symbolism: Its Meaning and Effect* (Cambridge: Cambridge University Press, 1927).
24. *Phenomenological Psychology*, p. 72.
25. *Ibid.*, p. 73.
26. *Ibid.*

27. *Ibid.*, pp. 72–73.
28. "The Forms of Spatiality," *ibid.*, pp. 3–37. Cf. also Chapter 2, "Lived Movement," and the account of action and space in Chapter 7, "The Upright Posture."
29. *Ibid.*, p. 8.
30. *Ibid.*, p. 16.
31. *Ibid.*, pp. 16–17.
32. *Ibid.*, p. 17.
33. Cf. *ibid.*, p. 23. See Chapter 3, above.
34. *Ibid.*, p. 28.
35. *Ibid.*, p. 30.
36. *Ibid.*, pp. 30–31.
37. *Ibid.*, pp. 31–32.
38. *Ibid.*, p. 32.
39. Cf. *ibid.*, p. 150.
40. *Ibid.*, p. 16.
41. *Ibid.* The second passage is rendered even more difficult by a change in paragraphing in the translation.
42. "The Upright Posture," *Phenomenological Psychology*, pp. 137–165; cf. "Born to See, Bound to Behold," *Tijdschrift voor Filosofie*, XXVII (1965), 659–688.
43. *Phenomenological Psychology*, p. 137.
44. *Ibid.*, p. 138.
45. *Ibid.*, p. 141.
46. *Ibid.*, p. 145.
47. *Ibid.*, p. 146.
48. *Ibid.*, p. 147.
49. *Ibid.*, p. 148.
50. *Ibid.*, p. 162.
51. *Ibid.*
52. *Ibid.*, p. 163.
53. *Ibid.*
54. *Ibid.*
55. Quoted in *ibid.*, p. 164.
56. *Primary World of Senses*, p. 96.
57. *Ibid.*, p. 317.
58. *Ibid.*
59. *Ibid.*, p. 329.
60. *Ibid.*, p. 328.
61. *Ibid.*, p. 317.
62. *Ibid.*, p. 147.

5

Kurt Goldstein

1

Goldstein's philosophy, like Straus's, sprang directly from the demands of his medical practice, and especially from his experience in one specialized area: the investigation of brain-damaged individuals, in particular of brain-damaged veterans of World War I, whom he studied as director of a Veterans' Hospital in Germany. At the same time, his interpretation of these studies led him straight to a philosophical theory of the organism and its structure as fundamental, in its way, as Straus's theory of sensing or Plessner's theory of organic modals. The work in which he developed this theory, *Der Aufbau des Organismus*, was written in the Netherlands in the first year of his exile from his native country. It was published in 1939 in an execrable "translation" (reprinted in 1963) and with

219

a preface by K. S. Lashley.[1] Yet, although his death in New York City in 1965 concluded a distinguished career in the practice of neurology, the theory which had emerged thirty years earlier from his medical experience, and on which for thirty years the latter had been founded, has remained too little heeded by English-speaking readers. True, his inclusion in the *History of Psychology through Autobiography*[2] marks his admission to the inner circle of American psychologists, and many of his special studies are widely known. He has been influential also, as has Erwin Straus, among psychotherapists of the "existential" school.[3] His general theory of biological knowledge, however, remains, in English-speaking countries, largely unknown, or at least unassimilated.[4]

What is that theory? Instead of trying to guide the reader through the major steps of his argument in *Aufbau*, as I attempted to do with Plessner's *Stufen*, I shall first take a brief look at some of the empirical data which inspired it, then summarize its principal theses, with the corollaries they entail, and finally consider its general philosophical implications.

2

Goldstein's lifetime of experience can hardly be summarized, and certainly not by a layman. His German experience included the examination and long-term observation of thousands of patients, some of whom he saw again in 1958 after a quarter-century's interval, and his publications on the subject of brain damage extend from 1905 to 1950.[5] A case described in his William James lectures, however, may serve as one among countless instances to illustrate the kind of behavior which his theory was in the first instance meant to interpret. He writes:

> The patient whom I have in mind is a man thirty years of age, with a lesion of the frontal lobe. His customary way of living

does not seem to be very much disturbed. He is a little slow; his face is rather immobile, rather rigid; his attention is directed very strictly to what he is doing at the moment—say, writing a letter or speaking to someone. Confronted with tasks in various fields, under certain conditions he gives seemingly normal responses, but under other conditions he fails completely in tasks that are apparently very similar to those he has performed quite well.[6]

The performances of which he is, and is not, capable can be illustrated, Goldstein continues, by a simple test:

> We place before him a small wooden stick in a definite position, pointing, for example, diagonally from left to right. He is asked to note the position of the stick carefully. After a half minute's exposure the stick is removed; then it is handed to the patient, and he is asked to put it back in the position in which it was before. He grasps the stick and tries to replace it, but he fumbles; he is all confusion; he looks at the examiner, shakes his head, tries this way and that, plainly uncertain. The upshot is that he cannot place the stick in the required position. He is likewise unable to imitate other simple figures built up of sticks. Next we show the patient a little house made of many sticks, a house with a roof, a door, a window, and a chimney. When he is asked to reproduce the model, he succeeds very well.[7]

What is the meaning of this extraordinary difference in performance? It cannot be a deficiency in memory, perception, or action, Goldstein argues, since copying the house demands in all these respects, especially in memory, greater capacity than the much simpler performance of replacing the single stick correctly, in which the patient failed. A further experiment provides the answer:

> We put before the patient two sticks placed together so as to form an angle with the opening pointing upward. The patient is unable to reproduce this model. Then we confront him with

the same angle, the opening pointing down this time, and now he reproduces the figure very well at the first trial. When we ask the patient how it is that he can reproduce the second figure but not the first one, he says: "This one has nothing to do with the other one." Pointing to the second one, he says: "That is a roof"; to the first, "That is nothing." [8]

What the patient has lost, it becomes plain, is a grasp of abstractions; he is deficient in what Goldstein calls "the abstract attitude." A conformation that has concrete meaning he can observe, remember, and reconstruct, but a much simpler arrangement which would have to be mastered as a line or lines in abstract space is beyond his powers. But what sort of "loss" is this? It results, obviously, from injury to a particular cerebral area, but it is not a "local" loss, like that of an eye or a leg. It is a loss in the patient's total capacity to handle his environment. Where the normal person approaches a problem through the abstract attitude and proceeds to handle it through concrete behavior, the brain-damaged individual is helpless before an abstract problem, though perfectly capable of handling one that is directly embedded in the concrete meanings of his everyday life.

Goldstein's distinction between the abstract attitude and concrete behavior proved a fruitful one not only for the study of brain-damaged patients but in other areas as well. Infantile autism, for example, he believed to be the result, not of abnormal relations between mother and infant, as many had supposed, but of failure to develop the abstract attitude, which normally matures in the first year of life.[9] In anthropology, he found the distinction useful (as he argued in an essay in honor of Paul Radin) in supporting Radin's differentiation between "thinkers" and "non-thinkers" in so-called "primitive" societies.[10] The members of such cultures are no more "primitive" in their thought processes than we are; but their institutions are so organized that the performance of abstract tasks is principally delegated to certain classes or individuals, while concrete performances are left to the lay majority. Although this is analogous to the division of labor between infant and mother, the analogy should not be misapplied. In the latter case, the one individual has not yet developed the capacities whose activities have therefore to be left to the more mature member of the pair. In "primitive" societies all the individuals concerned are equally mature and would be equally capable of abstract thought, did their social roles demand it; but the society is so organized that abstract behavior is reserved for an elite who have been specially trained for its execution, while others are content with concrete tasks.

3

What concerns us here, however, is not so much the applications of Goldstein's distinction between abstract and concrete behavior, important though these are. What concerns us here primarily is the methodology and, therewith, the philosophy which Goldstein's observations in this field led him to develop. Neurological practice, one infers from his account, had been addicted to particulate observation and particulate explanation; such observation and such explanation would be powerless in the kind of case he was used to dealing with, and he formulated, in opposition to it, a set of methodological principles of a different cast. He states them in his "Autobiography." The first postulate, he writes,

> is *to consider initially all the phenomena* presented by the organism, giving no preference in the description to any special one. At this stage, no symptom is to be considered of greater or lesser importance for the diagnosis. It must be left to future investigation to determine to what extent one symptom rather than another is essential for understanding the underlying defect of a function.[11]

This postulate entails, as we shall see, a more flexible and comprehensive empiricism than traditional empiricist methodology allows. So does the second:

> The second methodological postulate concerns *the correct description of the observable phenomena.* It was a frequent mistake to write down what amounted to the mere description of the simple positive or negative results obtained from an investigation that issued from a theory. A correct result may be ambiguous in respect to its underlying function. Therefore only a thorough analysis and presentation of the way in which the effect, whether success or failure, was achieved can provide clarification of the performance.[12]

This is clear from the context of the example cited above. Goldstein comments:

> The older psychopathological protocols usually confined themselves to a consideration of whether or not the patient answered a question correctly. This plus-or-minus method is inadequate, no matter whether the answer is correct or false. If we regard a reaction only from the standpoint of the actual solution of a task, a correct answer can be presented in spite of a wrong procedure. That may lead us to overlook a deviation from normality since the individual may fulfill the task by a detour which may not be evident from the answer.[13]

Finally:

> The third methodological postulate is *a careful description of the present condition of the organism in which the answer appears.* Many errors would have been avoided in psychopathology if these postulates, quite definitely stated by Hughlings Jackson in a similar way decades ago, had not been so frequently neglected.[14]

Goldstein notes two possible objections to this method. One is that one can never tell for sure when an examination has been completed, and the other is that one cannot by this method examine as many cases as one could by other and more mechanical means. The reply to both objections is contained, as we shall see, in Goldstein's fundamental theory of biological knowledge. To the first: The knowledge of living things is itself an aspect of biological performance, which is essentially under way and incomplete: so be it. To the second: It is the comprehensive understanding of the individual which is the basic aim of such knowledge. Awareness in depth of the individual's success and failure is more important than a superficial grasp of some syndrome or other spread over a large number of cases.

It is the third of his three methodological maxims which generates the fundamental principle of Goldstein's biological philosophy. *Each organism,* he insists, *must always be studied as a whole.* Several misunderstandings must be avoided here. First, Goldstein insists that in his basic thesis he is making, as we have just seen, a methodological and *not* a metaphysical assertion. As a physician, or even, he believes, as an experimentalist, one must approach the individual with reference to its whole nature, even if what one wants to study is the operation of some special part. This axiom, and the theorems that follow from it, constitute for him a cognitive norm, *ein Erkenntnisideal,* not a dogma about "reality." True, conformity to such a norm issues in knowledge of organisms different from the results of a more analytical procedure, in terms, say, of neurophysiology or biochemistry. In this sense, the statements we make about living things, and therefore our beliefs about their nature, will be correspondingly different. The emphasis on the whole is therefore no mere "as-if." Admittedly also, Goldstein sometimes appends to his empirically grounded expositions excursions into ontology which surprise even a sympathetic philosophical reader; of this more hereafter. Yet I think we should respect his claim to be proceeding from an operational point of view, in terms of the demands of medical and scientific practice.

A second warning: as his statement of methodology should make clear, the *whole* of Goldstein's axiom is the *individual* whole, in its ongoing interchange with its environment, of course, but still the individual, not the universe, not even, in the first instance, a community of individuals. He is no Spinozist, but a physician confronting *this* patient (rather than this patient's Babinsky reflex or this patient's inability to name colors and so on). Although the phrase *Ganzheitsmethode* which he uses to describe his method is rendered in his William James lectures as "holistic method," perhaps "comprehensive" is better. Whatever the term, the point is, it is not some vague inclusiveness he is talking of. He is recommending as primary to biology attention to the living individual rather than to its parts in isolation: analogously to the insistence of some biochemists that experiments should be conducted as far as possible in vivo rather than in vitro. In the study of organisms, he is insisting, whatever is partial is distorted, if not artificial; the only real object of study is the whole.

Yet thirdly, as a practicing biologist, he insists, one must deal clinically and experimentally with the specifiable particulars of the whole. As we shall see, he is never suggesting the abandonment of precise methods, which *can* only handle parts, but only the constant reference through these to the nature of the whole.

The first principle of Goldstein's philosophy, then, is the emphasis on the whole. This maxim has very precise consequences. First, the holistic approach, systematically carried into practice, reveals a *relative constancy* of the whole organism's achievements in its interaction with the environment. Depending on the whole situation at the time, the "same" external stimulus may have very different effects; yet in the whole situation we find a constant pattern maintained. With respect, in particular, to the action of the nervous system, Goldstein reports, we discover a changing figure-background relation which can be understood only in reference to a constant mean around which the performances of the organism fluctuate. Interaction of organism and environment geared to such a constant Goldstein calls the basic law of biology: *das biologische Grundgesetz.*[15] And it is clearly a principle which only the holistic approach could have discovered, since only the whole organism in its over-all reception of and action upon its medium can display and maintain such constants.

Once we recognize this constancy of over-all performance, moreover, we can see that what it represents is a *preferred behavior,* whether of individuals of this species, of this individual itself, or of this individual at this stage of its life history. It is the preferred behavior to the performance of which the organism directs its central effort, with the routine activities entailed in such behavior serving as background to the central performance. Thus, Goldstein insists—and this is a corollary of the principle of preferred behavior—any organism can execute only one performance at a time, not, however, at an instant, but over a stretch of time, and sometimes in different forms at different times. For plainly, as we have had occasion to remark in earlier chapters, process, the passage of time, is essential to the study of behavior.

Examples of preferred behavior are legion. The migratory behavior of the arctic tern described by Portmann and the breeding behavior of the Emperor penguins are examples of species-preferred behavior. Some individuality appears, even in such relatively fixed action patterns, in the behavior of the digger wasp quoted from Baerends, also in Chapter 1. The smiling of the human infant, which has been described by Goldstein in an essay closely following Buytendijk's and Plessner's studies,[16] exemplifies a more personal behavior, which, though species-specific, yet represents the first truly individual encounter of one human being with another, which will deepen uniquely in each lifetime to such richness of encounter as each person may attain. Each such instance, however it may transcend the limits of appetite, and however universal, therefore, its bearing and its achievement, is nevertheless individual and unique. It is the preferred performance of just this person, which aims at expressing maximally its essence and no other. Yet at different times in one person's life also such patterns differ, first, clearly, as he develops from smiling infant to mature statesman or lover or poet or what you will. And second, as Goldstein's experience taught him, in illness preferred behavior differs radically from its character in health: the patient who has lost his normal capacity for abstract behavior learns in his own way to perform competently what tasks he can, much as the blind learn to hear obstacles in their path and so move competently in what is usually a sighted world.

The implications of Goldstein's concept of preferred behavior are important. To begin with, the orientation of behavior toward a preferred performance shows why biology can never be wholly quantitative, why some reference to a qualitative aspect is essential. Homeostasis, the maintenance of a state of equilibrium, might perhaps be wholly quantified; but what is involved here is not just maintenance of the given state. What is involved, basically, is *the best expression of this organism's essential nature.* Orthodox biologists will accuse Goldstein of "essentialism," and they will be quite right; but, he insists, his is an *empirical* essentialism. He imports no "types" from a Platonic heaven, but seeks, concretely and experimentally, to understand the preferred behavior of *this* organism as it is expressed in a given situation.

If we compare Goldstein's clinical procedure, say, with that of orthodox psychoanalysts on the one hand or of orthodox animal psychologists on the other, we find, I think, an analogy with the situation in taxonomy which may clarify the approach to the "essence" of the organism that he had in mind. Ernst Mayr has contrasted certain types of pre-evolutionary taxonomy on the one hand, and on the other the efforts of the re-

cently active numerical taxonomists, with what he believes to
be the correct procedure in classifying organisms.[17] The older
approach entailed a priori weighting of characters and thus allowed insufficient flexibility in the taxonomist's activities,
whether in the museum or the field. On such criteria, for example, where we approach a specimen with certain fixed colors
and shapes in mind, it should be impossible to judge that a
male and female mallard belong to the same species. The numerical taxonomist, in contrast, who supposes himself to work
with no weighting at all and to feed any and all characters
indiscriminately into his omnivorous computers, is equally at a
loss in the face of such a common-or-garden fact. But what the
competent taxonomist does, and in fact, Mayr claims, has always done, is to practice a common-sensical a posteriori
weighting, studying what, on all the empirical evidence, he
finds to be a population (reproductively isolated from other
populations) for the characters in terms of which it can be distinguished from other populations. In behavioral science a similar trichotomy obtains. The Freudian works theoretically, if
not always in practice, in reference to rigid a priori patterns:
behavior must be Oedipal or libidinal or sublimative or what
not. The experimentalist, on the other side, supposes himself to
work purely empirically in terms of isolated stimuli and isolated responses, to which he supposes that he brings no over-all
theoretical concepts which would distort his purely factual results. Goldstein, looking at whatever data may appear relevant
in a given situation, is weighting after the fact whatever
features of a given performance and of a given individual's
repeated or altered performance in a given or altered environment appear, in the light of the whole picture, to have a genuine bearing on that individual's essential character. This is
again a posteriori weighting of the phenomena, as distinct from
a priori weighting or, allegedly, no weighting at all.

But a closer analogy—indeed, it seems to me, an *application* of Goldstein's method, although it has, so far as I know, no historical connection whatsoever with his work—is the study of what are sometimes called biological clocks, that is, of physiological periodicity. The first systematic work in this field, according to a paper by Halberg and Reinberg,[18] was that of Chossat (1843), who established the fact that pigeons maintain a rhythm in cloacal temperature until death even though they are totally deprived of food and water. Since then chronophysiology has developed dramatically, and especially in recent years, both in extent and in the objectivity and precision of its techniques. In particular, the application of computer techniques has permitted much more complex studies than were possible earlier: "Just as the use of microscopic techniques brings into view the cellular structures and spatial organization of a tissue, so the recourse to techniques of electronic computation brings into view the temporal structures of a function or the organization in time of a functional system." [19] Thus instead of investigating a single rhythm as a function of time, the chronophysiologist now studies and quantifies precisely, in human as well as animal subjects, many rhythms of different frequencies, from high-frequency rhythms with a period shorter than half an hour, through those of medial frequency ranging from half an hour to two and a half days, to low-frequency rhythms.

Now, not only do such studies emphasize the temporal aspect of organic phenomena, which all our authors also stress, but in their present refined form they stress the unique nature of the whole organic system as a complex network of spatio-temporal events. Such studies would be on principle impossible except in terms of a comprehensive method; indeed they are precisely studies of physiological and behavioral *constants* which exhibit a pattern of *preferred performances*. Such rhythms as sleep and waking, body temperature, sensitivity to drugs, E.E.G., and so on do not, of course, represent "performances" in Goldstein's sense; it would be absurd to say of them that the organism performs only one at a time. Quite the contrary; it is just their variety and multiplicity that makes them interesting. On the basis of Goldstein's methodology, however, one would expect that the whole system of such rhythms could be interpreted as organized background for whatever figure characterizes the preferred behavior, in the macroscopic sense, of the organism in question at a particular level of its activity. Whether or not this will prove to be the case, the point is that older, isolating methodologies, which investigate given parameters outside the context of the whole individual's performance, would be incapable of imagining, let alone of executing, such analysis. Goldstein's methodological maxims, and the philosophical principles which underlie them, are clearly presupposed in the chronophysiological approach. At the same time this work is as precise, as "objective," and as empirical as the most hardheaded reductivist could wish. It seems to me therefore an important vindication, displayed in a substantive body of precise analytical results, of his philosophy.

I mentioned earlier Goldstein's anticipation of the objection to his method that it can never be complete. Of course, no empirical study is ever complete. Goldstein emphasizes this feature in *Aufbau* by characterizing the holistic method, further, as *dialectical.* For, as Kierkegaard argued against the Hegelians, any fruitful dialectic is always incomplete. No organism, Goldstein argues, ever entirely achieves the complete expression of its nature, nor does any investigator ever understand it wholly. But the biologist must try systematically, through his action, to comprehend his living subject in its action. First he must start from some reference to a whole context, but then his empirical results will alter and enrich his concept of the whole, and so on indefinitely. The interplay of experiment and theoretical insight is here so far identical with the procedure of any science, biological or no; only the insight involved here is tied more concretely to individual existents in individual situations, and the degree of incompleteness of the resultant knowledge is therefore greater. Only abstract systems can be completed. Biological knowledge, tied to the ongoing existence of the concrete whole, is always in process. In the words of Ch. Nicolle, "Nous avançons sur une route qui marche elle-même." [20] True, biology is oriented to the whole, and in this sense complete, situation of its subject, while physical investigation is indifferent to most aspects of the given experimental situation it confronts, and in this sense is less "total." But, just because it attends to individual wholes, which are themselves developing, biological knowledge as such is *necessarily* incomplete. One cannot describe, let alone explain *in toto*, a process that is itself under way.

Biological knowledge is incomplete—and dialectical— further, not only because it studies concrete action, which is always in process, but because it is itself biological action. Not only in the situation of doctor and patient, Goldstein believes, but everywhere, biological knowledge and biological action are inseparable. For if even the quantum physicist interferes through his experimentation with the object of his investigation, so much the more does the biological experimenter and (as every conservationist knows) the biological technologist. He transforms the world of his subject, which may in turn (since he too is a living being) transform his own habitat and ultimately his own nature. Canguilhem makes this point in terms of an example from Girandoux's *Electre:*

> The beggar, the tramp, who stumbles over hedgehogs crushed on the road, meditates on this original flaw in the hedgehog which drives it to cross roads. If this question has a philosophical sense in that it poses the problem of destiny and death, it has, however, much less biological sense. A road is a product of man's technical ability, one of the elements of the human environment, but this has no biological significance for a hedgehog. Hedge-

hogs, insofar as they are hedgehogs, do not cross roads. They explore, in their hedgehog way, their hedgehog environment according to their alimentary and sexual impulses. On the contrary, it is the roads of man which cross the world of the hedgehog, its hunting ground and the theater of its loves, just as they cross the world of the rabbit, the lion and the dragon-fly. Now the experimental method, as is indicated by the etymology of the word "method," is also a sort of road that man the biologist traces in the world of the hedgehog, the frog, drosophila, paramecium or streptococcus. It is then at the same time inevitable and artificial to utilize, in order to comprehend the experience which is the organism's own existence, concepts, intellectual tools, forged by this cognizing animal, the biologist. This is not to conclude that experimentation in biology is useless or impossible, but, remembering Claude Bernard's formula "Life is creation," it is to say that the knowledge of life must be achieved through unforeseeable changes, by striving to perceive a becoming, the sense of which is never so clearly revealed to our understanding as when it frustrates it.[21]

But let us return to "preferred behavior." Goldstein sometimes speaks of a preferred behavior in terms of the adaptation of the organism to its environment. And, of course, where, either through injury to the organism or through a drastic change in the environment, the normal interaction of the two is interrupted, restoral of equilibrium must take place. Adaptation in this sense, especially in illness, is directed toward the organism's survival, and for many, perhaps most, biologists, that is its necessary point of reference. Organisms are conceived as adaptation machines and nothing more. We must distinguish, however, in Goldstein's view, between the minimal though necessary achievement of survival and the achievement at which preferred behavior normally aims.[22] *Preferred behavior is that achievement which best expresses the nature of the individual.* Only when its normal functioning is impaired, when it can no longer aim at its best expression, does the organism fall back on survival as all it can obtain. Thus for Goldstein biological phenomena are explicable as functions of survival only in conditions of disease or failure. Where an individual has lost the capacity for that preferred behavior which would best express its nature, it may creep into its shell, so to speak, and try to keep going at whatever possible level remains available to it. That is how, as he found, brain-damaged patients act. The situations they can handle are limited; they confine themselves, therefore, if they can, to rigid routines where the danger of "catastrophic reactions" can be avoided. All living performance is ordered: its figure-background character already says so much; but the existence of the brain-damaged is "abnormally" so. Thus they often maintain an exaggerated tidiness, keeping their possessions in elaborately organized arrangements. Goldstein tells, for example, of the patient who, though he usually set great store by his visits home, could not leave the hospital on one such occasion because his room was to be changed, and in the move some of the treasures so carefully stored in his cupboard might be put out of place. Others, he reports, cannot bear any asymmetrical arrangement. If the doctor lays a pencil down askew, the patient straightens it at once, and if prevented from doing so becomes visibly uneasy. Where the more flexible order of ordinary living is debarred, a tighter order becomes the indispensable framework of the patient's life. In this way he keeps himself going "at all costs." But the healthy individual would not be content with this minimal self-maintaining order: he seeks a maximal achievement, despite the risk of failure, or indeed, sometimes, of death.

Goldstein's demotion of "survival" to a manifestation of disease parallels Portmann's insistence that self-maintenance as a criterion of life is secondary to the primary criteria of centricity and display. An atomistic biology—whether its "atoms" be reflexes, DNA molecules, or what you will—can consistently envisage nothing beyond the self-perpetuation of its constituent particulars. But a living thing—not a "type," but an individual, developing organism, looked at in itself, as figure against the background of its unique interaction with its environment— exhibits to the naturalist not only such a monotonous maintenance of indifferent particulars but comprehensive features of appearance and achievement which constitute the entity whose emergence and whose maintenance such devices as those of inheritance or homeostasis subserve. "Appearance," admittedly, what Portmann calls display, does not enter into Goldstein's exposition. As a neurologist he is concerned with the organic basis of performance. Thus one of Portmann's two major criteria of life is missing from his account. But preferred behavior is plainly the visible expression of centricity, to which, as for Portmann, self-maintenance is secondary. And only in incapacity, whether induced through illness or (as we shall see) through experimental manipulation, does the secondary performance take over from the primary and appear as the whole significance of the living thing's existence.

The concept which best describes the relation of the healthy organism to its natural environment, therefore, is not so much "adaptation" as "*adequacy.*" Preferred behavior when achievable and achieved is the most adequate expression of this organism's nature in its ongoing relation to its surrounding world. In Strausian terms, it is the realized norm of the I-Allon relation for this individual. But nothing in life is perfect, and such adequate expression is always partial or may even fail completely. Where it does so, we have *catastrophe.* The normal structure of action collapses, and the organism is unable to act. Experimental neurosis, for example, seems to be an excellent illustration of such catastrophic response to a situation which the animal is unable to control. Anxiety, Goldstein believes, marks the awareness of imminent catastrophe; it is, he holds, a common phenomenon in all sentient organisms. It is, one might say, the awareness, at some by no means necessarily self-conscious level, of the risk inherent in sentient life. But catastrophe as a continuing state is insufferable. The response to it is a withdrawal into some kind of order, however rigid, in which the individual can maintain, not the preferred behavior of its healthy condition, but some lesser coherence. Hence, as we have already noted, the excessive neatness and rigid dependence on routine of brain-damaged patients.

4

Much of the text of *Aufbau* is directed to the refutation of alternative theories, and an inspection of some of these arguments may help to bring the comprehensive approach more clearly into view.

On the reigning evolutionary perspective in biology Goldstein has little to say directly. But I have already mentioned his relegation of "survival" to a secondary place in the explanation of organic performance; from this it is plain that he is, to say the least, not interested in the history of life as such. His approach, like that of most of our previous authors, is wholly neozoological. Two remarks, however, give some indication of his attitude in this respect. First, he begins his study with man rather than with other organisms, not only because of his own starting point as a physician but on principle. The lower can be understood, he holds, only from the higher, not vice versa. This is the method, as we have seen, that Portmann follows also in his speculation about centricity. It is also the method which, in the view of A. Vandel, one ought to apply to the study of evolution itself.[23] Vandel calls this procedural maxim the "law of recurrence." His point is that, being where we are in the evolutionary story, we must start from our own condition and look back at its genesis. To claim to begin, with no concept of evolutionary advance, from viruses or bacteriophage or from no life at all, is to pretend to a kind of total objectivity which can only lead us to self-deception and confusion. It is more honest and

more consistent, he argues, to admit our place at the pinnacle
of evolutionary development, that is, as the species which has
achieved the highest degree of individual psychic development
on this planet (the insects being our equals in inventiveness,
but on a specific rather than an individual basis). From this
position we then reflect on the conditions which may have led
from other less reflective forms of life to our own.

Now, Vandel's reason for this maxim is that of a reflective
evolutionist; Portmann's reason for the parallel approach in the
account of centricity is that of a neozoologist, but, as his studies
of human and animal development make plain, entirely compatible with an evolutionary (though not with an orthodox neo-
Darwinian) approach. Goldstein, however, displays, where he
touches on the subject at all, a positive antipathy to evolutionary views. Thus in his final chapter, on "Life and Mind," after
insisting on the unity of human nature, the absence in the individual organism of a fixed "hierarchy" of organs or organ systems, he introduces in conclusion a brief section of "Phylogeny
and Ontogeny," where he sets down his point of view on these
two topics (considered separately, not in terms of any alleged
"recapitulation"). "The problem of development," he writes,

> is usually so regarded, that an advance in development is as-
> sumed from lower to higher organisms, an actual coming to be
> of the latter from the former. Given that, on the one hand, all
> the objections we have been considering are opposed to such
> attempts, it is, on the other hand, in principle incomprehensible,
> how the more perfect is to arise from the less perfect. It would
> be at least more intelligible were the imperfect to proceed from
> the perfect.[24]

One is reminded of Kingsley's whimsical hypothesis, clearly
conceived for the amusement of his friend T. H. Huxley, of a
land where animals develop from primates back into protozoa:
from a strict Darwinian point of view ("no higher and lower in

evolution," as Darwin himself warned himself in a note on the notorious *Vestiges*), this should be perfectly conceivable, just as conceivable as what in fact has happened, namely, the development of the more complex and more centered from the less so. From Goldstein's point of view, however, it would be *only* such an inverse evolution that would be intelligible, for only such an inverse evolution would be consistent with the order of knowing:

> In the progress of knowledge it is certainly so; it is the absolutely basic idea by which we let ourselves be guided, and which was forced upon us by observation, that the imperfect becomes intelligible as a variation of the perfect, and that the converse, on the contrary, is never possible.[25]

This is neozoology with a vengeance! How can any biologist dismiss as unintelligible the fundamental principle of a vast field of research, if not, as many biologists believe, the fundamental principle of biology as a whole? Yet Goldstein insisted that the theory of evolution had hindered rather than facilitated biological research:

> I do not see, moreover, how the reduction of one phenomenon to another, the assumption of the "development" of the one out of the other, in any way advances knowledge. Usually it has only impeded further research. . . . Here too I would insist, as we demanded for the study of reflexes, that every phenomenon must be understood in itself. If we cannot do that, then it would be better to admit that there is something we cannot explain, rather than to lead research into false paths.[26]

Of course, Goldstein was writing, it should be remembered, in 1934, before the new "synthetic theory" had triumphed, and long before the population genetical and biochemical revolutions had seemed to give it framework and underpinning in two equally significant directions. Yet he made no remark in the

Preface to the 1963 edition to indicate any alteration in this
point of view, and there is no reason to hold that he did alter it.
As he said in the first edition, "We must be content with these
few words on the problem of development, which is one of the
most obscure and in which a host of prejudices hold sway." [27]
If we *were* to compare species, he had argued then, a comparison of different classes as representing different degrees of ap-
proximation to a common prototype (like Buytendijk's "ideal
biology") would be more fruitful than an endless running after
causes. But the search for archetypes (mortal sin from the orthodox evolutionist's point of view) does not in fact interest him
either. What he is after, once more, is simply the study of each
organic phenomenon as a whole, but for its own sake. From
this point of view ontogeny is indeed worth studying; but the
theory of evolution, claiming to know the whole of living nature, goes, he holds, far beyond any evidence that we, in our
limited situation, could procure and so confuses and distracts
by its wrongly "holistic" speculations. Better, he believes, to
heed a maxim of Goethe's: "It appears to us that one thing has
been *produced* by another, which, however, is not the case, but
one living being *gives another the occasion* to be and forces it
to exist in a definite condition. Thus every existing thing has its
own being in itself and therewith also the concordance (*Übere-
instimmung*) according to which it exists." [28]

These are fighting words. We shall see more later of the philosophical context which partly explains them. Meantime one
can give, perhaps, two historical reasons for what must seem to
many contemporary biologists a positively antibiological point
of view. First, Goldstein grew up at a time when a dogmatic
nineteenth-century version of Darwinism had indeed dominated much of German research to its detriment, and of course
the neurological atomism he opposed was conceptually a product, or at least an affiliate, of such oversimplified evolutionary
views. Second, his own work depended so much on the intui-

tive and self-correcting assessment of the individual case that one cannot expect him to have looked sympathetically at the renewal of Darwinism, which does, if with much more refinement and ingenuity than its older forebear, represent a totalization of biological knowledge antipathetic to the tentative and concrete nature of such knowledge in Goldstein's view. Certainly, neither populations nor macromolecules, the alternative objects of the modern evolutionist's attention, are whole organic individuals, and only with whole organic individuals is Goldstein primarily concerned.

It should be remarked in passing, however, that the French physician and philosopher Georges Canguilhem, who may be considered philosophically as in effect Goldstein's disciple, shows, in his subtle historical studies, a juster grasp of Darwins' influence and a more reasonable admission that evolutionary theory has been in fact a major factor in the formation of modern biological method—even, therefore, of Goldstein's. For, he argues, it was Darwin who transformed the concept of environment (*milieu*) from a primarily mechanical and Newtonian to its modern biological meaning.[29] And without this concept, first clearly articulated by Uexküll and used, if with some difference, by Goldstein himself, the modern conception of the organism would be impossible. In the present context, however, one can only admit that Goldstein himself saw no such historical connection of his own theory with the ideas of evolutionists. Putting him alongside evolutionary thought, we are faced, not only with a different emphasis from the orthodox one—as in the case of Portmann, Plessner, Buytendijk, or Straus—but with a positive antipathy. At the same time, Goldstein's emphasis on the understanding of the individual seems, at some level, certainly unacknowledged by himself, akin to many evolutionists' opposition to simple over-all categorization, their rejection of such simplistic theories as orthogenesis, for example, their emphasis on the diversity of life, the "opportunism" of evolutionary processes, and so on. One can only hope, therefore, that the philosophy entailed in Goldstein's concrete, empirical method may yet find a fusion with the best, and equally tentative, empirically directed orientation of evolutionary thought. There are, as I have suggested earlier, basic conceptual confusions in dogmatic evolutionism, which can be overcome, I believe, only through conceptual reforms as radical as those suggested by the authors I have been expounding. But that the philosophy of biology which might eventuate from such reform would be in principle antievolutionary, denying either the fact of evolution or its importance for a biological perspective in philosophy, seems to me as inconceivable as the evolutionary perspective itself appears to have been to Goldstein. Since, however, as Goldstein himself insisted, biological method is dialectical, one can only hope for a synthesis to follow the antithesis which he so powerfully presents.

All this, of course, is peripheral to Goldstein's own concerns. What he is most concerned to refute, himself, as a neurologist, is the interpretation of behavior in terms of reflexology. Indeed, this was a common concern of all of our authors who were active as physiologists or psychologists thirty years ago. I have mentioned Straus's arguments on Pavlovian theory and have reported in detail the papers of Buytendijk and Plessner from the years 1925 and 1935, respectively. Goldstein's arguments, directed primarily to the physiological rather than the conditioned reflex, differ in many respects from theirs, but since his book is available at least in quasi English I shall only mention them briefly here.

His principal point, as I understand it, is twofold. On the one hand, reflexes in fact occur, at least very often, he argues, only when parts of the organism are investigated in isolation. "Reflex" reactions therefore characterize only an artifact: distorted and isolated parts, not the living whole. In this respect the data studied in reflexology are analogous to the data studied in disease: the situation of illness and the situation of the experimental subject are alike in the distortion which they display relative to the normal behavior of the healthy organism, or, what is for Goldstein almost the same thing, the organism unhampered by interference by extraneous agencies that impede the realization of the constants characteristic of its preferred behavior. Whether it be brain damage or the artificial environment of the laboratory that prevents the subject's normal realization of his essence matters little. The abnormal isolation is the same and is equally disturbing to the adequate organism-environment interaction that characterizes the individual in his natural (or, in the human case, natural-cultural) situation. An organism investigated in reflexological terms is, for Goldstein, very like a brain-damaged patient who can live only in the rigid routine of the veterans' hospital. We must try to understand him, but not pretend that he is the same man who had once marched hopefully to glory—and catastrophe!

Second, if the situation studied by the reflexologist is distorted and artificial, it is also in fact by no means so well established as its adherents declared. It is difficult, Goldstein argues, to find reflex behavior in nature and equally difficult to maintain it. It is unnaturally rigid where it is found and, compared to more spontaneous behavior, unnaturally labile. Indeed, as we saw Buytendijk and Plessner also arguing, one has often to interpolate all sorts of purely speculative theoretical factors, inhibitions, radiations, and what not, in order to explain the actual phenomena in its terms. What is more, Goldstein reasons (reflecting again his dislike of the claim to derive the complex from the simple), where there are reflexes they are more common in higher than in lower organisms. Taken in context, a reflex is nothing but "the simplest reaction of living substance as such." [30] Such simple reactions, however, occur chiefly in boundary situations, where danger approaches at some particular point. But since higher organisms are more intricately and delicately integrated into their environment, such local reactions to slight disturbances occur more frequently in them than in simpler organisms, which are more likely to react globally and with less differentiated sensitivity. Thus the allegation that complex behavior is made up of these simple units, and complex organisms of simpler constituents behaving in this "simpler" way, has, Goldstein argues, no foundation in comparative biological fact. Indeed, the data tend to its refutation rather than its support.

Nor will conditioned reflexes do better as units of complex behavior. They share the characteristics of isolated processes: extraordinary rigidity and precision and at the same time extraordinary lability. They are inhibited by processes more "natural" to the organisms that exhibit them, easily lost through injury or other new conditions, and so on. Finally, Goldstein argues, when repeatedly administered they produce sleepiness: a sign of catastrophic reaction, which aims at excluding stimuli in general. So far are they from being the ordinary units of behavior!

What, then, is their significance? They may teach us something, Goldstein says, "about the formation of especially unnatural achievements and thus indirectly about the nature of the organism in question." [31] To begin with, since conditioned reflexes seem to be functions of the cerebral cortex, they must characterize only higher organisms—and indeed, Goldstein believes, chiefly man. Pavlov's experiments, he holds, fail to show us whether the natural environment of the dog would ever present conditions suitable for the formation of such reflexes. So far as we know, he insists, it is only through man's interference in the animal's life that they arise. If, on the contrary, "we could succeed in demonstrating conditioned reflexes which had originated in animals without the influence of man, this would permit, retroactively, an inference to an especially 'advanced' species resembling the human." [32] This is a startling—

indeed, in the light of the vast experimental literature on animal learning, a paradoxical—statement. For, except for experimenters like Buytendijk, most animal psychologists have proceeded confidently on the basis of the conditioning experiment as their principal tool. Are they displaying no more than the distortion of animal behavior by human experimenters? With respect to the study of animal behavior in the laboratory, it would be difficult to refute either Goldstein's thesis or its contrary, since we experiment on animals only when we do experiment on them. Ethological field work might provide some evidence, although even here the prevalence of behavioristic concepts would tend in the main to weight the evidence against Goldstein's thesis.

What can be evaluated and put to good use by philosophers and educators, however, is the interpretation of conditioned reflexes in man which accompanies Goldstein's rejection of their natural role in animals. Conditioned reflexes, Goldstein argues, are typical of *drill* as distinct from *practice*. In man they do become assimilated to "natural" performances:

> The formation of conditioned reflexes in man plays a not insignificant role for education and self-discipline. It demands a definite attitude, an adaptation even to unaccustomed, unnatural situations, of which in fact man alone is capable. Conditioned reflexes represent the highest achievements of such adaptation. In the infant, where this attitude has not yet developed, they are attained through the *external compulsion of the educator*. Thus the toilet training of the child can be *formed* as a conditioned reflex. But *it can never remain so*. If that were the case, it would never acquire the wholly routine character which it has later on. This is effected only through the integration of the achievement into the whole of the organism, in relation to which it is determined through insight, will, and so on, that is, through entirely different factors than those which are constitutive for conditioned reflexes. In general, the effect of drill becomes securely established only when it can be built into a natural

achievement, when the effect of practice can become effective along with it. Human insight into necessity can secure to the strangest connections the power to run their course independently, undisturbed by obtrusive influences. Only severe shock can destroy these connections.[33]

Such integration of associations into total behavior, however, is always dependent on the accompanying activity either of the individual himself or of other human beings: "The connection never arises of itself, externally, passively, without cooperation on the part of the person himself or his human environment." [34] The assimilation of conditioned reflexes, in other words, requires a kind of imaginative insight of which, Goldstein believes, other animals are incapable, but which is essential to the development of the human person and of human culture.

Yet conditioning, or drill, as Goldstein calls it, although essential to the development of the individual, must be distinguished from a different sort of training, which he calls *practice*. Both are directed to the best possible achievements in their kind, but only practice, as distinct from drill, aims at those achievements which express the essence of the organism and enable it to develop to the fullest degree that its environment permits. Thus it is practice rather than drill which leads to preferred behavior and therewith to the experience of fulfillment of the individual's being. Only training, therefore, produces comprehension or learning in the fullest sense of that term. Drill, on the other hand, as exemplified par excellence in the conditioned reflex, is achieved through the isolation of a part of the organism and in relation to some isolated aspect of the environment. It is always laborious and is also unstable unless assimilated to the natural achievement of the organism as a whole. Witness the artificial conditions under which animals, at the sacrifice of their individuality, are subjected to conditioning experiments. Even here, Goldstein points out, the conditioning is stable and even permits a certain enjoyment on the part of the subject, if it is integrated into the animal's natural achievements. In man, as distinct from other animals, however, in Goldstein's view, drill plays an especially important part in learning. For man is relatively deficient in natural adaptation to his environment; he *has* to be conditioned. Yet at the same time such conditioning, to be effective, must be integrated into the personality of the learner. Drill must always be subordinate to practice, and the acquisition of isolated skills to the preferred performance of the individual as a whole. In subordination to this double need, it happens fortunately, Goldstein argues, that man is uniquely capable of isolating parts of his own organism and exposing himself to stimuli which can be repeated at will under recurrent conditions, so that the same conditioned responses can be again allowed to run their course. Thus "inadequate" performances have their important uses and are not in fact so inadequate in our case, so long, of course, as they are duly subordinated, through will and insight, to what we recognize to be the necessities of our world. Thus we need drill, but in the sense of self-drill, in self-conscious service to our comprehensive purpose of self-fulfillment and adequate performance.

Clearly, this distinction between drill and practice, between conditioning and significant learning, may well assist the educator to resolve the apparent antinomy between meaningful learning and mere rote: since it shows how routine learning should be and can be integrated into more comprehensive and significant performances and, indeed, indicates why there is no human learning without some drill—a principle which teachers as well as students, in their rush to promote "creativity" and "meaningful learning situations," are too much inclined to forget. No modern educator can help shedding a tear for young Charles Darwin, exposed to the meaningless conning of Greek verbs when his heart was with beetle-collecting; but woe betide the student, or the teacher, who supposes that one could become either a humanist or a scientist without a good deal of rote learning and routine acquisition of skills, "meaningless" in themselves, but essential as underpinning to the achievement of any substantive performance. Everybody knows that it takes drill to get an Olympic gold medal; so does it to achieve any goal worth pursuing, and Goldstein's theory of learning should help to show us why.

Philosophically, too, it opens up new vistas. The Humean paradigm of learning is in effect the conditioned reflex, which Hume, and animal psychologists after him, considered to be common to men and other animals. Philosophers who would rescue our mental achievements from reduction to "mere" habit have sometimes tried to add to, or even to substitute for, the common ground of drill some other, uniquely human activity. But to reject the associationist pattern for other animals, to accept it as uniquely human *and* assimilate it to a larger pattern of responsible learning—this forms a new perspective both on the difference between our intelligence and that of other animals and on the nature of human learning itself. Contemporary linguists, discovering that the associationist theory fails to account either for the infant's mastery of speech or for the mature language user's original use of language, have reverted to a classical theory of innate ideas and postulated what looks like some secret mental activity, of the ghostly variety, to explain the operations which do in fact plainly transcend the powers of a Humean "mind." [35] But this is to return to the kind of dualistic solution which has already proved intellectually unstable, as well as false to the psychophysical unity of man. Goldstein's theory not only (as we shall presently see) stresses this fundamental unity, though without reducing the "mental" to the "physical," but integrates into a comprehensive view the associationist factors which do play a significant if subordinate role in the formation of language, as of all other culture-borne performances. Merleau-Ponty's chapter on language may be mentioned as one application to the interpretation of speech in Goldstein's theory; doubtless much more could be done with it in this field. (Not that Merleau-Ponty mentions this particular aspect of Goldstein's argument; but the latter's influence is clearly pervasive in Merleau-Ponty's work and may well have played its part here.)[36]

Other partitive, or reductivist, theories also come under attack. "Drives," in Goldsteins' view, have no facultylike independence, but can be subsumed under a single "drive" for the expression of the organism's essential nature. "Instincts" he rejects equally as rigid partitive concepts, untrue to the unified nature of organic performance. His argument here, I think, must be admitted to be weak; it antedates modern ethology and has not been revised in the light of the revolutionary developments of that discipline. Whether Goldstein's attack would stand up against the investigations of "fixed action patterns" in birds, fishes, insects, and so on seems very dubious. It may be, indeed, that such work itself goes astray if it hypostatizes its basic units and shapes them into rigid models.[37] But neither does a "holistic" approach seem to apply as directly to nesting behavior, say, as it does to the more flexible, insight-directed behavior of members of a human culture. Where, as Portmann points out (for instance, in territory possession), even in the relatively rigid behavior patterns of birds, the heightening of the individual's existence may be involved as well as techniques of survival, a more comprehensive approach may well be indicated, at least in part. As I have myself pointed out elsewhere, such personal assessment of the subject's behavior does creep into the work of even the most "objectivist" ethologists,[38] and it may be correct to argue, as Goldstein or Portmann would do, that it is only within a reference to the life of the whole organism that partitive processes, whether fixed action patterns or others, can fruitfully be analyzed. But it would take a much more substantive investigation of methodology in this field to support this conjecture; it must suffice here to refer, as I have just done, to my account of Portmann's *Animals as Social Beings* for an indication of an approach to animal behavior consonant both with modern ethological theory and with Goldstein's philosophy of organism.[39]

More central to the defense of Goldstein's own position—which does, after all, depend primarily on his interpretation of human behavior—is his critique of psychoanalysis. He objects to the use of the term "unconscious," because it is negative, and merely relative, he believes, to what one defines as "conscious," but chiefly because, he feels, the Freudian theory, for all its undoubted therapeutic achievements, produces a thoroughly confused account of the way in which the human organism in fact operates. If we look at behavior, not in terms of abstract a priori constituents, but in its whole physiognomy at a given period, we find three components in its whole action toward and within its world. We have, first, the performances which constitute conscious, voluntary behavior. Conspicuous among these, of course, are actions in which the abstract attitude predominates. But this is never the whole. We find also attitudes or inner states, the texture of our feelings, moods, and so on: what Heidegger calls *Befindlichkeit.* And finally there are *processes,* somatic events experienced only indirectly. Thus in an everyday proceeding like my typing this manuscript, there is my conscious effort to report on Goldstein's theory, my general attitude toward my present task, toward writing in general, my state of attentiveness or otherwise, the backache that is distracting me, and so on; and finally there are the somatic events in my nervous, muscular, and circulatory systems, for example, of which I cannot myself be conscious but know must subtend my personal efforts and affective attitudes if I am to exist at all. These three aspects have been described in the European tradition as "mind," "soul," and "body." In Plessner's account, for example, they are represented by my eccentric position relatively to the body that I both have and am, my animal positionality as both having and being a body, and my physical (or physiological) existence as a body. On the traditional usage Goldstein comments:

> There is nothing wrong with this usage, so long as one is clear about the fact that it is not three isolated spheres of being that are in question, which stand somehow in a secondary way in relation to one another, but that it is a question here of abstractions, each of which represents an artificially isolated aspect of the total organismic process. They appear as separate because one or another slips into the foreground more or less as "figure," while the others then form the background. Here too background and figure belong together, and the figure can be "normal" only for the corresponding ground. What becomes figure always depends on the situation, on the kind of interaction necessary at the time.[40]

Here again, as he had found essential in his medical practice, Goldstein stresses the importance on the one hand of keeping the whole in view and on the other of recognizing the plasticity of the figure-ground relation which integrates the other two aspects of the totality into the comprehensive pattern to which one of the three is for the time being central. True, each aspect can, at times, be relatively isolated. Thus when we investigate consciousness, objective behavior is in the foreground. But we can give in to our affective attitudes: then "we no longer have an objective world, we live in immediate relation to the world; every state is 'experienced,' but is 'not conscious' in the sense just described." [41] Goldstein is here dealing, it would seem, with a distinction at least very similar to Straus's between perceiving and sensing, or better perhaps to that between the gnostic and the pathic elements in our awareness of the world around us. Finally, Goldstein explains, we can concentrate on the course of bodily processes; abstracting still further from the normally functioning whole, we can view our body in relative isolation as a physical object or let it proceed in its routine interaction with the environment. In each case, however, specific patterns can be discovered in the two subordinated spheres; and derangement of the normal functioning of any one aspect can occasion disturbances of the others.

This way of looking at human behavior is, again, similar to Merleau-Ponty's account in the *Phenomenology of Perception,* with its stress on the relation between "thetic" and "non-thetic" aspects. It could also be fruitfully compared with Polanyi's theory of tacit knowing, where, because of their essential bearing on the task to which we are focally attending, we are said to be subsidiarily aware not only of our inner attitudes but of the bodily processes on the smooth functioning of which our performance depends. Such comparisons, however, would take us too far afield at the moment. What concerns us here is the use Goldstein makes of this analysis for the critique of Freudian theory.

There can be, he argues, no such phenomenon as "the invasion of the unconscious," since aftereffects of each aspect of the total behavior are actualized only in that mode in which they first occurred: "Just as these processes belong to definite modes of behavior of the organism in which they arise, so *they can be recalled and produce after-effects only in the same modes.*" [42] On the other hand, of course, since figure and background always form an integral whole, changes in background can influence the figure and thus affect future performances, but only through the whole.

At the same time, Goldstein insists, all comprehensive human activity begins with a conscious attitude. This may later lapse into background and provide a general framework for future behavior; but the "lower" levels, both attitudes and processes, must be set going, he believes, by the central, conscious behavior of the human person. On the other hand, attitudes and physiological processes may be defectively integrated into the whole behavior of the person or put out of their normal focus through injury or unusually strong stimulation. This is especially likely in childhood, since the child's behavior is not yet conscious in any well-defined way:

> The child comes immature into the world, its first reactions are certainly not yet of an objective nature, it has either no world or a very "diffuse" one. Its behavior will still be essentially characterized by processes in the bodily sphere, and by inner experiences (attitudes) of the kind we have described, although here too of course relatively imprecisely specified because of the still relatively simple interactions with the environment; the whole is more deeply embedded in a sphere of the affective kind than in that of the objectively conscious world. But what the child finds before it as phenomena is certainly very intensive, for this if for no other reason, that in view of the imperfect centering of the whole that happens to confront it, its experience proceeds in relatively isolated parts. It is isolated processes, such as the satisfaction of hunger . . . that are natural, that lead to an adequate equilibrium and are therefore the most actively determining factor in the assessment of stimuli. The child's behavior patterns therefore exhibit also the characteristics of response in relatively isolated parts. We see abnormally violent reactions, reactions of abnormal duration, a greater dependence on external stimuli, more primitive modes of behavior and, finally, the occurrence of reactions in opposing phases, a change of response which we have recognized as characteristic for isolated processes.[43]

Here, too, as in other cases of isolation, catastrophe can easily take place, as it does with brain-damaged individuals. Tasks which demand greater conscious centering than the child as yet commands produce violent aversion. And naturally such responses also leave their traces in the organism.

On the other hand, the child can be "conditioned" to form new patterns which it integrates as it matures, or which it resists not so much consciously as through inner attitudes that conflict with its new patterns of behavior. Such "repression," however, is not so much an "invasion of the unconscious" as it is the substitution, at least in normal development, of new patterns for old. The old are not so much repressed as discarded:

> The fact of elimination of earlier reactions is usually called *repression*. So long as we mean by this a displacement, a separation, the phenomenon has not been correctly characterized. As long as this is all there is to it, the "repressed" processes are nevertheless still effective, and we know how little success we have with such active prohibitions. So-called "repression" in fact takes effect only when the organism, maturing in a new adaptation to the external world in which the "repressed" behavior has no place, achieves a new configuration to which the repressed phenomenon does not belong. What is present, therefore, is not continual repression, but *the continual formation of new patterns*. The so-called repressive factor is formed neither by external prohibitions, nor through a censor, nor through an ego or super-ego, but through the emergence, increasing with increasing maturity, of that configuration of the organism which corresponds to the type "man" and its special configuration in the environment in which the child grows up. This configuration can of course be called "ego-formation." And in this process prohibitions, like other events in the external world, of course play their part. The effect of earlier responses, however, are not "forgotten" through repression, since they cannot be recalled, nor can they become effective, because they are not contained in the attitudes of later life.[44]

It may well happen, however, since maturation is a delicate and dangerous process, that infantile or childish attitudes remain unassimilated and come in later years to be revived if the individual is brought into a situation similar to that in which they were generated, whether in neurosis, psychosis, or psychotherapy. But these are not "repressions" drawn back into an original conscious form out of a kind of secret unconscious reservoir; indeed, the self-conscious form in which the psychoanalyst elicits them could not have been characteristic of the not-yet-mature childish "consciousness":

> That it is not thoughts repressed in childhood which here crop up out of the unconscious, follows, indeed, from the very fact that their content is of such character that the child could not have had such thoughts. It does not contradict this point to admit that the thoughts here expressed [by the neurotic patient with the help of the analyst] are partly determined by factors which owe their origin to events in childhood. Thanks to their imperfect centering, responses of a substantive nature which arose in childhood and are now relevant to the new situation may crop up, be recalled and brought to the fore. Then we get the impression that the patient has regressed to an infantile state. But there is no regression, there is only the same form of response, but now differently, that is, pathologically, determined —or in other words, in isolated parts of the whole. The adult patient, however, can never regress to a really infantile state.[45]

What we have in the neurotic individual, then, is not "repression" of some definite, once-conscious content, let alone "regression" to infantilism, but an *ambivalence* which characterizes the *whole* of his behavior in his present state—the result of imbalance, of imperfect assimilation of earlier patterns into his mature behavior, but not of their "repression." And this ambivalent behavior is as multifarious, as complex, as any other behavior of the mature human being:

> The most various thoughts, concepts, feelings of contradictory significance belong to the ambivalent behavior of the neurotic, which is released in the analytic situation, as they do to the behavior of every human being. Among these naturally there are also some of sexual content, and here again especially such as take their specific coloring from the ambivalent relation to the individual's parents, the appearance of which is certainly favored by the strong disposition which is formed in the so-called Oedipus situation. It may be for this reason that this complex so often appears in the free associations of the neurotic. But this

*by no means says that this complex is the determining, uncon-
sciously acting reason for the ambivalence as such.* It is a consequence of the analyst's *interpretation* that he places sexual ambivalence and in particular the Oedipus complex into the center
and sees the ambivalence which occurs in free associations with
other contents, or in the behavior of the patient on other occasions, as *dependent on the ambivalence of his sexual thoughts or
impulses,* instead of seeing the latter, like other phenomena, as
the expression of the same basic process, namely *ambivalence as
such.*[46]

We should follow here, Goldstein argues, the same methodology as elsewhere, that is, we should take all symptoms as
equivalent, instead of drawing out, artificially, one particular
aspect of the whole as primary. Given this theoretical predilec-
tion, experience will always "confirm" the Freudian theory, just
as it does reflex theory: it can appear in no other mold. But,
Goldstein holds, such a phenomenon as the "Oedipus situation"
could be reasonably interpreted without the cramping apparatus of the unconscious and all its paraphernalia:

There are in the child preferred forms of reaction. To these belongs that which is produced by the so-called Oedipus situation:
the contradictory attitude of the child to the object "father." But
this is not repressed; later pattern-formations allow the ambivalent attitude that had once been present, and with it its special
content, to become ineffective, because they do not belong to
these new patterns. In the same way something we have learned
comes back to mind only when the situation to which it belongs
is present.
So we at once recall a foreign language in an environment in
which this language is naturally spoken, but do not recall it in
another environment, to which it does not belong, but where it
has to be fetched forcibly back into consciousness in a kind of
contradiction to the environment. Of course infantile attitudes
have not vanished; they are retained in dispositions or habits,
many even perhaps in especially powerful habits. But they are
meaningless, not there, that is, not effective, because they do

not belong to the milieu of the mature individual, because ambivalent attitudes as such recede as maturity increases.[47]

Thus, he concludes:

> *What appears as unconscious is nothing but the entry into a re-*
> *sponse of an earlier reactive pattern of the organism, when the*
> *situation is appropriate to it.* It is a question of nothing but a
> certain form of recall, of memory. *The emergence of the uncon-*
> *scious is nothing but the effect of strong dispositions to certain*
> *forms of reaction,* which do not belong to the situation objec-
> tively like other stimuli but become effective if they are strong
> enough in themselves or if the centering of the organism is weak,
> just as unusually strong external stimuli become effective in such
> cases. If they do not become effective, they can also, like the
> above-mentioned external stimuli, exert a disturbing influence
> on normal responses. Anxiety then arises as the expression of
> the constantly threatening danger of catastrophic reactions. If
> the effect of these stimuli is prevented, because the situation is
> unsuited to their emergence, then they can transform the indi-
> vidual's responses so effectively that they take a wholly abnormal
> course. Then to avoid catastrophe we may get *substitute be-*
> *havior patterns,* which have the same character as those we have
> met in the case of the organically diseased.[48]

The comprehensive theory of the organism, therefore, Goldstein believes, can interpret the phenomena of neurosis as well
as of physiological injury, within the compass of a single, if
flexible, approach, without the elaborate and overabstract superstructure of psychoanalytic dogma.

One further critical exposition should be mentioned briefly:
that is, Goldstein's discussion of Gestalt theory. Plainly, his
holistic view has much in common with this school of experimental psychology, but the differences are also important. In
Chapter 10 of *Aufbau* he analyzes these differences; I think we
may summarize them here by pointing to his emphasis on preferred behavior as not only comprehensive but actively so. The

tendency of Gestalt theorists, particularly Köhler, to explain *Gestalten* in terms of field theory and ultimately in terms of physical isomorphism diverges sharply from Goldstein's more dynamic biological approach. The convergence of his holism with that of the gestaltists, in fact, recalls the reliance on their discoveries by Merleau-Ponty or Polanyi rather than the philosophical position which, with some exceptions, they themselves developed.[49]

5

It remains to look a little more closely, in conclusion, at the philosophical implications of Goldstein's theory. Now, plainly, and as I have already pointed out at a number of points, these coalesce in many respects with the concepts and arguments of my previous subjects. It is, to a great extent, though not wholly so, a common perspective on the foundations of biology, both epistemological and ontological, to which I have been hoping, in these essays, to direct attention.

Methodologically, for example, the authors I have dealt with all share in one way or another allegiance to the phenomenological slogan: back to the things themselves! They all urge us, in reflecting on the methods of biology, to moderate our admiration for the daring abstractions of physics and turn our attention to the visible richness and complexity of the living world. Both Straus and Buytendijk rely explicitly on phenomenology as a philosophical and psychological method; Plessner in fact studied with Husserl, and though his method is his own, it clearly bears traces of phenomenological influence. Portmann, in turn, has been influenced by all of them as well as by the demands of his own zoological practice and its incompatibility with the accepted Galilean view of science. Even Goldstein, who is, in training and experience, the least "philosophical" of our subjects, expresses, in his autobiography, sympathy with

Husserl's late concept of the "life world" and confidence that his method is convergent with the phenomenological in this phase of its development.[50] Admittedly, as I warned in the previous chapter, one should not take the direct and informal intuitive methods of writers like Straus (or Goldstein) as in fact equivalent to those even of "late" Husserl; but that is not the point in question. The point is simply that there is in all these cases a common direction, not unconnected with the spread of phenomenology, in the negative sense that it entails a rebellion against a cramped and confined tradition, and in the positive sense that it seeks an ampler and more adequate approach to the structure of the experienced world.

Ontologically, also, there are numerous common themes. Goldstein, in emphasizing the attempt to observe and understand the whole organism and rejecting the claim to "explain" it through its parts, is taking, implicitly, a position on the mind-body problem entirely congruent with that of Straus, Plessner, or Portmann. And his explicit treatment of the problem bears out this impression. In its insistence on psychophysical unity—but not, of course, in the sense of Laplacian materialism—his chapter of "Life and Mind" runs parallel to themes we have already met in Straus, in Plessner, indeed in all our authors. There is a common emphasis, also, on the importance and subtlety of the temporal aspect of living things. And so on.

At the same time, there are differences of emphasis and, indeed, some special difficulties that should be mentioned with respect to the ontological foundations of biology as well as to questions of the uniqueness of biological knowledge.

First, method. The intuitive confrontation with their living subjects—the *vision,* both sensible and intellectual, entailed in biological method—has been, it should be clear, from the outset on, one of our common themes. Goldstein too insists on the importance of a unifying, imaginative perception in the biologist's work: of what Goethe called *Schau.* That is why he insists that biological research is "acausal": it is not directed primarily to the enunciation of laws of mechanical cause and effect relations, but to the intuitive awareness of the physiognomy of living things.[51] Not that biology rejects the exact methods of other sciences. On the contrary. But the analytical methods of all experimental science, as valid in biological research as everywhere, must, he argues, be applied by the biologist in constant relation to his intuitive aim. The example of chronophysiology which I mentioned earlier may recall here what is intended by this maxim. I might refer the reader here also to Agnes Arber's book *The Mind and the Eye*.[52]

Goldstein's presentation, however, more explicitly and centrally than the others I have been treating, attempts to describe such a method *under way*. He is a passionate empiricist: what concerns him is less the intuition from which a biologist sets out or at which his mind rests ultimately or at some points along the way, than the very road itself that he takes in confronting and handling his living subject. Hence his insistence, as we have seen, on the *dialectical* nature of his method: it is so essentially in process that it transforms its very instruments in the course of using them. If this seems paradoxical, it is the paradox not only of biology but of all empirical science, as against the traditional dream of an ultimate and unequivocal knowledge of an ultimate and unequivocal real. If everything were changing, Plato argued in the *Cratylus*, there could be no knowledge, since "knowledge" itself would be changing. But so it is; and so much the more so are the ancillary concepts which it uses in order to achieve whatever "knowledge" will turn out to be. But in physics, the subject matter, being a high abstraction from the real flux of the real world, is relatively stable: it is the knower who is changing.[53] In knowing living things, on the contrary, we as living knowers are confronting, and acting upon, living subjects, who are themselves changing and therewith changing us. Not that such change, on either side, is Cratylean and chaotic. It is orderly, or, better, rhythmical, in rhythms which themselves develop through the very interplay of knower and known. Eliot's concept of tradition seems to represent, from this point of view, the very quintessence of life: there is no living subject, or creature of a living subject, which is not altered in some measure by another living being's knowledge of it, and conversely the knower develops—or sometimes degenerates—through his knowledge; he is in some manner essentially affected by what he knows.

Such a process, I repeat, can *use* analytical methods of any degree of precision you desire. Indeed, Goldstein emphasizes, biology is no less exact than other, more exclusively quantitative sciences. Even though its aim is holistic, its techniques are exact and even partitive. For empirically one *can* deal only with one or a few parts at a time. But biology can never be *wholly* precise, first, for the reason just mentioned: because it depends for its significance on the developing insight into a developing subject. Second, moreover, just because of his complex and multidimensional subject matter, the biologist cannot confine himself, qua biologist, to any one set of abstractions. Knowledge from anywhere *may* be relevant to any given problem in its biological context. This is the theme, touched on by Goldstein, but more extensively elaborated by the late C. F. A. Pantin in his distinction between "open" and "closed" sciences.[54] The biological sciences are open, in that physics, chemistry, geology, cybernetics, *any* discipline may be of use to the biologist, and he may use it with any degree of subtlety; but if it is to yield biological knowledge it must be applied relatively to the biologist's aim of understanding living systems in their immersion in a living, as well as a nonliving, world. That is a third point, moreover: the reason why biology can use insights and techniques from anywhere is not only that the organism is so complex but that to *be* an organism is to be receptive to and active upon an *environment* which is itself almost infinitely complex. Not only the relation of subject to experimenter but the whole interaction of the subject with its environment—and where possible its natural environment—must be taken into account.[55] Hence, again, Goldstein's dislike of partitive methods. Unless used (as, of course, they may be) with biological tact, they result, not in the study of organisms—which, studied *a*part or *in* parts, are no longer organisms—but rather in a game played with counters of one's own making.

Like any empiricism, which emphasizes its own tentative and conjectural character, Goldstein's methodology is easily susceptible to philosophical criticism, especially when he himself tries to unite it with reflections of a more speculative cast. Before facing the difficulties which arise in this connection, therefore, I shall compare his theory briefly with Michael Polanyi's theory of intellectual commitment as developed in *Personal Knowledge*.[56] By showing their common ground I think I can also suggest, as Goldstein's argument alone would not permit me to do, a line along which some of its seeming inconsistencies could be resolved.

I have rendered *Ganzheitsmethode* as the *comprehensive* method, a rendering suggested by Polanyi's description of organic being as "comprehensive entities," and I mentioned previously several parallels between Goldstein's views and Polanyi's. The phrase implies also, what is essential to Goldstein's epistemology as to Polanyi's, the double meaning (absent, I confess, in the original) of comprehensiveness (in the subject matter) and comprehension (by the scientist). True, neither Goldstein nor, under his influence, Merleau-Ponty articulated as completely as Polanyi has done the epistemological tools for describing such a method and putting it to philosophical use. Yet Goldstein's method is, I submit, in effect the elaboration for biology of Polanyi's account of scientific discovery, with the same distinctiveness for the case of the biological sciences that emerges from Polanyi's more inclusive argument. In both cases the aim of scientific knowledge is not prediction, or the formulation of exact laws for their own sake, but *understanding*. In both cases, analysis is the servant of intuition—intuition understood, however, not as a detached *nous*, but as groping, as "sallying forth" under the guidance of imagination in a fashion unspecifiable by explicit rules. Knowledge is analogous to perception, and perception indeed is the primordial case of knowing, which at its most universal and sophisticated is still "vision." In both cases, also, the developing, active nature of the living being introduces into the search for biological understanding a new logical level that is missing in the sciences of the nonliving world.

But the parallel, or the identity, that I want to stress here is yet another, which marks the distinctive empiricism of Goldstein as against that of my other subjects in this book. For Goldstein, as for Polanyi, scientific investigation is an extension and a refinement of the process of *acquiring practical skills*. All biological knowledge, I noted earlier, is for Goldstein a case of biological action. This is true, however, not only because, as we have seen, the scientist is himself alive and interacting with his living subject but because learning to understand living things is a process that resembles very closely the fashion in which we acquire, in practice, other, nontheoretical skills. It follows, in other words, the pattern of everyday practical activity. For Polanyi, of course, this is the case for all knowledge, if more strikingly so for the disciplines that deal with life. Goldstein, as a practicing physician, is more exclusively concerned with biology and leaves the physical sciences, on the whole, to separate theory and practice as they like.[57] But there is no doubt that the process he describes for biology is the same process that Polanyi has described in *Personal Knowledge* for a broader range of disciplines. I shall not carry this comparison through in detail here; but suffice it to mention an everyday instance of a skill which they both cite as paradigmatic for learning: the case of cycling, an example analyzed by Polanyi in his chapter on "Skills," and of which Goldstein writes:

> This kind of cognitive process [that is, the method he has been describing], which may at first sound rather mystical, can be stripped of this mystical character by reference to a very banal biological process, by reference to the learning of any skill. For instance riding a bicycle. For a time we make undirected movements of our body, that is, such as are determined by particulars, which are not essential to bicycling, until we are suddenly able to keep our balance and to move forward in the right way. All these first attempts have nothing directly to do with the genuine achievement. They are, to be sure, not aimless and are necessary, for only through continuous modifications of our movements do we come to the right performance. But as false movements they never lead directly to the right one. The right movements appear suddenly, when adequacy between the organism's behavior and the environmental conditions appears. This adequacy is experienced by us. The behavior in this situation contains the right knowledge of how to behave in cycling. We keep trying to bring this about until it becomes the unique performance which we have embarked on with the project of riding a bicycle. This attainment of adequacy in the power of the organism in relation to environmental conditions, a basic biological phenomenon which alone makes possible the very existence of organisms, is essentially related to the biological knowledge we have been seeking. In the cognitive process too we take in practice all sorts of wrong paths until we have suddenly achieved a picture that "fits." [58]

Polanyi's exposition of the same case, it is true, contains in little the epistemological machinery which he proceeds to elaborate and analyze throughout his book, while with Goldstein it serves as a hint which is not worked up further into a general epistemology. But I hope that I will not mislead the reader too far by taking it here as the starting point for a further comparison; some of the differences will become apparent as I proceed. The common point, and that to which I wanted to call attention by introducing this example, was just the assimilation of theory to practice.

Now, admittedly such an assimilation brings with it formidable problems; it has done so from Plato (how can the philosopher-king apply knowledge among the shadows?) through Hume to Dewey. And these problems arise in an acute form in Goldstein's case. Let me approach them therefore from the point of view of Polanyi's theory of intellectual commitment, where they occur, indeed, but in a somewhat milder form. The crucial question is: if theory is assimilated to practice, knowledge to skill, how can we claim for it the universality that makes it knowledge, not blind habit? How can we ever make a claim to the discovery of the truth? Positivists have solved this problem by denying that scientists seek truth, by reducing knowledge to prediction. This both Goldstein and Polanyi would emphatically refuse to do.

First, despite their "pragmatism" in relying on the skill-like nature of learning, they both distinguish, as some pragmatists have failed to do, between pure science and technology. Science is for them certainly not prediction in the sense of technical control. Biological technology, in particular, Goldstein argues, uses living things for human ends; biological science, in contrast, seeks to understand living things, whether men or animals or plants, for the sake of understanding, not to master them, but to submit to them, to *let them be*.[59] To put it in Polanyi's language, we seek to dwell in the objects of our knowledge, rather than to manipulate them for utilitarian ends. True, both pure science and technology are skills, but with purposes as different as have the skills, say, of composing poetry and of setting type. Both have, indeed, both ulterior purposes and an intrinsic and self-satisfying order: the poet wants to be published and read, and the typesetter takes pride in his art for itself. But in their ultimate foundations and the source of their cultural meanings they are and must be kept distinct.

Nor is pure science to be conceived, secondly, as prediction for its own sake, as a zero-sum two-person game with nature, which we can win or lose but which has no meaning beyond this meaningless result. Its aim, once more, is understanding, and understanding not as a subjective satisfaction, but as an insight into what really is. Such insight, however, transcends our particular accomplishments and lays claim to a validity that is compelling, or ought to be compelling, on other knowers as well. When Goldstein speaks of a fundamental law of biology —the search for organic constants—or of the interaction in man of abstract and concrete behavior, he is enunciating principles based on insights which he expects, or hopes, his readers will share and will implement, if they are themselves biologists, in their own research. But if the method of discovery is as personal and as thoroughly in process as these writers suggest, how can it issue in truths demanding universal assent? (What does *my* riding a bicycle prove for everyone?) That is the nub of the problem. Polanyi attempts to solve it by insisting on the universal *intent* of our cognitive assertions. No one ever knows for sure that he knows, but we do *claim* that we do; and if we make this claim responsibly, in the light of the best evidence we can muster as competent—though, of course, not as infallible—practitioners of a particular discipline, that is the best we can do and all we feel called on to attempt to do. Thus in his account of intellectual commitment Polanyi distinguishes the *subjective,* my inner, fleeting feelings, from the *personal,* the active commitment which entails responsible submission to something which I appraise to the best of my ability as existing beyond me. The personal as distinct from the subjective does not arise, and cannot exist as such, without an impersonal pole to which the person's activities are directed and with which in discovery they claim to have made contact.

Admittedly, the concept of universal intent is a difficult one.[60] It seems to allow us no definite criterion by which to distinguish real from illusory discovery or error from truth. Nor does it. It is the *claim* to universality, the self-discipline (Goldstein's *Übung*) inherent in seeking it and the transcendence of individuality, the submission to something greater than ourselves entailed in claiming, or, better, in hoping, that we have found it, that distinguishes our intellectual lives from the existence of other sentient creatures. But there is no automatic, self-guaranteeing criterion of "evidence" by which I dare affirm that this time I really have it, that this is ultimate knowledge, once for all wrapped up for all time to come. As Goldstein might have put it, the progress of cognitive achievement is dialectical. Nor is this an ideal, but an existential, dialectic, which must be every day renewed, which aims at the universal, yet can never guarantee to have achieved it and must constantly be alert to try again. But it is not, for that, "irrational," since reason is just the hope and the method of finding meaning *in* history, not beyond it. The paradox that confronts us here is parallel to, if not indeed the same paradox as, that of freedom.[61] We can neither resolve the freedom-determinism problem nor dismiss it, because we are it.[62] The very problem itself constitutes our moral lives. Similarly, the conflict between the contingent, particular aspect of the scientist's search for knowledge, the fact that it is *his* search here and now out of these given skills and traditions and these given superstitions and ignorances, and its transcendent, impersonal aim, the fact that what he seeks to know is what there really is and that when he has expressed what he has found he may be providing insights, even deeper insights than he himself could know, for others now and to come—this conflict expresses a basic polarity of our condition which is the very fiber of our lives as intellects. Such basic polarities we can only seek to formulate and to weave into the fabric of a broader tapestry, but not to dispel by any less imperiled formulation. The problem of self-evidence, like the problem of freedom, is neither soluble nor a pseudo problem; it is what we are.

I have introduced Polanyi's theory of commitment here by way of introduction to a difficulty in Goldstein's theory, not because Goldstein too expresses a concept of universal intent, but just because he does not. This solution, uneasy though it is, of the problem of particular and universal in scientific knowledge is not available to him, and so such statements as he makes of the universal pole of his methodological commitments appear as anomalies within the extremely individualistic and empirical orientation of his method. The paradox is further aggravated, moreover, by his emphasis on human biology, and in particular on his medical practice, where it is the preferred behavior of this individual rather than of the species that is primarily in view.[63] I have already mentioned the description of preferred behavior as that performance which best expresses the essential nature of the organism as a whole and have argued that such "essentialism" is, as Goldstein declares it is, truly empirical, rather like Mayr's a posteriori weighting in taxonomy. It is not, in the first instance at least, a metaphysical essentialism. And Goldstein emphasizes over and over again that his aims are not metaphysical at all, but wholly empirical. Biological knowledge, he holds, is entirely "positive," and he seems to mean this (with some inconsistency, of which more later) in the sense of *positivism:* asserting the empirical facts rather than seeking speculative principles to explain them. Yet when he comes to tell us more about the intuitive aspect of biological method and of the object of his search for preferred behavior, he may take a leap into what sounds to the ordinary reader like fathomless speculation. Thus in his concluding remarks we read:

> The facts we were seeking were those which enable us to *describe univocally the being of an organism,* to "understand" it. Starting from the concrete, from the particular, we were always trying to define the organism in general, to get it in view in its essential nature. In this process what we discovered at first was *the structure of the "particular."* We could define it only with

reference to the whole of the organism to which it belongs, in its structure as well as in its qualitative character, as a being of the organism in an "unnatural" condition, in "isolation" of certain, often quite arbitrarily selected segments. We found it also inappropriate to build up the whole out of such parts; all the particulars pointed beyond themselves to the whole, to a ground which is of another nature from themselves, and in reference to which alone they achieve coherence.[64]

So far, so good. But what is this "other," at the grasp of which our research has aimed and on reference to which even the understanding of the particulars as particulars depends? Goldstein continues:

> Of what nature this other is, purely empirical observation can no longer give any answer whatsoever. For empirical research it is enough to define this ultimate ground (*Urgrund*) in the first instance as a *cognitive ground,* which enables us to comprehend all the particulars in their relation to the organism as appearances under certain conditions, and at least as not contradictory to one another. We can say further: this cognitive ground is no concept in the abstractionist sense; it has the character of an image, the character of an archetypal image (*Urbild*). As such it contains more than its "parts," which are indeed its appearances, ever allow us to know. And as the situation permits it and demands it, it reveals itself to an ever stronger and more differentiated degree. Here we found parallels to what Goethe brought into concrete but ideal view in its *Urpflanze* as the source of the differentiation of plants in manifold individuals, as well as to the profound speculations of Parmenides.[65]

Now, except perhaps to an Agnes Arber, such a statement will seem to the biologist, or indeed to the philosopher of science, *naturphilosophischer Unsinn*. Such a vision appears arbitrary and subjective, even though Goldstein hastens to remind us that its *content* can be sought only by means of the isolating techniques of empirical research. For how, apart from a leap into the subjective, does one acquire a vision of the *Urbild* to which one's techniques are to give content? Isolating empirical techniques do not by themselves yield *Urbilder;* indeed a major motif of Goldstein's argument has been to refute partitive theories just because he insists that the work done on isolated parts of organisms cannot give us knowledge of the whole. The higher (whole) cannot be understood from the lower (parts). We have to start from the whole. But if his work is empirical, and therefore, as he admits, partitive in its methods, if the only particulars one can actually study are parts; if he is continually immersed, as he constantly declares he is, in the analytical details of practical research and if he nevertheless rejects, as he certainly does, the imposition on the facts of abstract theories like C-R theory or psychoanalysis, where does he get his *Urbild* from and how does he use it *in* his daily work? Usually, as I have already noticed, if he speaks of archetypes at all it is to dismiss them as not of primary interest. He does indeed speak on one occasion of Cassirer's theory of symbolism and suggests that the symbols used by the biologist are of a more Gestaltlike character than the physicists' mathematical formulae.[66] This is only to put the *Urbild* story in other words, but it fails to bridge the gap between the empirical method and the guiding vision. That there *is* a gap is, of course, undeniable: any theoretical vision transcends its data; in this respect no one has answered, and no one can answer, Hume. But these gaps *are* bridged: that is scientific discovery, and an adequate philosophy of scientific method must tell us how, not leave us with careful footsteps all on one side and the light that should guide them on the other side of an impenetrable wall.

Goldstein does make one attempt to show how, in biological knowledge, this gap is bridged. In a very obscure passage he compares biology with quantum theory in respect to its nondeterministic character, taking the reliance of these two disciplines on probabilistic foundations to indicate their tentative and nongeneralizing character.[67] But statistical knowledge is just as universal as knowledge of a classical deterministic type. And besides, however tentative the biologist's conclusion, his *Urbilder* are not statistical. There is no help here.

If, however, I may rely on their common identification of the advance of knowledge with the learning of a skill to assimilate Goldstein's comprehensive theory to Polanyi's theory of intellectual commitment, I can suggest, and indeed have already partly suggested, a way out. Two points are involved: one, the universal intent of all cognitive statements, and the other, the place in biology of class concepts or norms.

I have already spoken in general terms of the first point. Let me just apply Polanyi's interpretation now to Goldstein's troublesome *Urbild*. The scientist—any scientist engaged in original research—is guided in his daily work by an intimation of a *Gestalt*, a coherence of some kind on which he focuses, relying on his empirical data as clues to this imagined unity. While he is engaged in designing a given experiment, or keeping it running, or tabulating its results, he has, of course, to focus on his daily tasks, and the primary vision has become subsidiary. And admittedly science has by now become such a huge enterprise that, almost in the fashion of Radin's "thinkers" and "non-thinkers," many individuals practice science for a lifetime, and quite respectably, without ever transcending the more routine situation: someone else has done the imaginative work, has conceived the *Urbild* which guides the task in question: how then should they know there is one? For the creative scientist, however, that imaginative vision must be the motive force which constantly presides over his analytic work. In his everyday situation it becomes one of the subsidiary clues to what he focally undertakes: in Goldstein's terms it has left traces in his attitudes and even his physical performances, and so he may lose sight of it for a time. Yet without its guiding power the undertaking as a whole would be impossible. For it is the bearing of the particulars on the general conception that both makes them significant and at the same time, as Goldstein says, allows them to give content to the guiding vision. Hence when the scientist comes to formulate his results, he asserts them with universal intent, seeing his original hunch now tied down and embodied in the evidence which bears on it. His *Urbild,* he is now confident, is not an empty vision, but a reflection of the lineaments of a substantive reality. He may be mistaken, but he has firm hope of being in some good part correct, both because of the coherence of his vision and because of the solidity with which it has been tied down to the empirical evidence.

This account, admittedly, stresses the theory-laden nature, from the beginning, of all statements of fact of interest to science, and this is just what Goldstein most of the time appears to wish passionately to deny. Yet surely his own "theory" of abstract and concrete behavior is also a theory? And for all his insistence on an extreme empiricism, on sticking to the phenomena and describing them all, he admits nevertheless the discrimination involved in fact finding. He is explicitly opposed to a random, "trial and error" empiricism, an approach to "facts" which has no guidance from any vision. Thus what he is opposing, in the last analysis, is not theory as such, but first, the isolating sort of theory which is too impoverished in its own coherence and so can embrace only an exiguous and distorted set of "facts," and second, the abstract sort of theory, which tries to classify all human subjects too quickly under types rather than looking at them as persons, each trying to find an adequate existence in his own world in his own best way. But from a distrust of certain theories one should not leap to deny the theoretical content of science as such and therewith the universal intent which alone can give its pronouncements authoritative weight. What one needs is an epistemology which will take due account both of the richness of the phenomena and of the process by which the seeker after knowledge is guided through an empirical maze by the hope of substantiating a vision of coherence which at first he had only glimpsed, but which remains the ultimate focus of his search.

All this concerns, so far, the relation in general of the empirical and particular to the theoretical and universal. But there is a special problem in biology as distinct from physics which, again, looms as insoluble in Goldstein's exposition, but which can, I believe, be adequately dealt with if one integrates, as I have here suggested one may do, his argument in *Aufbau* to Polanyi's in *Personal Knowledge*. This is the problem of *norms*, or more particularly of specific norms, of what Polanyi calls judgments of "trueness to type." In speaking of preferred behavior Goldstein presents, as I have mentioned, the alternative of individual or species-specific constants. Yet, again, his emphasis has been almost entirely on the preferred behavior of the individual rather than of biological groups. In his concluding remarks, however, he touches again on the question of groups transcending the individual, both species and organic communities (which, of course, generally include more than one species). Continuing his account of *Urbilder,* he writes: "Only when we succeed in bringing the *Urbild* into view, and only so far as we succeed in this, can we even attempt to proceed to such questions as those of the relation of organisms to one another, their membership in species and class, their place in a hierarchy of life, and so on." [68]

Yet this process seems in his own terms quite unintelligible. Are we to leap into the universal, to understand kinds rather than particulars, with only this mysterious archetype to guide us? Again, Goldstein's emphasis all along has been on the individual organism we are confronting and on the tentative manner in which we feel our way forward in attempting to understand *this* individual as a whole. But reference to types rather than individuals, as well as to the universal import of our knowledge rather than its particularity, has been conspicuously absent. Yet just as all knowledge must claim universality if it is to be knowledge at all, so all biological knowledge must deal with norms, which are standards and therefore universal, not particular. Even if the biologist deals, medically, with this patient here before him, or, genetically, for example, with populations statistically analyzed, he has still to have behind him the recognition of this or that kind of organism or this or that kind of behavior.[69] He has to recognize, for example, the physiognomy of this illness, which must have some general, not just this particular, *Gestalt* if it is recognizable at all. He must know cv, redeye, or what you will from wild-type drosophila, or he could not begin to build up his populational statistics at all. Such biological universality, such normative judgments, must be integrated into the account of biological method at the start, not injected at the end. True, Goldstein does at one place deal with the problem of norms, clearly in a way of great interest to the physician and pathologist, that is, with the norms of health and disease. But even here his primary concern is with the individual patient: he defines illness in terms of individuals, as the inability of this person to exist adequately in his environment. What is illness for one may not be so for another. This is doubtless an excellent maxim for the clinician: witness Goldstein's influence on psychologists and philosophers of medicine; but it only aggravates the philosophical difficulty. For how can we move from "client-oriented therapy," where the *Urbild* is one person's only, to the concept of a species or of any broader class? In terms of *Personal Knowledge*, however, the direction can be reversed, yet without imperiling the individualistic basis on which, in the case of human biology, Goldstein rightly lays so much stress.

First, all knowledge claims universal intent and does so through reference to a coherent pattern which the knower responsibly assents to as indicative of a coherence in the real world. Second, biology, which deals with comprehensive entities, entails a more richly structured comparison. It has to assess, not the mathematical coherence of some few parameters in a highly abstract context, but the physiognomy of living beings, themselves centered to some degree in an individual existence. The universality in question here is not so direct nor so inclusive in its denotation. It embraces, in the first instance, the individual, morphologically, as one of a limited kind. The naturalist looks at the individual as a specimen with reference to a norm—not, indeed, a speculative or a priori norm, but a pattern which he has learned through practice to see in the particulars and from which nevertheless he can see deviations or differences in the case before him. (If I have learned to ride a bicycle, I can adjust my movements, and so modify and increase my knowledge, by riding a different machine, whether an old crock or a new and improved model.) This minimal normative judgment we find in all biology. Coming to the study of animals, and in particular of their behavior, however, we meet centers of sentience which we judge by more complicated standards, involving "rules of rightness" in behavior as well as trueness to type in shape or developmental rhythm. I need not go into the details of Polanyi's argument here; the point is that all the way through, from morphology through physiology to ethology to the study of man, we are already appraising specific constants, and in the case of animal behavior constants that represent preferred behavior of the species rather than the individual alone. But finally when we come to human subjects and attempt to understand the preferred behavior of the individual, we have a limiting case of the specific *Urbild*. For each human individual in his unique relation to his culture and his fellow men demands of the scientist, who is his fellow man, a unique understanding. We have here, then, a case where the norm of each subject must be studied and apprehended in itself. The relation of experimenter to subject is, or should be, one of full-fledged encounter.[70] So we seek a taxonomy of individuals as the special case of the biologist s search for a taxonomy of populations. Like Aristotelian intelligences or Thomistic angels, each man is in effect a species to himself.

Thus we have no longer, as in Goldstein's account, on the one hand a particular search somehow linked to a transcendent image and on the other the problem of species or communities left over from the search for individual norms. Instead we have a smooth transition from the universal intent inherent in all knowledge through the search for specific norms in taxonomy to the search for individual norms in the physician's study of this individual patient. Admittedly, as we have already recognized, there is always a gap left between empirical evidence and theoretical insight, as well as an ultimate insecurity in the claim to universality (even with respect to the claim that this is, on the whole, this person's preferred behavior). But if we see Goldstein's method as an instance of personal knowledge, we can at least alleviate the strange disharmony of his account in this respect and assimilate not only the particular to the universal but the physician's search for individual constants to the more general biological aim of understanding *kinds* of organisms.

The ontological implications of Goldstein's work are more difficult to assess, for from a vehemently antimetaphysical position, he takes occasional plunges into obscurely speculative pronouncements. All biological knowledge is positive: that is a major slogan for his method, and by it he usually seems to be saying, as I have already noted, that biology is positivistic, based on empirical protocols rather than a priori theorizing. But instead of contrasting this, as a positivist would, with metaphysical statements as nonsense, what he reiterates about metaphysics is the statement of its *negative* character. Now (although I do not in fact subscribe to this doctrine), I can see why and how one might call metaphysical statements empty or meaningless—but negative? What do they deny? The only answer I can suggest—and it is only a suggestion—is the following: Biological knowledge must be immersed in the complex reality of its living subject; it must beware of hasty theory construction, which purports prematurely and inadequately to mathematicize the full richness of the living world. Such premature, overabstract theories take off from a partial description of the phenomena and so return to their further inspection with a set against looking at the whole, and seeking the essential significance, of what is really there. That is Goldstein's basic objection to reflex theory and to psychoanalysis. Now, insofar as theories neglect certain aspects of their subject matter and refuse to look at them, they are negating those aspects. And if allegedly empirical theories do this, the more inclusive "theories" of avowed metaphysicians might be said to abstract from, to negate, still more of what the biological practitioner really finds. The metaphysician, the archtheorist, is, as, of course, empiricists have always accused him of being, the man with the closed mind and in this sense a negative thinker.

There is one other point that may be relevant. One of Goldstein's attacks on speculation is the passage in which, like Plessner, he opposes Drieschian entelechy as a concept dragged in to stop research in its course.[71] No such *deus ex machina* is wanted or needed, he argues; it is only a hindrance to further investigation and in this sense, again, negative in its effect. If the previous paragraph has interpreted his meaning correctly, the protest against "entelechy" would be one application of this general principle.

At the same time there are some metaphysical passages in *Aufbau* itself which I find it quite impossible either to accept or to reconcile with Goldstein's over-all position. For example, there is a paragraph about the organism not only as temporal but as being really in "eternal time," as existing before conception and after death, which I must confess myself wholly at a loss to interpret.[72] Is Goldstein after all a Spinozist whose stress on historicity is a stress on illusion? I cannot believe it. But on the other hand, if this is not so, why is he, while stressing the historical character of life, so throughly antievolutionary (not only anti-Darwinian) as we have seen him to be? Or another example: in the passage I have quoted from the concluding remarks, there is a reference to Parmenides which in turn refers to an "excursion" on Parmenides and the comprehensive method, which is totally mistaken historically and totally unilluminating, therefore, for Goldstein's own argument.[73] Goldstein there equates Parmenidean being with his individual organic wholes, and the chaotic world of opinion with the diversity of particular phenomena which have to be brought into relation with the being they express. That there is for Parmenides only one whole and no real change he seems to have missed entirely. In fact he takes Parmenides' dictum that only being is or is intelligible and that the path of nonbeing is nonexistent and unintelligible as a slogan for his own book. But surely nothing is less Parmenidean than Goldstein's method! Again, I simply cannot interpret this section, and I sympathize with the translators, who omitted it (along with the reference to it in the later passage).

On the other hand, as I have pointed out already, there *are* metaphysical reverberations which are significant, most of which, like Goldstein's treatment of the mind-body problem, show him taking a position congruent with that of the subjects of the preceding chapters. Let me conclude this account with an example from the chapter on "Life and Mind" which illustrates both this convergence and the emphasis peculiar to Goldstein's empiricism: the problem of the hierarchical organization of living things.

While insisting on the unity of human nature, Goldstein argues, he can also hold, without sacrificing the uniqueness of man, to the unity, in the order of knowing at least, of man and other animals. In the order of being also one can assert equally of every species that it is a unity, which must be understood in and for itself. We must take man, not as an animal with something different superadded, but as presenting to us, just as every living being does, a unique totality.[74] This premise must be kept in mind when we consider the question of levels of organization. With an eye always to the whole organism, we must beware, Goldstein warns, of fixed schemata of organs or organ systems. He advocates instead a functional criterion of rank. The loss of the abstract attitude in favor of the "lower" concrete type of behavior exemplifies such a hierarchy of functions. Goldstein here relates such psychological phenomena to their bodily basis and concludes that in general a distinction should be made between the significance for the organism of *flexor* and *extensor* movements. The relation to the whole is more intimate, he alleges, in flexor than in extensor performances: "The flexor movements have a clearer reference to the self, the extensor movements more reference to the external world" [75]—although, being Goldstein, he is not referring here to the use of particular muscles in particular cases, but to the configuration of the over-all performance:

> Thus the difference between flexor or adduction movements and extensor or abduction movements becomes for us an *expression of different attitudes of the organism to the environment.* Flexor movements stress rather the I over against the world, the grasp of the world from the point of view of the I, and so make possible the separation of I and world. This finds its special expression in the convergence of the eyes, the bending of the head, the act of leaning toward an object usually placed in front and beneath me, in fixating it and so voluntarily grasping the world. In contrast, extensor and addiction movements correspond to a certain surrender to the world, a passive being in the world, a condition in which the I is lost in the world. We have then in the eyes a lesser convergence, the head is bent backwards and the arms stretched out. We can visualize the difference best if we imagine

on the one hand the bodily and intellectual attitude of a person who is intensively looking at an object, and on the other hand that of a dancer, who touches the ground with the tips of his toes and in a sense lets the external world take over.[76]

Goldstein finds the influence of colors affiliated also to this distinction: green, which "favors the achievements of the organism," inclines us more easily than does red to flexor movements: "it allows the organism to be more 'in itself,' to act 'on its own,' while red promotes a stronger attraction from the outside." [77]

Now, if we compare this distinction between flexor and extensor performances with Plessner's argument on positionality, for example, or with the grandly generalizing outlines of Buytendijk's "ideal biology," we find it empirical in a sense that looks at first sight almost behavioristic. For even if it is not particular muscles that are denoted by the phrases "flexor" and "extensor performance," it is an overt, physical behavior that Goldstein seems to have in mind. On this very concrete basis, however, he seeks out a functional criterion of rank which is clearly not behavioristic in the orthodox sense and indeed closely resembles the criteria of organic rank of our other authors.

A defect in the organism, especially brain damage, Goldstein notes, obviously disturbs its total performance, and thus, disturbing essentially the *separation of I and world,* "it puts the organism more at the mercy of the world, makes it more of an automaton." [78] From this point of view, then, we can proceed to a comparison also of man and animal:

We neither see in animals so marked a differentiation in the use of flexor and extensor achievements, nor does a brain defect, for example, produce such a different effect on the two types of movement. Accordingly the animal seems to us also much more closely tied to its environment, lacking freedom and the possibility of behaving so as to place itself at a distance over against the world.[79]

We can say, therefore, that we have here genuinely an instance of a higher and a lower level of organization. Again, this is not a rigid division according to organs or organ systems, or abstract functional levels such as "sexual" versus "nervous-psychological." Of such "systems," either may become figure or ground, depending on the character of the performance to which the individual's energies are directed at the time; neither is in itself "superior." If we beware of such abstract isolation of single systems, however, we can, Goldstein believes, in reliance on the fundamental distinction between flexor and extensor performance, establish a double criterion of rank: a criterion of *degree of centering* and, allied to it, of *richness of content.* He approaches this by distinguishing in general three human types:

> In accordance with the different kind of centering, we can distinguish in general three principal types of human behavior, which we can see in the prototypes of the thinker, the poet and the man of action. In the thinker the "conscious," "objective" mode of behavior comes especially to the foreground. But woe to him if he neglects the unconscious, "lived" mode or that of action! Then his work becomes a mere proliferation of thought, floating in a void. In the poet the "unconscious" attitude is dominant; but woe to him if he fails to heed the "objective" sphere and the verification of thought in action. Then his work becomes an exuberance of feeling alienated from reality. The man of action, finally, is threatened by the danger of losing himself in the current situation of his milieu, if he does not at the same time grasp the world "objectively" and take account of its whole "felt" and "lived" being; then he becomes a destroying machine. If one or the other side comes to the fore so as to destroy the whole, then we have always a loss of value, above all always a state of being deficient in centering.[80]

Thus, he continues:

> *The strength of centering proves to be a yardstick for the level of being.* The highest centering is manifested in a number of at-

tributes which represent ultimately one and the same thing, but which are usually given a variety of names: like freedom, significance, action out of the whole personality, productivity, capacity for meaningful action, for meaningful change of attitude, adaptability to a more complex environment, and so on. To this yardstick we might then add a second, according to *capacity and richness*. We have already seen that these qualities are also dependent upon the degree of centering, that they themselves suffer losses from the loss of centering, but they nevertheless stand alongside the first criterion as a special moment, as expression of the qualitative organization of the organism. The more a man in the highest degree of centering comprehends the human world, that is, the environment that accords with human nature, the higher we place him.[81]

This twofold criterion, then, permits us to speak about higher and lower levels. This is manifested, again, in the difference between the healthy individual and the sufferer from disease, where the lesser being of the sick person is characterized over against the full value of the healthy state "by losses in world, by losses in the 'person' in the sense of a limitation of degrees of freedom, and finally by losses in centering."[82] It is manifest also, of course, in the difference between men and animals: the degree of centering and, we suppose, its richness (though this is much harder to establish) being higher in our case. Both criteria must, of course, once more be considered as aspects of a unity: indeed, they add up to Portmann's criterion of centricity, *Weltbeziehung durch Innerlichkeit*, and they can also be easily related to the criteria used by Buytendijk or Plessner to sort lower from higher, as well perhaps as to Straus's distinction between pathic and gnostic. But Goldstein issues a final warning: beware of attempting to apply even these flexible and functional criteria without first understanding the essential nature of the individual to be ranked, understanding him as a whole, and therefore in the light of *his* highest, preferred performance, the fashion in which he seeks maximally and most adequately to express that nature. That, in Goldstein's credo, is the first and last aim of biological research.

6

The philosophy of science is an extension of biology: it is the attempt to understand, especially with reference to their claims to truth, certain activities of a certain class of living beings, namely, those activities which can properly be described as scientific research or scientific knowledge. I shall therefore heed Goldstein's warning and refrain from placing any solemn generalizations at the conclusion of this book. My aim has been, in any case, not to produce a new philosophy of biology, but to suggest that the reflections of the scientists and philosophers I have been discussing are worth looking into for themselves and also for their bearing on current problems in philosophy itself as well as in the methodological and metaphysical problems that cluster around the foundations of biology. There are other authors I might have included, and there are many aspects of the thought of those I have included that I have had to slight. But I hope that my reporting has not been grossly inaccurate and that it may lead some readers to look further in their direction for help in emancipating the disciplines that deal with living subjects, whether plants, animals, or men, from the bonds of a rigid, physics-dominated metaphysics that has too long held them captive:

> . . . May God us keep
> From Single vision and Newton's sleep.

NOTES

1. Kurt Goldstein, *Der Aufbau des Organismus* (The Hague: Nijhoff, 1963, reprint of 1934 edition); hereafter referred to as *Aufbau*. Cf. *The Organism* (Boston: Beacon, 1963, reprint of American Book Company edition, 1939).

2. "Kurt Goldstein," in E. G. Boring and G. Lindzey, eds., *History of Psychology in Autobiography* (New York: Appleton-Century-Crofts, 1967), V, 145–166.

3. See, for example, Carl Rogers, *Client-Centered Therapy* (Boston: Houghton Mifflin, 1951).

4. But for his influence in Europe, see not only Merleau-Ponty but also Georges Canguilhem, *La Connaissance de la Vie* (Paris: Vrin, 1966), and *Le Normal et le Pathologique* (Paris: Presses Universitaires de France, 1967).

5. See the bibliography attached to the autobiographical essay (reference 2, above).

6. Kurt Goldstein, *Human Nature in the Light of Psychopathology* (New York: Schocken Books, 1963, reprint of Harvard University Press edition, 1940), p. 39.

7. *Ibid.*, pp. 39–40.

8. *Ibid.*, pp. 40–41.

9. *Autobiography*, (reference 2, above), p. 159. Cf. B. Rimbaud, *Infantile Autism* (New York: Appleton-Century-Crofts, 1964).

10. Kurt Goldstein, "Concerning the Concept of 'Primitivity,'" in *Essays in Honor of Max Radin, Culture in History* (New York: Columbia University Press, 1960), pp. 99–117.

11. *Autobiography*, (reference 2, above), p.151.

12. *Ibid.*

13. *Ibid.*, pp. 151–152.

14. *Ibid.*, p. 152.

15. *Aufbau*, p. 76.

16. Kurt Goldstein, "The Smiling of the Infant and the Problem of Understanding the 'Other,'" *Journal of Psychology*, XLIV (1957), 175–191.

17. Ernst Mayr, "The New Systematics," in C. A. Leone, ed., *Taxonomic Biochemistry and Serology* (New York: Ronald, 1964), pp. 13–32.

18. F. Halberg and A. Reinberg, *Journal de Physiologie*, LIX (1967), 117–200.

19. *Ibid.*, p. 123.

20. Quoted from Canguilhem, *La Connaissance de la Vie*, p. 31.

21. *Ibid.*, p. 39.

22. *Aufbau*, p. 276.
23. A. Vandel, *L'Homme et l'Évolution*, 3d ed. (Paris: Gallimard, 1958).
24. *Aufbau*, pp. 316–317.
25. *Ibid.*, p. 317.
26. *Ibid.*
27. *Ibid.*
28. *Ibid.*, n. My italics.
29. Canguilhem, "Le Vivant et son Milieu," in *La Connaissance de la Vie*, pp. 129–154.
30. *Aufbau*, p. 115.
31. *Ibid.*, p. 121.
32. *Ibid.*
33. *Ibid.*, pp. 120–121.
34. *Ibid.*
35. See, for example, Noam Chomsky, *Cartesian Linguistics* (New York: Harper and Row, 1966).
36. M. Merleau-Ponty, *La Phénoménologie de la Perception* (Paris: Gallimard, 1945), Part 1, Chapter 6.
37. Cf., for example, R. A. Hinde, "Energy Models of Motivation," in *Symposia of the Society for Experimental Biology*, XIV (New York: Academic, 1960), 199–213.
38. M. Grene, *The Knower and the Known* (New York: Basic Books, 1966), Chapter 8.
39. Cf. Chapter 1, above.
40. *Aufbau*, pp. 206–207.
41. *Ibid.*, p. 207.
42. *Ibid.*
43. *Ibid.*, p. 209.
44. *Ibid.*, p. 211.
45. *Ibid.*, p. 213.
46. *Ibid.*, p. 215.
47. *Ibid.*, p. 216.
48. *Ibid.*
49. Cf. also Goldstein's reference (in the English version only) to some statements by Wertheimer and Koffka which come closer to his own position: *The Organism*, p. 380.
50. *Autobiography*, pp. 162–163.
51. *Aufbau*, p. 256. In the same chapter there is also a rejection of biological teleology; thus biological method is said to be both acausal and ateleological (pp. 263–264). Yet Goldstein there accepts the notion of *Ziel*, though not that of *Zweck;* his attack thus appears to be directed against the concept of conscious purpose in biology, affiliated as it was to its contrary, mechanical causality (see my argument on this point in Chapter 2, above).

52. Agnes Arber, *The Mind and the Eye* (Cambridge: Cambridge University Press, 1954).

53. Although I should not venture to pronounce on this subject, I suspect that the case of indeterminacy in quantum mechanics does not make an essential difference to my point here. Presumably particles-or-waves do not develop in the same way as organisms, and so it is the limits of our cognitive powers rather than any alteration in the being of their object that occasions the breakdown of exact measurement in microphysics.

54. See C. F. A. Pantin, *The Relations between the Sciences* (Cambridge: Cambridge University Press, 1968); also "Organism and Environment," in *The Anatomy of Knowledge* (Amherst: University of Massachusetts Press, 1968).

55. See also the account of Buytendijk's method, Chapter 3, above.

56. M. Polanyi, *Personal Knowledge* (Chicago: University of Chicago Press, 1958); cf. also *The Tacit Dimension* (Garden City, N.Y.: Doubleday, 1966). I have limited myself here in the main to the formulations of the theory of commitment in the earlier work, rather than moving to the broader theory of "tacit knowing" developed in *The Tacit Dimension* and other titles published since *Personal Knowledge*, partly because it seems to me needed in the context of Goldstein's argument and partly because it is the argument of Part 4 of the earlier book, on "Knowing Life," that is closest to the ground Goldstein is covering.

57. There are a few passages where Goldstein does state his position for scientific method in general and compares the method of biology with that of physics; I have mentioned these, or most of them, in the course of this discussion. On the whole, however, his major concern is, of course, with biology; the comprehensive method is conceived as a biologist's method, and I think it is fair to say, therefore, that problems of physical or chemical methodology are for the most part left to fend for themselves.

58. *Aufbau*, pp. 242–243. Cf. *Personal Knowledge*, Part I, Chapter 4, p. 49. The passage just quoted from Goldstein contains some serious misprints which I have tried to take into account in my translation (as did the translator of *The Organism*).

59. A Heideggerian phrase.

60. See E. Pols, "Polanyi on the Problem of Metaphysical Knowledge," in W. H. Poteat, ed., *Intellect and Hope* (Durham, N.C.: Duke University Press, 1968).

61. See William H. Bossart, "Three Approaches to Phenomenology," in *The Anatomy of Knowledge*.

62. See my mention of this question apropos of Plessner on eccentricity, Chapter 2, above.

63. Not that this is usually the case; but it clearly was for Goldstein and clearly ought to be much oftener than it is.
64. *Aufbau,* p. 348.
65. *Ibid.*
66. *Ibid.*, pp. 248–251.
67. *Ibid.*, pp. 257–259.
68. *Ibid.*, p. 348.
69. Cf. C. F. A. Pantin, "The Recognition of Species," *Science Progress,* XLII (1954), 587–598, and my discussion in *The Knower and the Known,* Chapter 8.
70. In Buytendijk's sense. See Chapter 3, above.
71. *Aufbau,* pp. 259–261.
72. *Ibid.*, p. 349.
73. *Ibid.*, pp. 251–255.
74. Goldstein quotes Herder on the folly of imposing human reason as a separate power over and above the animal "soul": "this is indeed, however great the philosophers who say it, philosophical nonsense. All separate powers of our souls and of those of animals are nothing but metaphysical abstractions, effects. They are inferred, because they cannot be viewed all at once by our weak mind; they stand in chapters, not because they work chapter-wise in nature, but because a textbook can best develop them in this way . . . but it is the whole undivided soul that is everywhere at work." "If man had the appetites of beasts, he would not have what we now call reason . . . if he had a beast's senses, he would not have reason." *Über den Ursprung der Sprache* (1770), quoted in *Aufbau,* pp. 304–305.
75. *Ibid.*, p. 309.
76. *Ibid.*, p. 310.
77. *Ibid.*, p. 309. This is a theme taken up with enthusiasm by Merleau-Ponty in *The Phenomenology of Perception.*
78. *Ibid.*, p. 310.
79. *Ibid.*, p. 311.
80. *Ibid.*, p. 314.
81. *Ibid.*
82. *Ibid.*, p. 315.

Acknowledgments

Part of Chapter 1 was published in *Commentary*, XL (November 1965), part of Chapter 2 in *The Review of Metaphysics*, XX (Fall 1966), 250–277, and part of Chapter 4 in *The Review of Metaphysics*, XXI (Fall 1967), 94–123.

Grateful acknowledgment is hereby made to the following:

To Hutchinson & Co., Ltd., London, and to Suhrkamp Verlag, Frankfurt a.M., for permission to quote from Adolf Portmann, *Animals as Social Beings* (London: Hutchinson, 1961); and to Professor G. P. Baerends for permission to use a diagram (my Figure 1) adapted by Adolf Portmann from his work.

To Princeton University Press, Princeton, N.J., and to Routledge & Kegan Paul Ltd., London, for permission to quote from "Time in the Life of the Organism," in Joseph Campbell, ed., *Papers from the Eranos Yearbooks*, Bollingen Series XXX, Vol. III, *Man and Time* (New York: Pantheon, 1957). Copyright © 1957 by the Bollingen Foundation, New York. Reprinted by permission of Princeton University Press.

To Walter de Gruyter & Co., Berlin, for permission to quote, in my own translation, from Helmuth Plessner, *Die Stufen des Organischen und der Mensch*, 2d ed. (Berlin: de Gruyter, 1965).

To Francke Verlag, Bern, for permission to quote, in my own translation, from F. J. J. Buytendijk and Helmuth Plessner, "Die Deutung des mimischen Ausdrucks," *Philosophischer Anzeiger*, I (1925), 72–126, which was reprinted in Helmuth Plessner, *Zwischen Philosophie und Gesellschaft* (Bern: Francke Verlag, 1953).

To E. J. Brill Ltd., Leiden, for permission to quote, in my own translation, from F. J. J. Buytendijk and Helmuth Plessner, "Die physiologische Erklärung des Verhaltens," *Acta Biotheroretica*, I (1935), 151–171.

To F. J. J. Buytendijk for permission to quote, in my own translation, from his *Das Menschliche* (Stuttgart: Koehler Verlag, 1958).

To Martinus Nijhoff, The Hague, for permission to quote, in my own translation, from Kurt Goldstein, *Der Aufbau des Organismus*, 2d ed. (The Hague: Nijhoff, 1963).

To Basic Books, Inc., Publishers, New York, and to Tavistock Publications, Ltd., London, for permission to quote from Erwin W. Straus, *Phenomenological Psychology, Selected Papers of Erwin W. Straus*, trans. in part by Erling Eng (New York: Basic Books, 1966). Copyright © 1966 by Erwin W. Straus.

To The Macmillan Co., New York, and Macmillan & Co. Ltd., London, and Anne and Michael Yeats for permission to quote the last two lines of W. B. Yeats, "The Folly of Being Comforted," *Collected Poems of W. B. Yeats*. Copyright 1903 by The Macmillan Company; renewed 1931 by William Butler Yeats.

Index

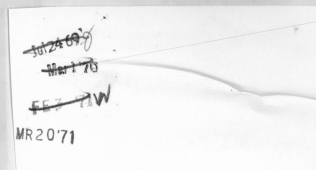